PRAISE FOR
THERE IS NOTHING TO FIX

"This is one of the best books on trauma ever written—and it's much more than that. Fast-paced, grounded in science, full of practical suggestions, and always hopeful, it is about living with courage and joy no matter what. Sue Jones draws on her personal history and vast experience with body-oriented practices to offer an original and effective program that is deeply healing while bringing us home to our true nature. Comprehensive, humane, and inspiring, this is a gem of a book."

—Rick Hanson, PhD, author of *Resilient: How to Grow an Unshakable Core of Calm, Strength, and Happiness*

"Suzanne Jones is a real-life superhero. She and I met in the context of the 2010 Haiti earthquake, and her efforts to develop a yoga intervention to help people affected by various forms of trauma. Her personal testimony informs a truly excellent description of the nuances of traumatic experience that become internalized in the body and spirit, which can feed the progression of mental unwellness. The road map to recovery that she describes, grounded in both science and ancient practices, is accessible and practically feasible for all people. This is a *useful* book."

—Giuseppe Raviola, MD, MPH, assistant professor of psychiatry, global health, and social medicine, Harvard Medical School

"*There Is Nothing to Fix* demands that we shift from a focus on trauma to engaging in the process of healing. Self-empowering and grounded in the blended wisdom of experience and science, it is a road map that recognizes the power of the individual to change the relationship they have with themselves as a pathway to happiness. I believe everyone will see themselves in Suzanne Jones's journey of healing through self-discovery and finding peace and power on the other side."

—Jeannette Pai-Espinosa, president, National Crittenton

"In *There Is Nothing to Fix*, Sue Jones cuts straight to the heart of our core human wounds and lays out an accessible and embodied path to healing. In a book that manages to be both deeply personal and startlingly universal, she reminds us that the price of our survival does not have to be our authenticity or our joy. Start reading, and whatever your age, gender, or circumstance, Sue's clear and compassionate voice will help you write a more powerful story for yourself."

—Jennifer Cohen Harper, author of *Thank You Body, Thank You Heart* and founder of Little Flower Yoga

"*There Is Nothing to Fix* is strongly rooted in both experiential and empirical evidence. Sue shares her story authentically, inviting readers in while also sharing tools of TIMBo in an accessible way. TIMBo is a valuable technique for embodied healing, and one that works—I have witnessed this both through personal accounts and empirical data, and I am honored to have had the opportunity to share the story of TIMBo through my research."

—Danielle Rousseau, PhD, LMHC, assistant professor, Department of Applied Social Sciences, Boston University

"Suzanne Jones has written a wonderfully accessible and comprehensive book on how to heal from trauma. She vulnerably shares her personal experience and how that led to the birth of creative interventions that are refreshingly available and effective. *There Is Nothing to Fix* is a very important read for everyone. I've been using TIMBo in my clinical practice and recommend the same to anyone who works with survivors of all likes."

—Mindy B. Loiselle, LCSW, coauthor of *Back on Track, Shining Through,* and *Rewind, Rebound*; author of *Care for Trafficked Children* (USCCB) and "The Trafficked Child: Trauma and Resilience" (*Forced Migration Review*)

"This book is a game-changer. The world needs *There Is Nothing to Fix*, and without a doubt, I will be recommending this book for years to come."

—Andrea Clemens, author of *Invisible Target: Breaking the Cycle of Educator Sexual Abuse*

"PTSD has produced hundreds of books and educational articles on the topic of overcoming trauma. However, there are only a handful that confront the 'monster' from the trauma victim or survivor. Suzanne Jones has climbed out of hell to provide a road map for those still suffering. Jones's voice in *There Is Nothing to Fix* is clear and concise and provides a deep insight into healing the scars of trauma. This book will change your life!"

—Ritchie Farrell, bestselling author, motivational speaker, and survivor

"With *There Is Nothing to Fix*, we have been given a gift: healing power that is accessible to all. This is everything! The book is brave, wise, and commanding. I am grateful Suzanne was able to harness the power of her traumatic experiences for this masterpiece. The positive impact on survivors everywhere will be profound."

—Maryrose Anthes, chief of the Human Trafficking and Exploitation Unit, Suffolk County District Attorney's Office

"A beautifully intentional narrative of how the wounds of trauma divert our development and create the vulnerabilities that so often lead to retraumatization, especially in intimate relationships where those wounds are so accessible. Through her own story, Suzanne carries us down a path of discovery in which we can find ourselves and the parallels to our own stories. *There Is Nothing to Fix* highlights in very tangible ways how to heal and find connection, clearly emphasizing what trauma-informed care systems everywhere are *relearning* . . . that it is only when we find safe, compassionate, and healing relationships does our recovery happen and lead us back to our authentic self."

—Toni DeMarco, deputy director, Child and Youth Services, Behavioral Health and Recovery Services, San Mateo County Health

"*There Is Nothing to Fix* is an inspired, inspiring, and revolutionizing book that everyone should read. In a world where many people seem to have lost the compass, with repetitive patterns of destructive behaviors at the mercy of their unhealed 'wounded child' craving desperately for love and connectedness, Sue Jones offers simple but radical and practical tools to help understand and grow in awareness through the body, which leads to healing, freedom, and happiness. Her story is a living testimony of TIMBo's effectiveness to heal ourselves in a world that overmedicalizes trauma; it's worth tapping into its potential."

—Jean Bosco Niyonzima, MD, MA, global clinical
governance adviser, Save the Children International;
cofounder and executive director, Ubuntu Center for Peace

"If, as Suzanne Jones writes in *There Is Nothing to Fix*, "healing hurts," then what she has succeeded in offering readers here for their journeys is a way through that pain to true sources of healing. Convincingly and vividly illustrated via personal narratives (her own and those of friends and clients), Jones guides readers as one would a friend—with gentleness, care, love, but also unflinching truth to, as she writes, "create space" to heal from various forms of trauma (from the intensely personal to the generational) "without judgment." This is a book to sit with, to hold in practice, to return to through different stages of processing, to share with others with whom we walk some part of the way. It will undoubtedly take its place as a new classic in how to engage somatic healing as an ongoing practice of wellness."

—Myriam J. A. Chancy, Guggenheim Fellow and HBA
chair in the Humanities, Scripps College; author of
Searching for Safe Spaces and *Framing Silence*

"It is absolutely incredible how Suzanne is able to explain and explore a journey of healing, and living a more fulfilling life, in a way that is raw and experienced within the reader. Every human being should read this book."

—Robyn Rees, family peer support coordinator,
Operational Stress Injury Social Support

"The narrative of *There Is Nothing to Fix* presents familiar emotions such as shame and guilt in the context of neuroscience in such a way as to depathologize them. I came away with not just an idea but also a credible recognition that all of these reactions are, in fact, the way it is supposed to be because it is the way we are built . . . What really seal the book's practical usefulness are the simple and powerful exercises for calming and soothing ourselves when we are angry, frightened, or hurt . . . Sue's perspective and suggestions provide everything needed to inhabit a world in which there is nothing to fix."

—Tom Lorello, director of clinical
operations, Lynn Shelter Association

"Suzanne Jones spent decades second-guessing her choices and worth before coming face-to-face with her self-destructive habits. With courage and determination, she punctures through the illusion of hoping for a better life and gets real about what it means to be human. *There Is Nothing to Fix* bristles with energy and compassion as Sue discovers practical, lasting adaptations to the fear and anxiety responses embedded in the human brain, as well as to the guilt and shame so deeply buried in our hearts. An invaluable guide to change from the inside out."

—Virginia Prescott, host of *On Second Thought*
for Georgia Public Broadcasting

"*There Is Nothing to Fix* does something no other book about trauma and the human condition does: it makes tangible the tapestry we are made of, all the threads and all the colors. It allows you to hover over it and dive into it. It encourages you to see the connections that you feel but can't always understand. It's in that seeing and understanding that peace can grow and that change can come. I'm grateful to Sue for writing in a way that can be seen and felt and internalized. What a gift!"

—Beth Niernberg, LMHC, former clinical
director, My Life My Choice

There Is
Nothing
to Fix

Best Wishes!

There Is Nothing to Fix

Suzanne Jones

Becoming Whole Through Radical Self-Acceptance

LA
KE

PUBLICATIONS

Published by LAKE Publications, Somerville, MA

Edited and designed by Girl Friday Productions
girlfridayproductions.com

Cover design: Emily Mahon
Project management: Bethany Davis
Image credits: Cover photo by Cig Harvey, www.cigharvey.com

ISBN (paperback): 978-1-7340835-0-7
ISBN (ebook): 978-1-7340835-1-4
Library of Congress Control Number: 2019915621

First edition

For Lucy

INTRODUCTION

Remember the spirit of childhood? The imagination, creativity, sense of adventure and optimism. As kids we see no limitations for our future—we exclaim we want to be a doctor, a glamorous actress, even the president of the United States! We see the world through a curious and colorful lens—full of possibilities. We run, laugh, play and feel free. But as we get older, that spirit dims, and we wonder where it went or forget about it almost entirely.

We are all born with an authentic spirit. Through our developing years, that spirit erodes as we sacrifice authenticity in favor of things we need as children to survive, like love, connection and belonging. All children adapt. Whether we have normal experiences or experiences of trauma and neglect in childhood, we develop adaptations in our bodies and later in our minds and behaviors. These adaptations help us survive; they are our superpowers.

The term *superpowers* comes from Dr. Nadine Burke Harris, pediatrician and current surgeon general of California.[1] When Dr. Burke Harris talks about childhood trauma, she flashes an ear-to-ear grin and says, "Batman was an orphan! Superman was a refugee! The X-Men lived in a group home! Trauma gives us superpowers!" Humans are innately genius. Our developed superpowers are a mechanism of the resilience that is a part of our biology. Whether we have identified our early life as traumatic or not, the survival adaptations that at one time kept us safe become maladaptive as we move into adulthood. Eventually they keep us disconnected from our authenticity. And in many cases—they hurt us.

This book describes how and why we go through this process as children. You'll read examples of how others have adapted, and you'll explore your own adaptive process. You'll begin to see how your negative thoughts and behaviors were once your childhood superpowers that kept you alive and connected. You'll understand how and why they have become outdated and are now negatively impacting your life.

You'll gain a clear understanding of the work involved in updating your superpowers so you can reconnect to your authentic self. As you travel the path back to your original self, you will gain *new* superpowers (which I call embodied resources) that will help you feel free and happy. These are things you've had inside you all along, and this book will help you discover them from within.

This book is also a story. It's a story of how I unwittingly grew from a vivacious and enthusiastic girl to an insecure and confused teenager and eventually a depressed and suicidal mother of two who lost my connection with the essence of my true spirit.

It's a story of a series of devastating and traumatic events that led me to seek answers to why and how I ended up wanting to take my own life. I found support for recovery in things like yoga, meditation and traditional talk therapy. But to find my path to freedom and happiness, there was a missing puzzle piece. As far and wide as I searched, I could not find it.

So I created the missing piece. It is not found outside of you—it is *inside* of you. I created a pathway called TIMBo (trauma-informed mind body), and it worked for women around the world, and then it worked for me. It continues to work—and not just for women. TIMBo is a pathway any and all of us can follow as we journey back to our true selves.

Although I will talk about trauma, this is not a book that serves only people who identify as trauma survivors. In fact, early in the course of my work I realized one thing: we are all survivors of trauma, because trauma is not about a traumatic event. It is not found only on a list of terrifying life experiences that qualify as traumatic.

Whether we are conscious of it or not, trauma lives in almost everyone's body. Maybe we inherited it from our parents and their parents, which would make us susceptible to encoding more trauma as our life continues. Maybe we felt traumatized by the supposedly normal parenting or schooling we received as children. Regardless, the way we develop trauma in our body is through any experience in which the body feels in danger. And the body can feel in danger even before we can walk, talk or think.

I have sat in circles with women who have stories that are difficult for me to fathom. But I have also sat in circles with women who claim they have had good families, good lives and happy childhoods. I have no doubt of that. But these same women also have crippling anxiety, are frozen in fear or can't bear to sit in silence or witness the suffering of another. These limitations were once their superpowers. Not making sense to you? It will as you continue reading through these chapters.

We all were once children, and we all have adapted. In that process we have lost parts of ourselves. This is the human condition. As Dr. Mark Epstein states in his book *The Trauma of Everyday Life*, "Trauma is an indivisible part of human existence. It takes many forms but spares no one."[2]

So this book is for you. It's for your father, your sister, your brother, wife, cousin, colleague and husband. This book explores the manner in which *all* human beings adapt to stay safe. There are times when I mention *trauma* or *trauma survivors* because there are categories of experiences recognized by the community at large as *traumatic*. The individuals who have experienced such traumas (physical, emotional or sexual abuse, violence at the hands of a fellow human, etc.) are more likely to develop superpowers in childhood that over the years turn toward self-destruction.

Regardless of your life experiences or level of dissatisfaction, confusion, suffering, anxiety or trauma symptoms, I promise you—this book will change your life. Not by changing the external circumstances of your life, but by changing your *relationship* to the external circumstances of your life. You will recalibrate your superpowers from prioritizing protection to cultivating resilience. To get through life, we need to go back to that child we once were and see their remarkable ability to adapt in response to all our life experiences. We need to thank them and set them free.

This dramatic shift begins with changing the relationship you have with yourself—and from there you will begin to experience significant improvements in the quality of your life and your ability to experience true happiness. You will feel confident in living a life as who you really are, and you will feel unafraid to let others truly see you. It takes work. But if you commit to using the tools, method and practices in this book, you can indeed find happiness. This path is radical because it is simple. It's radical because you already have what you need inside of you. And it all begins with changing yourself from the inside out.

PART 1

The Journey
Away from Self

CHAPTER 1

At Least I Was Loved

There are no bruises or broken bones. There are no violent outbursts, calls to 911 or restraining orders. It's a slow and steady erosion of your connection to reality. At first, he's too good to be true. He showers you with praise and gifts and makes you feel like the most incredible woman in the world. As your trust in him increases, he begins to work on isolating you. You become disconnected from the world around you. You push away your family and your friends and begin to see him as your sole source of support.

He's such a kind and wonderful person—of course he knows what's right and what's wrong for you. He tells you all the ways in which you can improve yourself. You believe him. When you tell him that you see things differently, he convinces you that you are mistaken or paranoid or selfish or overly suspicious. He's a master at biting sarcasm, belittlement and criticism that chips away at your self-esteem. He wraps it all up in a joke and delivers it with a smirk. When you protest, you are told that you are too serious or have no sense of humor. You realize you have a lot of work to do on yourself.

You commit to fixing yourself. By the time a few decades have passed, you've erased the girl you once were, the woman you once thought you were becoming. You do this because it is causing this person—a man who you believe is better than you—harm. You do not want to harm anyone, so thank God you have found someone who can point out the ways in which you are doing so. Without him you would have continued to be a subpar human in this world. Who would love a person like you other than this incredibly giving and sacrificing man? How lucky you are to have him—without him you would be all alone. An unlovable woman, unloved. At least you are loved.

THE GIRL I WAS

In 1988 I was a young woman ready to embark on an exciting new chapter of life. I had recently earned a bachelor of fine arts degree in graphic design from the Rhode Island School of Design. Between my junior and senior year, I'd spent a summer taking a filmmaking course at New York University. The thrill of living in that city was something I can still feel in my cells even today, more than thirty years later. So in late summer of 1988 I found my home in New York City.

The daily buzz of city living was like an addictive dose of adrenaline, and I loved everything about being a young, independent and enthusiastic city girl. New York immediately felt like home to me, especially since several of my best high-school friends had graduated the prior year and were already living there and loving life.

Ever since high school I'd felt a strong sense of belonging with these friends. We maintained close ties all through college—spending as many minutes of the day (and night) as we could with one another during summer breaks. Once I moved to New York City, my sense of community with this group continued and intensified. After feeling out of place all through childhood and college, I was finally living a life that felt right for me. If you've ever seen an episode of the popular nineties sitcom *Friends*, you can get a good sense of what my life in New York City was like. To me, life was perfect.

A NEW FRIEND

At the very start of 1991 I was introduced to a new friend in the city, and we hit it off immediately. There was an energetic connection that felt powerful, and if he hadn't had a girlfriend already, I surely would have wanted to fill that role.

As it happens, he also had a group of friends that had relocated to New York City after college, and they were very connected. *How great would it be if we got our two friend groups together?* we thought. This is how on January 11, 1991, I found myself at a local Irish bar on East Twenty-Third Street in Manhattan, sitting across from my new friend's roommate, Mitch.

Mitch had sauntered through the door with the demeanor of an I'm-too-cool-for-this-crowd rock star, and he looked the part too. He had thick shoulder-length brown hair and wore a worn leather biker jacket that groaned and creaked when he bent his arms. He was good-looking in a Kurt Cobain kind of way. That is to say his hair clearly hadn't seen a brush for who knows how long. His fuck-it attitude made me less concerned about basic hygiene and more caught up in the intrigue and mystery that seemed to surround him like a low-hanging cloud. He was tall and slim with angular features and aloof enough that he would feel like an incredible conquest should one woman catch his undivided attention. But something about him made my hackles rise. My aversion was immediate.

As the evening went on, I watched Mitch hit it off with one of my friends, Sean. Sean was my best friend in the city. When we weren't at work we spent most of our time together shopping, listening to show tunes, dancing and laughing until our bellies hurt. My aversion to Mitch began to soften. The following weekend we went on our first date.

Like many young romance stories go, we quickly began spending most of our time together. But I was not long out of a three-year relationship with a college boyfriend and was resistant to getting into another relationship. By the time I'd stepped into that Irish bar I'd been living, for the first time, in my own one-bedroom apartment in Brooklyn, loving my independent life and committed to staying single. I had plans. I wanted to spend the summer somewhere outside of the city. By now I'd spent a few summers in New York, and I craved fresh air, the sea breeze and to work, for a brief period, in nature. A relationship was going to mess up my plans.

But Mitch seemed too good to be true. His model good looks made him the object of desire to so many women. He came from money. I had grown up (with Sean and the rest of my New York City friends) in a depressed coal-mining town in Pennsylvania. Mitch came from a wealthy Boston suburb, which felt exotic and exciting. But best of all, Mitch seemed really crazy about me. How could I, a former ugly-duckling misfit from Nowheresville, Pennsylvania, be the object of desire to such a stunning and perfect- seeming man? I was like Mary Jo Kopechne—a small-town gal from my same hometown who was dazzled by the allure of the Kennedys.

Before long he began insisting that I explain to my former boy-friend (whom I was still friends with) as well as my friends that I had a new priority—him. He began teaching me how to be a better person by pointing out the basic behaviors I should have learned as a child. Things like saying *please* and *thank you* at the appropriate times. I was already putting him on a high moral platform, feeling like I had met someone who could point out ways to be a better person in the world. It was my family, he reminded me, that was to blame for many of these early flaws he identified in me. He assured me that it wasn't really my fault. I was ignorant.

Less than three months into the relationship he began introducing a concept that had, until now, been foreign to me—you don't have to love or even like your family simply because you are related to them. It was as if he was telling me the earth was square. Loving my family was a fundamental belief that I did not question, but after he suggested it a number of times I thought, *I guess so.*

I had told him of my plans to move to a coastal town for the sum-mer, and he asked to come with me. He was so considerate. He prom-ised he wouldn't get in the way. He just had never met a woman like me, he said. He made me feel like I was one in a million, a needle in a haystack. He would do anything to stay near me, he said. But of course, he assured me, if I *preferred* to go alone, he would be waiting for me when I came back.

I didn't want him to come. My instincts told me I should go alone. But a crushing feeling of guilt in my chest overrode my instincts. I felt like turning him down would be a selfish act. By this time, he had pointed out many such selfish behaviors of mine. I didn't want to be a bad person.

HOOK, LINE AND SINKER

A trip home to Pennsylvania to have all four of my wisdom teeth removed turned the tide of my commitment to Mitch. I had come home alone and was staying with my parents so my family dentist could perform the surgery. Several times a day Mitch and I spoke on the phone and professed how we ached for one another. He had to work at the mom-and-pop production company where he had been recently hired, though he insisted he wanted nothing more than to be by my side.

Just a few hours later he called me from a pay phone at the Port Authority Bus Terminal in New York City, telling me he was about to get on a bus. He would be by my side in less than three hours. This (I told myself) was a truly selfless and incredible human being. In the face of such goodness, how could I turn down his desire to come on my summer adventure with me? When we returned to New York we began our search for coastal towns that we could call our home that coming summer. We visited local bookstores and looked at books filled with idyllic pictures of coastal villages in New England and the Chesapeake Bay.

In May of 1991 we began living together in a house on Mount Desert Island, home to Bar Harbor, Maine. I had sublet my coveted one-bedroom apartment and had every intention of returning to it in the fall.

JUST ME AND THE PERFECT MAN

We spent every moment of every day together that summer. We had made a trip up in early spring and secured jobs on a sailboat that took tourists around Frenchman Bay. We marveled at the scenery, the Porcupine Islands and the sunsets. From the middle of the deep harbor, we glided under the power of the wind and gazed toward the village of Bar Harbor.

We made friends together, explored the hikes and trails of Acadia National Park together and took day trips up and down the coast together. We enjoyed quiet dinners with just the two of us in our rented house on a wooded street. I was twenty-five years old, and he was only twenty-three—yet we felt so domesticated and grown-up.

But we were barely into that first summer when Mitch started to make it clear he had problems with the way I did certain everyday things. One day, Mitch told me he had a problem with the way I put away groceries. He didn't like how I'd empty all the food out of the bags and put it away first, leaving the paper bags on the floor. After the bags were empty and the food put away, I'd go back and fold up all the bags.

Mitch responded to this practice as if I had been raised by wolves! He insisted that the only way to put groceries away was to empty one bag, fold it up, put the food away and then move on to the next. I pushed back. I told him I'd made it through twenty-five years of life putting groceries away in the same manner, and nothing catastrophic had ever happened. To me, it seemed a silly complaint.

But he pressed. It was clear he wouldn't move on with his day unless I saw the error of my ways. I thought the whole thing was ridiculous, but it seemed to really matter to him. The conversation and its lack of resolution wore me down. I didn't agree with him, but I sure didn't want to have another stupid and exhausting argument about groceries, so I made sure I never made *that* mistake again. It was just a small adjustment. In the end it wouldn't be too much for me to do. If he preferred the groceries be put away that way, it was no big deal.

Gone were the days of living an exciting and independent life in New York City, replaced by an enmeshed life with this "perfect" man. It wasn't exactly what I'd had in mind when I envisioned my summer away. It felt more like an extended vacation with my boyfriend. I'd be back to New York City that fall—at least that was my plan. My friends were waiting for me, even though Mitch made sure to constantly disparage them, with a twist of humor to indicate it was all in good fun.

Summer turned into winter, when we decided to honor the full-year lease that we had signed. Wintertime on Mount Desert Island was dark and isolated. Nearly all the shops were closed and boarded up. The hum of the busy tourist town quieted to a feeling of total hibernation.

Seasonal workers (and many of our friends) returned to college or their next wintertime work destination. I began to feel confined to our house and had only one person for company—him.

That same winter I gained an uneasy feeling that this man had an unhealthy obsession with sex. I found phone bills with hundreds of calls to 900 numbers—the nineties version of what would become online porn and easy access to sexual partners. When I confronted him he convinced me that I was an oversensitive prude who didn't have a healthy relationship with sex. I believed him. I did my best to keep things exciting (sexually speaking), but the winter wasn't half over before I began to get a what-have-I-gotten-myself-into feeling. I argued with my instincts: It was probably just the winter. Or me. Or both.

Around this time, I also started to realize I didn't like the way I felt inside when Mitch talked to me. His proclamations of *You're not making any sense! You don't know how to communicate. What are you talking about? Are you seriously telling me you believe that?* left me feeling misunderstood and stupid. At the time I didn't know this is exactly what abusers *want* you to believe about yourself. It is only then that they can truly control you.

I decided not to ask him to change the way he spoke to me. Instead, I would end the relationship and free myself of the constant feeling of being stupid and flawed. I would free him of the constant struggle to understand my feelings, my point of view, how I made sense of the world—how I put groceries away. So after a day of cross-country skiing where I once again felt like I had completely fucked up what we had hoped would be a nice day together, I plucked up the courage to tell him what had been on my mind. I told him I didn't like the way I felt when he talked to me, I didn't expect him to change, and I felt the answer was to end the relationship. He began to cry. He professed his undying love for me. He promised he would change. He begged me to give him a chance to show me. So I did.

His tears and pleas fueled my growing "realization" that what he had pointed out to me was probably true. I was a selfish and inconsiderate person. What kind of person would I be if I didn't give him a chance? That winter turned into another summer working together. So when we were twenty-six and twenty-four, we once again found jobs working together at a local restaurant that catered to the droves of tourists who visited Bar Harbor each season.

We saved all our tips from that summer job so we could travel the coming winter. I did not want to spend another winter in Maine and was eager to get back to the city that I loved. But while we traveled around Spain it became increasingly clear that Mitch did not want to move back. We argued about it. I felt misled and betrayed. *This wasn't in my original plan!* During that trip we argued about everything. Stupid fights. We would argue until I broke down in tears and conceded.

By this time I had become dependent on him emotionally and financially. At the same time, I'd become more distant from my family, isolated from my close friends and removed from any career goals I had developed in New York. My pull toward New York felt strong, but my connections were fractured. He was my connection to the world now.

Even though I was starting to feel uneasy about how I felt with Mitch, I also wanted him to love me enough that he'd want to marry me. He resisted whenever I brought up the topic. It's not that he didn't want to marry me, he said. It was that he didn't want to marry any-body. How could I argue?

I started to become more aware of what seemed to be bizarre and even cruel treatment over the next year or so. For instance, on several occasions he'd spontaneously ask me to marry him—always after a night of drinking and partying with friends. *He finally asked!* I would think with excitement and couldn't wait to talk about it the next day. But when I would bring up the subject the following morning he'd laugh and tell me he didn't really mean it. He was just drunk.

By the summer of 1993 we had been living in Maine for a couple years. With his encouragement, I had agreed to pull away from my family and friends and now had only a small social group that we had met together. There was no more me; there was only us. Mitch and Sue. Sue and Mitch. A package deal.

My ability to have any reality check or reference point from the outside was limited. Remember: this was before cell phones, the inter-net, FaceTime or Facebook. Connecting with support networks was not easy.

When he finally asked me to marry him for real, I had a dim feeling of reluctance. But by then I was so isolated, and it seemed like he was all I had, so I agreed.

LOSING MYSELF IN THE GASLIGHT

The coming years in Maine ushered me slowly and steadily away from the girl I once knew, and the insidious abuse of the marriage had dimmed my natural inner spark. All that was left was a continuous existence of numbness that ultimately ran on a daily drip of fear, guilt and feelings of never being good enough.

Sex was the only time I felt worthy of his love and affection, yet it was unfulfilling and unpleasant for me. Before long, he used my aversion to physically engaging with him as further proof that I was a selfish woman. He would regularly tell me that I was not doing what a good wife would do. When I asked him if perhaps he could touch me sometimes in a nonsexual way, he told me there was no such thing as nonsexual touch.

By this time my sense of self and my ability to hold firm to my previous points of view had given way to believing everything he told me about the world and about myself. Every positive comment was connected to my physical attractiveness or desirability. He groped me and grabbed me all day every day. I tried getting thin. I tried gaining weight. None of it changed the way I felt. My life with him became a constant commentary on all the ways that I was flawed, coming up short and making his life miserable.

His complaints told me that I needed to work on myself more, fix myself, find the formula for being a good, kind, caring, generous and loving wife—and later a good mother. Nothing ever seemed to work.

He developed extremely close relationships with various women in town that made me feel uneasy or insecure. When I confronted him with this, he convinced me that I was being paranoid and overreacting. He would tell me that he was the kind of guy who related better to women than men. More in touch with his feminine side than most men. I would feel like a jealous and unreasonable woman.

Later when the internet began to be available, I would discover suspicious things on our computer—sexually explicit photos or messages from what seemed like *real* women. Again, he would either make up an excuse, become enraged at having his privacy invaded or claim ignorance. He would often say things like "To tell you the truth, I have no idea what that is." I was so consumed with the guilt of not trusting him or the shame of invading his privacy that each time this happened I felt simultaneously recommitted to fixing myself and a growing conviction that it would never be possible.

After a few years he had an arsenal of statements to use against me. He would tell me "You yourself said . . . ," to which I might reply, "I've changed my mind." He would tell me I couldn't do that. Normal people didn't say one thing and then change their mind. It's not the way it works. I got the message and became wary of getting ensnared in a conversation where I might say something I hadn't completely thought through. So I began to try ending a conversation the moment I felt confused and overwhelmed. He told me that I couldn't just end a conversation because I didn't like the way it was going. He told me how things were, as if he were the authority. I believed him. He knew better. If he said that's not how it works, then it must be true. I gave up. It was safer to stop talking.

As hard as I tried we couldn't agree on where to relocate. I finally agreed to stay in Maine for good. I spent a year writing a business plan, getting investors and opening a little cafe in Bar Harbor. By the summer of 1994 we had bought a house together, gotten married and were expanding our community of local friends.

I was a twenty-eight-year-old woman trying to learn how to run a business while it was in operation. I struggled with employees, with customers and with the crushing feeling of being completely responsible for whether the venture succeeded or failed. I needed someone to talk to about the stress that was crushing me, but he couldn't listen to my feelings of being overwhelmed, so I shut up. Again.

The first spring my restaurant was open, Mitch had agreed to help me by working the evening shift while I worked the morning shift. I began stopping in to say hi to Mitch, and each time a woman named Leah was there. I would walk in, the place quiet with the exception of Leah leaning over the counter as if she were trying to get as close to Mitch as she could while remaining on the customer side. I began to feel insecure, worried and confused. Where did this woman come from? Who was she? Why was she always there? Mitch laughed my concerns aside.

But one day he said to me, out of the blue, "Guess what Leah told me?"

"What?" I answered.

He said Leah told him a more vulgar version of this: if he were her boyfriend, she would never stop sexually pleasing him.

Immediately I said, "No she didn't." What he suggested was absolutely absurd to me. "No woman would ever say a thing like that to any man."

Still he insisted, and still I called bullshit on it. But he didn't give up and spent what seemed like forty-five minutes convincing me that she did in fact say that to him.

Eventually I believed him. Why else would he put so much effort in convincing me?

I broke down crying. I was scared, alone and now threatened.

Mitch began laughing at me. He told me he couldn't believe how gullible I was. I looked up at him and said, "What's *wrong* with you? What kind of person thinks that is funny? That is just messed up and cruel!"

Mitch responded with anger, accusing me of being oversensitive and having no sense of humor. I believed him.

I was being beat down. Every criticism began to feel like a mallet slamming the top of my head, every comment a blow. I was losing my center, existing in an increasing sense of fog and avoiding connecting with him at every turn. Occasionally he would profess his love for me, buy me unexpected and lavish gifts and tell me he couldn't live without me. That I was the love of his life. In those moments I forgot about all the rest.

MOTHERHOOD SEALS THE DEAL

Two years into our marriage, at the age of thirty, I became pregnant. When my son was born I struggled with postpartum depression, and Mitch stepped up. My friends and family marveled at what a wonderful husband and father he was. As a stay-at-home dad he began hanging out with all the new moms and local young families while I worked myself to exhaustion every July and August. Not a day went by that he didn't remind me that I could be spending more time with him and our son. Technically he was right. His trust fund could support our family, at least in the short term. But I was committed to making my endeavor a success. He continued to remind me of how selfish I was for keeping the restaurant. He called it my hobby.

The third winter of parenthood, Mitch decided to take a two-week photography class in Cuba. A trip away from home was very unusual for him, and while he was gone I just couldn't shake the feeling that I would rather he didn't come back. A mutual friend came to visit me during those two weeks, and I tearfully confided in her. The relief I felt from the crushing weight of his criticisms and constant need for more gave me a tiny taste of what freedom could feel like.

I felt like a horrid person for feeling this way. I was married to a man who—along with his tendency to point out all my flaws—told me that I was the love of his life. I had a little boy, no sustainable income of my own, no friends of my own and now more of a connection with his family than my own. Leaving seemed impossible.

One day Mitch told me he wanted me to become pregnant again. I had suffered with severe postpartum depression and an undiagnosed hypothyroid condition after my first son was born. I was extremely nervous about going through that again, but Mitch gave me what seemed like an ultimatum. He said if we didn't have another child it would be a problem. I chose to have another child.

As our family grew we decided to renovate our house from top to bottom. Because we would have to move out during this process, I saw an opportunity to revisit a dream I had when I was single and living in New York. We would move to Italy for six months. This wasn't quite what I had in mind back then, but it was something.

We found a farmhouse to rent outside a little town in the hills of Umbria. After less than two weeks of living in Italy I knew I could never go back to Maine. I felt like I had escaped prison. The thought of going back was suffocating. One day I collapsed on the kitchen floor of our farmhouse and choked through my sobs, "I can't go back. Please don't make me go back!" He finally agreed. We would move to Boston after our six months in Italy.

CHAPTER 2

"Go Fix Yourself"

After twelve long years I finally felt free from the isolation in Maine. We moved into Cambridge—a historic town across the river from Boston and home to Harvard University. The aliveness of Cambridge was a reminder of my long-lost life in New York City. Almost instantly I began to find activities and communities that helped me feel a little more connection to that city girl from long ago.

I took painting classes, violin lessons and Italian lessons. Right away I noticed how much I enjoyed doing things that didn't involve my husband.

Developing more autonomy and loosening my dependence on Mitch coincided with an increasing aversion to any physical intimacy with him at all. Sex had come to feel like a chore or a quota I was required to fill. In return I received his love and commitment to staying married to me.

I still claimed responsibility for being the problem. Once again, I committed to fixing myself. I had to find the source of my sexual aversion. Was it the sexual molestation by a family acquaintance that I had a vague memory of? Sexual molestation by a doctor I experienced at sixteen? Sexual harassment by boss after boss? Or maybe it was something that happened to me as a baby or young child? Something I didn't remember?

We went to a number of therapists, including a sex specialist. Mitch professed his undying love and support for me. He maintained that he would do whatever it took to help me fix myself. I became increasingly hopeless that I would ever be normal. Each day took me one step further into despair.

A GLIMMER OF HOPE

For almost a year and a half I felt despondent about being such a problematic and sexually dysfunctional wife. And then one day—January 8, 2005, to be exact—I tried my first yoga class. It is a date I will always remember, because from that day forward my life began to change.

I had attempted yoga after my first son was born while living in Maine. But back then I used a DIY book and practiced in the isolation of my home. My local yoga studio in Cambridge was an entirely new experience. It was a welcoming environment and a clear community, and practicing in a room with fifty to eighty people felt life altering. I began to feel physically alive and connected, at least to myself. The inspiring words of my teacher left me feeling like life could be different. That *I* could be different.

What happened after that seems like a whirlwind of divine intervention and a light-speed unraveling of everything I knew. A few days after that first yoga class I reconnected with a friend named Daniel, who had just separated from his wife after she told him she was gay. It started as an intense friendship. I was a supportive ear for Daniel as he struggled with the recent split from his wife. But soon he was supporting me as I confided all my feelings of despair about my marriage. His response took me completely by surprise. It wasn't *me* that was not normal, he said. It was the things my husband said and did and alluded to that were not normal.

Still I didn't want to upset my marriage. I didn't want to rock the boat. But I was now talking with a man who listened to and heard me in a way Mitch never did. And he didn't make me feel completely crazy like Mitch did. Where Mitch might tell me, "That doesn't make any sense at all. That's just not normal," Daniel would say, "That makes absolute sense. You're really smart and articulate." Smart and articulate? *Wait, what?*

It was like I had been living in an oxygen-deprivation tank for a dozen years and now was breathing fully oxygenated air. This new way of seeing myself and my situation was simultaneously completely foreign and a massive relief. I continued yoga, and with each class I continued awakening to the truth. I was not happy. I was not living the life I wanted to live. Most memorably, I was not the person that I knew I was deep down. I had lost that vivacious and independent city girl. I was a shadow, and I knew I wanted out.

Leading up to this point my husband and I had several intense arguments about my "selfishness." I wasn't living up to what being a good wife meant. I wasn't backing him up on parenting approaches, and I wasn't being compliant enough when it came to how he wanted things to be. I was desperate to find a solution that would make him happy, telling myself that if Mitch were happy, I would be happy too. Sex made him happy, so I tried everything—things I am ashamed of. There might have been a temporary period of him feeling satisfied, but it was short-lived.

I finally suggested that if it was sex that was so important to him, we could work out an arrangement. I was done trying to be what he wanted. I loathed being close to him. I recoiled at his touch and never initiated sex. I pretended to enjoy sex even though I didn't. I found ways to get myself to orgasm quickly so it would be over. I couldn't do it anymore. The thought of him going outside the marriage to satisfy his need for sex felt like a relief to me. But once again his eyes teared up, and he softly cried and told me he couldn't think of such a thing. He told me he was born monogamous. And once again I felt like the most vile and selfish woman in the world.

One day he asked me to have sex with him in his usual unromantic and hey-let's-have-a-game-of-tennis way. I'd already told him many times this approach did not work for me, and I told him again now. I couldn't just go upstairs with him, lie down and let him have his way. I wouldn't. In response he told me that 99.9999 percent of the problems in the marriage were because of me, and if I would just fix myself, everything would be great.

There was a dissatisfaction brewing in me. I don't know if it was because I had begun practicing yoga, a mind-body practice that awakens you in ways that allow you to see the world through a different lens. Or perhaps the move to Boston was showing me that there was a bigger world out there, and I wanted something better. It could have been that my increasingly intimate relationship with Daniel was showing me what a mutually loving and respectful relationship with a man could be. Maybe a combination of all these things was converging like tectonic plates.

Finally, on Valentine's Day 2005, I found the courage to tell my husband I thought I was in love with Daniel. At the time I did not intend to leave the marriage—mostly because I did not want to hurt my children.

Once I told him I might be in love with another man, he became so venomous that I couldn't bear being near him. Through his rage he spat things like "Why did you make me marry you?" He proclaimed that I wasted the best years of his life. Then, on the turn of a dime, he would call me, crying, professing his love and asking, "How can you do this to me? Can't you see how much you're hurting me?"

Every day I talked with two people: Daniel and my youngest sister. They were both lifelines during a time when I felt completely lost in the dark. I credit my sister in particular for saving me during this time. She pointed out that I sounded like an abused woman. *Abused woman?* I couldn't grasp it. I told her of my husband's increased grasp for total control now that he knew I was in contact with people outside his sphere of influence. He demanded that I cease contact with Daniel and flew into a rage when he checked my cell phone call history and saw that I wasn't complying with his demands. My sister told me I could take a break from the marriage—she reminded me that I was a grown woman who could rent an apartment and take a time-out. I couldn't fathom it. Just the thought felt excruciating.

I went home to spend time with my family—time that Mitch classified as abandoning my children. I spent the better part of a week with my parents and close family friends, describing how my husband talked to me. How he treated me. All through a never-ending stream of tears.

"You've been brainwashed," they told me. *Brainwashed?* I was scared. I was confused.

Daniel was showing me there was a different kind of relationship that was possible, but feelings of worthlessness have deep roots. No matter how wonderful Daniel was, I was still convinced that when he saw the real me, he would be repulsed and flee as fast as he could in the opposite direction. Years spent being reminded of how broken I was convinced me that no one but Mitch could love me. Leaving Mitch to run into the arms of Daniel meant risking that Daniel would eventually drop me like a hot rock. In my mind, I couldn't fathom turning away from the only love I felt I would get.

Looking back, I think my sister knew what I could and couldn't hear. Somewhere in our hours and hours of phone conversations she suggested this: sometimes you have to rebreak the bone for it to heal properly. That was it. I could hear that. I could conceptualize leaving the marriage to fix myself and *then* determining if the marriage was healthy or not. I rented an apartment. Mitch agreed to let the kids remain in the family home while we took turns staying at the apartment. I told Daniel I couldn't work on myself and decide on my marriage while I was in a romantic relationship with him. We stopped talking.

SUICIDE SEEMED LIKE THE NOBLE CHOICE

While I was separated from Mitch, I felt lost and alone, spiraling into a dark pit of self-loathing and crippling guilt. I still saw this man as the knower of all that was right and good; I took every criticism he handed me as an absolute truth. So, after so many years of trying to fix myself, I was ready to surrender to the fact that I was unfixable. That I would never be a positive presence in anyone's life. That I was hurting people by simply being alive.

One June evening I methodically planned every detail of my final day on earth. I would wait till the kids were with their dad, clean the house from top to bottom, take a bath, swallow all the pills I'd been collecting and drift away, feeling satisfied I was making my husband's and children's lives better. I would finally be doing the right thing.

While I waited for that final day to come, I continued with intensive therapy that I had begun in March. My therapist, Joan, referred me to a psychopharmacologist who told me I was a danger to myself. He prescribed antidepressants and made me promise to hand my pills over to Joan that very day. That evening I met Joan on a street corner, and I reluctantly handed over my bag of pills. *There's more where that came from,* I thought.

Though I was still in a deep depression, I got out of bed each day only to get to yoga class—my singular place of relief. Stepping on that two-by-six-foot mat each day was my refuge. I told myself I could just lie there and sleep if I wanted to. Sometimes I did, but most days I breathed and moved. Each day I began to see more clearly.

With time, space and a commitment to my overall health, I began to question the things that Mitch had been telling me over our fourteen years together. Talking with others helped me consider that Mitch's behavior was unusual, unhealthy and even abusive. One day I decided to google *emotional abuse.*

There it was in black and white: Sarcasm, check. Criticism, check. Belittling, check and check. There was more:

A partner that wants to know where you are at all times and checks in constantly.

A partner that says hurtful things about you in the form of jokes.

You walk on eggshells to avoid disappointing your partner.

You've lost sexual desire for your partner (oh, did I ever).

And on it went. Each line I read was like another punch in the gut. Maybe my sister was right—I had to break the bone to heal it. The bone was me, and I needed to heal myself. I needed a chance to become strong again.

THIS TIME IT WOULD BE DIFFERENT

I committed to healing my own wounds—wounds that were a result of fourteen years of slow-drip abuse. I continued practicing yoga, experiencing new relationships and new communities, and I wanted desperately to get myself to a healthy enough place so I could come back to the marriage and change things. My greatest worry was for my children. I wanted them to have an intact family.

After ten months of gaining strength, clarity and a piece of my adult self back, I returned to my marriage with a list of conditions, which included things I would not tolerate. Sarcasm, criticism and belittling were at the top of my list. I would also not engage in conversations of character assassination (something at which he was very skilled). He agreed to my conditions.

I felt strong. I would not listen to him telling me who I was, what I did and why I did it. I was the authority on me, not him. I held him to these promises, pointing out to him each time he engaged in these behaviors and reminding him that he had agreed to my conditions.

I continued with my yoga, increasing the amount of time I practiced each week. I no longer felt that my husband's word was the absolute truth. Slowly I began to see things in him that I hadn't seen before. Things like cruel psychological treatment of me and the children, sexually inappropriate images and language around the house and in front of the kids, and alarmingly disrespectful behavior for no apparent reason.

I began paying attention to small things. Things that in the past could lead to me feeling like I was crazy. For example, Mitch routinely complained that I slammed the toilet lid down every time I went to the bathroom in the middle of the night. The old me would have felt like I was losing my mind because I was so careful to place that lid down without a sound. But this time I very consciously noted that I was not making a sound, yet still he told me that I was slamming it and waking him up. Every time it was the same. I did not take the blame, yet I couldn't explain why he would insist that I was waking him up. I silently began asking myself if this really was the person I wanted to spend the rest of my life with.

AN OLD MEMORY BREAKS ME OPEN

In February of 2006, two months after I had returned to my marriage, my favorite yoga instructor suggested I attend a weeklong teacher-training intensive in Hawaii. "It will deepen your practice," she said. I couldn't have known what she meant. I signed up without hesitation.

We spent the start and finish of each day practicing yoga and going on silent meditation walks along the shoreline. Between these practices, though, we were guided through exercises of self-investigation and engaged in discussions where we were invited to share our insights.

Through these exercises, I began to notice something painful about myself: each time I considered speaking in front of the group, I was convinced that nothing I had to say could have any value. When I did choose to speak, I was consumed with shame and regret afterward, convinced that what I said was entirely asinine and not in the least useful to anyone.

As the days wore on, I started believing that my very existence at this training was ruining the experience of all the other participants, as if I were a bad apple in a barrel, creating rot in the rest of the healthy apples. In response, I began to isolate myself. I sat farther and farther away from anyone at meals. I pulled away from connecting with anyone by retreating into the safety of silence or allowing myself to get swallowed up in crowd activities.

The most visceral memory of that week was a traumatic childhood memory that resurfaced and the intense grief that erupted in me, regardless of my protests or efforts to suppress it. Every day I would run to the bathroom stall, fall apart for a few minutes, pull myself together and join the group once again. I was confused by the intensity of the emotion this old memory was stirring in me and angry that I couldn't make it stop. I thought I had dealt with it long ago in psychotherapy. The memory just kept bubbling up to the surface on a tsunami of grief. The more I ducked into the bathroom to sob, the more I knew I was only releasing a modicum of the pressure inside. I could tell there was so much more, and it felt scary, overwhelming and puzzling.

It wasn't necessarily the incident itself that was unearthing so much grief. It was the realization of how it had shaped me and how that shaping impacted my life in the years to follow. Even now, it is hard for me to write about this moment in my childhood, but it was such a milestone in changing the course of my life I couldn't leave it out.

One day when I was about twelve years old, my father asked me to tend to a chore. As a sassy, budding adolescent I rebelled by giving a smartass reply. Suddenly my father flew into a fit of rage the likes of which I had never experienced before and haven't experienced since. He'd always been the disciplinarian of the family, conducting routine spankings, which were an acceptable form of punishment back in the late sixties and early seventies. But what happened next was not discipline—it was an unleashed, terrifying assault.

My memory is of my father throwing and kicking me out of the living room, up the staircase, onto the bed, off the bed and back down the stairs, all the while screaming at me in an uncontrolled rage. True to how traumatic memory works, I vividly remember pieces of that incident: my face hitting the shag rug, my back hitting the bed, my father's shoes making contact with my body, his terrifying rage (more than his specific words), my scrambling like a crab to get out of reach and my screams of "No, Daddy, no!" More than anything, I remember feeling like he might kill me.

In that moment, when I felt like I might die that day, there was one thought that remains crystal clear in my memory: if my father—who is supposed to love me and protect me—wants to actually kill me, there must be something so rotten in me that I won't be able to fix it. The feeling of being rotten was consuming my yoga training experience, and the resurfacing of this memory allowed me to realize how many years I had carried this belief with me.

As I grew older and eventually left the household, my relationship with my father became something that I love and treasure. He is a kind, generous and loving human being. He is an outstanding grandfather. But the truth is there was that one day in my life when I didn't recognize him.

As much as that incident impacted me, it was the total silence that followed that sealed shame and unworthiness into my self-belief system. Years later I learned that both my sister and my uncle (who witnessed the event) went to my mother and told her what happened that day. I don't remember her saying a word to me.[1]

The perceived deafening family silence after that trauma was proof, in my mind, that it was something about me that made it all happen.

The reason that particular memory kept visiting me during that teacher training was that even though I thought I'd dealt with it in talk therapy years ago, it still lived in my body and was defining my experience of that week. Every time I opened my mouth to contribute something to the group (i.e., made myself vulnerable), I was consumed with feelings of shame.

Thoughts flooded in: *What you said was just stupid. You don't have anything meaningful to contribute. Just shut your mouth. Everyone thinks you're an idiot.*

But because I was given a week of space to sit with these sensations, thoughts and actions, I had an epiphany: I was creating an experience for myself because of a belief I had about myself that may not actually be true.

In keeping my mouth shut and isolating myself from the group, I created proof for myself that I did not belong. And because this old memory kept surfacing that week, I connected the feeling of profound shame directly back to that moment when I was twelve—the moment when I told myself that I must be somehow fundamentally rotten.

Finally, during the last lunch of the last day, I confided in a woman I had come to trust. I told her what was happening for me, avoiding the specifics. She encouraged me to stand up and talk about it. She told me she would be right there with me and that I could just look at her to help me get through it. Knowing this woman was willing to be an anchor for me gave me the courage to consider taking her advice.

I waited until the last possible moment on that last night of the training to raise my hand and get up in front of 125 individuals. I stood onstage gripped in fear. The world shrank. Everything went a bit dark, as if I were suddenly in a tunnel. I looked at my friend, which gave me the strength I needed to start talking. Then I completely fell apart, choking on sobs while telling of that memory with my father and the insights I was having around my self-belief. I don't remember what the leader of the training said to me. I don't remember how I got myself off that stage. I only remember sobbing, looking at my friend in the audience and rubbing my thumb on the cap of a pen I happened to be holding.

The next thing I remember was being at dinner and feeling exhausted and embarrassed. Then something happened that I can trace back to as the underpinning of all that TIMBo is built upon. One by one, people came up to me to thank me. *Thank me? For what?* They told me that witnessing my grief and hearing my insight was incredibly helpful for them. That it inspired them to understand their own self-damaging beliefs about themselves and where they might have come from. They called me courageous and inspiring. It was hard to take it in—I felt like a total hot mess. I left that week scratching my head, thinking, *I don't get it.*

While I didn't know it at the time, I began to feel worthy of connection because I allowed myself to be profoundly vulnerable on that stage. That felt like an excruciatingly dangerous risk to take. My courage to be vulnerable in front of all those people was helpful to them, though it felt nothing like courage at the time. In hindsight I recognize that when I was up on that stage, I was showing humanness stripped bare. I let myself be seen as raw and imperfect. The power in that moment for them was in knowing that they were not alone in how they felt—they could relate to the experience. There was a beautiful moment of shared humanity.

THE FLOOR COLLAPSES

During this time, my self-esteem increased a little each day. Shortly after that teacher-training experience, I started a nonprofit called yogaHOPE that offered direct-service yoga classes to women in life transitions. I was especially passionate about bringing yoga to women who might feel broken, like I did. Women in substance-abuse treatment, homeless shelters, domestic-violence safe houses and prison.

All the while, I was collecting a community of local yogis that served as a constant reminder that I did, indeed, have some worth in the world. I was increasingly happy in my life. I told myself I would tolerate my marriage and focused on all the "good" things—like the fact that we were a family and our kids seemed happy. I stood up to the emotional abuse and reminded him of his promise whenever he slipped into old behavior. I truly expected things to get better.

Mitch seemed like he was trying—at least he told me he was. He continued to call me the love of his life. I believed him every time. How could I possibly leave this dedicated man, breaking up my family and hurting him and my children in the process? I couldn't do it.

Just over two years after that training, I experienced the greatest devastation—and ultimately the greatest gift—of my life. It was like any other day. Work, kids and chaos swirled around me and my husband as we tried to get ourselves out the door for a weekly therapist-imposed date night. He ran out to the car to fetch a toy for my youngest, then six years old, who was pitching a fit. I had just gotten home from my little office and ran upstairs to change my clothes. What happened from there was a swift and utter destruction of everything I thought I knew.

It started with my eye catching a strange subject line in his in-box, which he had left up on the computer. It ended just a week or so later with the confusing and crippling realization that my husband—the man who, despite his flaws, I believed to be a truly loyal and dedicated husband and father—had been betraying me for the entirety of our relationship. *I was born monogamous* was a lie. *You are the love of my life* was a lie. *I'm in pain because you are withholding sex* was a lie. Everything he said and did was a lie. Those women "friends" he often introduced me to were his lovers.

After sending an email to several dozen mutual "friends" explaining my discovery, I started receiving call after call from women, telling me through their tears how sorry they were for what they had done. Some of these friends were women we had met together—wives or girlfriends of couples we hung out with. Some were women I had employed at my restaurant in Maine. Some were women he introduced me to, claiming they might need a place to stay for the summer or a summer job. One was a midwife—my midwife! He wasn't a sensitive man in touch with his feminine side. He was a predator.

I couldn't help but think back to three years prior, during our period of separation, when I had nearly taken my own life because I felt like my presence on earth was hurting my loyal and devoted husband. At best, I felt like the chump in a Ponzi scheme or a long con, but mostly I felt stunned and comatose. It was as if a tornado had ripped through my life, taking only seconds to leave it in a pile of ruins. Here I was, standing in the middle of the rubble. This feeling of being completely broadsided left me flat on my back. This was the place from which TIMBo was born.

THE QUESTIONS THAT LAUNCHED A NEW LIFE

To say that I never suspected his deception would not be true. There were many red flags along the way. So I was faced with a host of burning questions. Why was I not able to leave, even after I recognized the emotional abuse in my marriage? Why did it take the discovery of my husband as a lifelong liar, philanderer and wielder of intense psychological cruelty for me to leave and never look back? What was going on inside of me that for seventeen years I did not see this man for who he really was? And why did I desperately want to believe that I was the problem that needed to be fixed?

For one whole year I struggled with these questions. I also struggled to be present for my children. I struggled through the slog of the divorce. And I deeply struggled (and did for many years to follow) with having to turn over my children every week to a man I now despised. I had been living each day thinking *Why me?* and experiencing immeasurable rage and drop-to-your-knees sorrow. But I told myself there was nothing to grieve because all of it was a lie.

After a year of what could only be classified as immobility, I felt ready to move on. I wanted to stop being angry. I wanted to find peace in my life. I wanted to bypass the painful grieving process required to heal. I just wanted to feel OK.

What I wanted was impossible, but I wouldn't learn that until years later.

THE DEEP DIVE

Instead of grieving and compassionately being with all the feelings I was experiencing, I began to intellectualize. I knew that others had false beliefs about themselves that took root in early life and impacted them into adulthood. I understood this because I had witnessed it in my 2006 teacher-training experience in Hawaii.

For me, the belief that I was somehow fundamentally flawed led to a series of life decisions that ultimately brought me to what felt like rock bottom. Everything was gone in one fell swoop. Rock bottom was what I had in common with the women I cared about. Substance-abuse recovery, homelessness, prison and domestic-violence shelters can all be considered places where women land after hitting their rock bottom. And if my end point of rock bottom started in early life experiences, then I could hypothesize that it was the same for all the women that I worked with. I yearned to find out more.

So in May of 2009 I directed all my energy toward a deep dive into women, trauma, trauma theory, trauma-informed programming and gender-responsive programming. I had been slowly learning about these things over the past year but didn't know enough. I called upon my growing yogaHOPE community for help. I told volunteers that I needed everything they could find on women and domestic violence, women and homelessness, women and addiction, women and eating disorders, incarcerated women, women and child abuse, and women and sexual assault.

Each day my volunteers sent me articles, book recommendations and links with information on all these subjects and then some. It was clear that the common denominator to all these issues was early life trauma.

Once again I asked my team of volunteers to help me—this time I wanted them to find everything they could about women and trauma. I spent a year reading books that remain a profound influence to me. Dr. Gabor Maté's book *When the Body Says No* taught me what stress in the body really is. Dr. Maté connected stress in the body with disease and early death in a way that was completely life altering for me.[2]

I read Peter Levine's *Waking the Tiger: Healing Trauma* and learned that trauma is an extreme version of stress in the body. Dr. Levine taught me about how trauma is stored in the body and how it can be healed through an inner awareness of the body.[3]

I found articles on trauma-informed programming and gender-responsive programming. I learned how women are wired to heal in relational contexts, how choice is the key to recovery, and how leveling power dynamics is critical for effective women's programming.[4]

I read Babette Rothschild's *The Body Remembers* and Belleruth Naparstek's *Invisible Heroes*, which gave me insights on women, PTSD and the use of guided imagery for healing trauma.[5]

Another book that especially stood out and would ultimately become instrumental in shaping my future was Caroline Myss's

Anatomy of the Spirit. Like Dr. Maté, Myss also correlated specific emotional, psychological, physical and spiritual stress patterns with diseases. However, she also introduced me to the idea that disease is connected to blocked chakras, or an imbalanced chakra system.[6]

Given my yoga background, this instantly made sense to me. Simply put, chakras are energy centers believed to run along the trajectory of the spinal cord (from the pelvic floor to the crown of the head). Eastern practices such as yoga and qigong are practiced, in part, to balance the chakras. According to Myss, "Every thought and experience you've ever had in your life gets filtered through these chakra databases. Each event is recorded into your cells."[7]

CHAKRAS: A BLUEPRINT OF YOUR LIFE

Jacqui Bonwell, a yoga teacher here in Boston, is a former Department of Health and Human Services social worker turned inspirational local yoga guru. Her no-nonsense, pick-yourself-up-and-get-your-own-back-because-ain't-nobody-gonna-do-it-for-you style of teaching was drawing droves of students who badly needed to hear her firm yet inspiring words of encouragement.

Jacqui was single-handedly responsible for sparking the transformation and evolution of many of my closest friends. She also seemed to know everything there was to know about the chakra system.

In July of 2010, I emailed Jacqui and asked for help in developing the framework for a program I was developing (a framework we now call the Emotional Anatomy Pyramid). She enthusiastically agreed with a resounding yes. I explained my idea to her and emphasized the importance of accessible and simple language. I knew in my bones that whatever materialized from all this research, I wanted it to transcend culture, religious beliefs and social class. I wanted it to be a place where women could relate to one another simply because they were *women*— who all shared feelings inherent in the human experience.

Jacqui began by sending me all the information she had on the chakra system. I then asked her to help me distill each chakra down to the basic elements of emotions associated with both a balanced chakra and a disrupted chakra. Together we pulled out the simplest descriptive emotion that could be applied to a disrupted chakra. The list looked like this:

Chakra one: fear
Chakra two: guilt
Chakra three: shame
Chakra four: resentment, grief
Chakra five: feeling stuck
Chakra six: denial
Chakra seven: doubt

As I looked at this list, I could identify moments through my life that correlated with all these emotions. I felt like I just might be on to something.

THE BIRTH OF TIMBO: A TRAUMA-INFORMED MIND BODY PROGRAM

What started with a quest to answer the nagging question of *What did I believe about myself that blinded me to the truth about my husband and instead kept me focused on fixing myself?* yielded so much more than an answer. What came of this personal quest was an understanding of what I had in common with every human on the planet—the trajectory of my emotional development and the impact it had on my life.

A year later, a couple of volunteers and I piloted the first TIMBo program at a women's correctional facility outside of Boston. In the eight years since that pilot, TIMBo has become an internationally acclaimed approach to life and relationships that is built on a simple, revelatory theory and can be experienced as a practice, a language, a method, a community and a culture.

Through the chapters of this book, you will come to know the elements of TIMBo as best as I can describe them in written word. There is tremendous healing potential in using this innovation, especially when experienced in the presence of other human beings—witnessing courage, risk-taking and vulnerability. Then practicing them yourself, in your own time.

As I came to witness the profound healing of the TIMBo journey in the women who stepped into my world, I wanted to understand exactly what was fueling that healing. It was clear that I had created something incredibly effective. I knew that it worked, but I still wanted to know *how* it worked. If I was going to have effective trainings, I needed to be able to explain how and why this program worked, so I dove into literature on the subject.

Over the next several years I pored through countless influential books on the neurobiological development of the mind, the social brain, the neuroscience of human development and the science of exercise, all the while having one *aha* moment after the other. I share these insights with you through the chapters of this book.

In addition to the many incredible texts that I read and reread in helping me understand why TIMBo works, I discovered something else. By sitting in circle after circle of TIMBo groups—in prisons, Haiti, homeless shelters, trainings, substance-abuse treatment centers and Kenya—I learned that as human beings, we all on some level feel not good enough. We all strive to "better" ourselves, because we all want to feel loved and accepted. I also learned that this yearning is not frivolous—it was at one point in our lives a matter of survival.

CHAPTER 3

There Is Nothing to Fix

The best way to introduce the powerful, life-changing impact of TIMBo is to look at our wiring. Like every living being on the planet, human beings are born with a basic operating system, full of functions we don't need to think about but which are crucial to our survival. Our heart pumps blood through our veins and arteries, our lungs pull in oxygen and send out carbon dioxide, and our digestive system provides our body with nutrients and excretes anything we don't need.

Our primitive survival system is a part of this basic operating package as well, allowing our body to respond to perceived danger without thinking about it. We share all these basic functions with every living animal, from lizards to meerkats to our fellow humans. Without any one of these functions, we would not survive.

I remember watching a show called *Mutual of Omaha's Wild Kingdom* when I was a kid. The host, Marlin Perkins, would narrate scenes of big cats hunting—stalking and taking down prey like zebra or antelope. The primitive survival function of the prey animals was evident in their hyperalert responses to their perception of danger. Their heads lifted up. Ears like satellite dishes swiveled this way and that to catch the sound of pending danger. Their legs were at the ready to leap into action. Finally, they would run for their lives. Sometimes animals would go limp if caught, playing dead in hopes of the lion easing the pressure of its crushing jaws enough for the prey animal to spring into action and escape.

These responses in the prey animals do not require cognitive function; they are automatic actions responding to neurological stimuli that the animal has learned mean danger. We humans have this mechanism of stimulus and response as well. It develops along with all the other automatic functions in our body and is run by our autonomic nervous system.[1]

Whether we are reptiles, animals or humans, our actions are a response to the danger we perceive outside of us as well as the sensations experienced in the body itself—sensations produced by the primitive survival response.

Here's how it works. The systems of the human body (hormonal system, nervous system, muscular system, immune system, etc.) are all influenced by one another. When the nervous system responds to an external or internal stimulus, it influences what hormones, neurotransmitters and biochemicals are produced.[2] It is the production of any hormones or biochemicals and their distribution through the organs and muscles of your body that create internal body sensations.[3]

Perhaps you can recall falling in love. Or holding your newborn baby for the first time. Hormones such as oxytocin and vasopressin produce a warm, gooey feeling in your body that drives your urge to snuggle and be physically close. Flirting with someone you find physically attractive can produce arousal hormones such as estrogen, progesterone and testosterone, creating sensations in our bodies that drive a desire to intimately connect. It's not very difficult to call up memories of these good body sensations.[4]

Conversely, you can likely recall stimuli that have produced feelings associated with being suddenly alert or afraid. Experiences such as being chased by a dog, nearly hitting something with your car or even waiting for an important phone call could all produce a surge of adrenaline or feelings of anxiety. Stress hormones like cortisol and chemicals like glutamate pump through our body so that we can be alert and on guard.[5]

These stress hormones and biochemicals immediately prime your body to fight or flee.[6] If we are trapped, powerless or helpless, our body resorts to a third survival strategy—freeze. You may recall the feeling of a hot whoosh through your body and the sudden racing of your heart. In these moments, you may lose your sense of time. The world can seem to shrink instantly to only what is immediately in front of you, and you don't think about your actions; they are automatic.

Sensations such as these are produced due to your body's *perceived* need to get out of danger, and it's a good thing we have this mechanism! Remember: this is a primitive system. It operates from the oldest part of the brain—the reptilian brain, also known as the primitive brain. This is an evolutionary biological phenomenon that we share with all living creatures. It is brilliant and crucial to our survival. However, in our modern society, there are times when danger is not imminent, yet we feel distressing body sensations that we either are not aware of or have no healthy tools to manage.

I'm talking about the heavy feeling in the chest when we feel like we've done something wrong or when we feel responsible for the emotional health of another person. The sick feeling in the pit of our stomach when we feel the shame of disappointing someone or feeling excluded. The red-hot burning in the chest when we feel anger or resentment over something that felt unfair—a betrayal or an injustice. And in some cases, the soft, fuzzy feeling of dissociation when we feel trapped in a situation that we feel no hope of getting out of. Feeling "nothing" is still a sensation in the body.

All of these feelings originate in how our neurons have learned to connect with one another when we perceive an external threat. We are learning not with our cognitive mind, but with the primitive systems of our bodies. In fact, from the moment after birth, everything but our basic operating system is learned and remembered, and everything we learn and remember is informed by our experiences. The term for this is *experience-dependent learning.*[7]

OUR BODY REMEMBERS

Ask anyone who has had food poisoning what happens when they think about, see or smell the food that caused such a violent reaction in their body. Chances are they will tell you they can never eat that food again. For example, several years ago, my family went out for our annual lobster dinner in Maine, and later that evening, my youngest son was violently ill. I can attest that he will never touch a lobster again. If you have had food poisoning, you have probably made that same vow.

This is not only because you consciously remember being sick after eating that particular food but also because your body simply won't allow you to enjoy that food. It's likely that even the smell of such food causes your stomach to turn, reproducing the feelings of illness with startling accuracy.

In this way, our body receives sensory cues of a past negative experience and makes us remember the danger to our survival by reproducing the physical, visceral experience for us. Sensory cues aren't limited to the smell or look of a food but can include the sensory aspects of the negative experience, such as sea air—like that of the lobster pound where we ate our dinner—or sounds of seagulls or lobster boats motoring through the harbor.[8]

These sensory triggers also cause our bodies to re-create pleasant past feelings and memories. When I hear a song associated with a significant period of my life or a specific life experience, I am immediately transported back to the feelings of that time. This positive body memory experience can also be triggered by a smell or a taste, the quality of the air, etc. How many of us have turned up a song on the radio (for me it's REO Speedwagon's "Roll with the Changes"), belted out all the lyrics and felt awash with nostalgia, while our passengers (perhaps our children) looked at us with a complete lack of understanding as to what we were so excited about?

From an evolutionary perspective, it's more useful for our survival if our brains remember the dangers we've encountered rather than our positive experiences.[9] The reason we remember these experiences through our senses is because the sensory system of our brains and bodies develops early, while our survival system is also developing, enabling us to sense and remember (in our bodies) danger from the earliest stages of life. Therefore, it is through the senses that we experience life and create memory.[10]

THE FLOOD

In 1972, I was six years old and lived in a northeastern Pennsylvania valley town that ran along the banks of the Susquehanna River. My parents were the proud new owners of a little ranch house right next door to the riverbank. I still remember the pink kitchen, the layout of the living room, the three bedrooms on the first floor and the basement family room with the TV and all our toys. My older sister was seven, and my brother was just three years old.

One June night, after several weeks of driving rain, we were roused by our parents and told we needed to leave. It was the last night we would ever spend in our house—the rains of Hurricane Agnes had filled the river to its breaking point, and no amount of sandbagging could hold the waters. Our little home was filled to the roof with floodwater, and after the waters receded, stinky, sludgy mud.

If you ask anyone who lived through that historic flood to smell an item, they could tell you whether it had been in the flood. The smell of the flood—particularly the sludge covering and permeating every item left in the home—was distinct and unforgettable for those who lost everything. My parents spent multiple days spraying my sister's first Holy Communion dress with a power washer, trying to get the mud out of it after the flood had soaked it through. No fiber of that dress was unsullied by the sludgy flood mud. And no matter how desperately they tried to clean that dress, using all manner of cleansers, scrub brushes and power washers, they were never able to get the smell of the flood mud out of it. This particular smell can instantly transport anyone who lived through Hurricane Agnes back to those terrifying days even now, almost fifty years later.

Dolores

Before the flood hit our little neighborhood, it was full of families with kids about my age, including my best friend, Maria, who lived about a block away. Maria and I were in first grade together and walked hand in hand to school every day. We did the same on the return home to her house, where her mother would make tuna sandwiches (for her) and bologna and mayonnaise (for me).

Maria's father had died a few years earlier of an autoimmune disease, and her mother (and my piano teacher), Dolores, put her life together as best she could. She managed her grief by creating the perfect home. This perfect home Dolores had so painstakingly created was also destroyed in the flood.

A few years after the flood, Dolores remarried. She gave birth to two additional children (Maria's stepsister and brother). After raising her children to adulthood, Dolores and her second husband bought another little house down in that same Pennsylvania valley. Being empty nesters for many years now, they wanted something small and manageable near their grandkids—somewhere they could imagine spending the rest of their years. They found an adorable cape just a few blocks away from where we had all lived together in 1972. It was in decent shape. All it needed was a little updating.

Still maintaining her passion for creating the perfect home, Dolores began the process of updating their new place with the same care and controlled decision-making that she had put into her home that had been destroyed by the flood.

Around this time Maria reached out to me for advice. Her mother had recently called her and was so upset she could barely speak. Through her tears she told Maria, "I need to talk to someone. I don't know what to do!"

Maria went through all the possible catastrophic scenarios in her mind before asking her mother what had happened. But she had to wait awhile before Dolores could control her panicked, sobbing cries. Maria was finally able to get her to calm down a bit and asked her what was going on. Finally, Dolores was able to choke out the words "Flood mud!" Dolores had decided to install central air-conditioning. When they opened up the heating ducts in the house, they were still filled with dry, caked forty-year-old flood mud from the wrath of Agnes. The smell was overwhelming. I explained to Maria that smells or other sensory triggers can activate old memories in the body and that perhaps the smell of the flood mud could be the reason for her mother's strong reaction to finding it. Maria asked if I would talk with Dolores and explain some of these ideas to her.

In a follow-up conversation, I helped Dolores understand that her body perhaps had viscerally remembered how Hurricane Agnes had torn apart all semblances of her home and security—not to mention the safety associated with perfection and any tangible connection to her deceased husband—in one fell swoop. In an instant, the moment lit up with every sensory memory of the flood—the smell, the sight, the sound and the feeling. Her experience of panic, loss, uncertainty and unpredictability felt life-threatening and real. But it wasn't the truth.

Dolores's response to what she found in her heating ducts was informed by all of her early-life experiential learning and her neuro-biologically learned and remembered responses to real or perceived danger. After the death of her husband and prior to the flood, Dolores steadfastly engaged in the process of making a perfect home. It pro-vided her with a sense of purpose, control and safety. But well before her husband's death, Dolores (the daughter of a violent alcoholic) already had correlated perfection with survival.

Dolores learned to feel in control by creating a façade of exte-rior perfection, while living in a constant state of fear and stress in response to her unpredictable family environment. Her family kept the violence and alcoholism of her father a secret, telling the children that what happens in the house stays in the house. Her father's violence was directed primarily at her older brother. While Dolores felt guilty about never being on the receiving end of the violence, she also recog-nized that her father saw her as his perfect little angel. Maintaining the facade of perfection became a matter of survival. The body memory of fear, stress and panic from her early childhood with her father, in conjunction with the body memory of the devastating premature loss of her husband, dramatically converged in Dolores's present moment all those years later.

This could be due to the environment of chaos and unpredictabil-ity in a home, coupled with the survival strategy of maintaining per-fection, or it could even have originated as far back as her neurological development in the womb. If Dolores's mother was experiencing the stress and trauma of living with a violent man, that neurological blue-print would be passed to unborn Dolores.[11] Whatever the case, it's not necessary to know the origin.

The most important takeaway from this story is to understand that as children, our bodies (and later as we develop—our brains) have normal responses to abnormal experiences. Since we don't understand what makes us respond to things as we develop (namely, our experience-dependent survival wiring), this dynamic turns on its head. As adults, we have abnormal responses to normal experiences.

PRIMITIVE WIRING IN A SOPHISTICATED SOCIETY

Sensory memory explains why the smell of flood mud evokes such a visceral response in those of us who lived through the flood of 1972. It was the mechanism behind Dolores's breakdown and panic when she found the flood mud in her heating ducts. Dolores's response to finding that flood mud was different than someone else's might be.

TIMBo theory accounts for the fact that as infants and young children, we often have survival responses to normal (for this society) experiences.[12] Consider a childhood surgery for an example. The majority of people would agree that if an infant needed lifesaving surgery, performing the surgery would be the right thing to do. Few would argue that the experience would be too traumatic; most would agree that saving the life of a child is the priority.

When we think of an infant as a biological organism, we acknowledge that the brain of an infant is not developed enough to cognitively understand that the experience they are going through (surgery, in this case) is a lifesaving one. The neurobiological response of an infant is primitive, and having their body cut into by a surgeon at eight months old is likely to be experienced by the body as the opposite of lifesaving—as in life-threatening.[13]

This is not to say the answer is to choose not to have a lifesaving surgery for a child! It simply means that it is possible to have neurobiological stress responses to things later in life that are rooted all the way back to that surgery. Since the experience is only remembered in your body, not your brain, you might think that something is wrong with you. In fact, nothing is wrong with any of us. The truth is that our primitive biological systems have just not caught up, evolutionarily speaking, with our modern society.

These biological survival responses remain from the earliest days of our childhood and become a part of our wiring, which we call *implicit memory.*[14] This implicit memory and the stress responses it activates begin in our developmental years but are carried far into our adult lives.[15] The problem is this survival system has become outdated and, more often than not, is interfering with our true human nature—so much so that the system that once secured our survival is now leading to illness and feelings of despair and disconnection.

I believe the havoc caused by this outdated wiring is the fundamental basis behind much of the human suffering in the world. Emotional distress, discomfort and even symptoms of PTSD, anxiety and depression are all rooted in this primitive survival system. It is certainly the source of most of the pain and suffering we see in every person that comes to a TIMBo training or program.

Yes, many of the women who come to TIMBo have experienced devastating traumas in their childhoods or at some point during their lives. But as I said, it's important to see that many others would not claim to be trauma survivors, yet their pain and suffering is expressed alongside those who do identify as trauma survivors.

It's also important to acknowledge there are indeed traumatic and abnormal experiences in childhood that are the root of pathologies later in life. But just as often, if not more often, there are normal experiences in childhood that are the basis of our stress responses in adult life. By normal, I mean these experiences are common, not intended to harm and a part of the everyday fabric of our society. Even so, our outdated biological survival wiring will perceive these normal experiences (by society's standards) as a threat to survival. When we understand this about ourselves, we can begin to hold compassionate awareness in moments when our bodies are signaling to us (via distressing sensations in our bodies) that our life is in danger.

At the most basic level, body memories can be understood as sensation inside the body, and the key to managing our stress and suffering is in changing our perspective of and response to the sensations in our body.

This is why *It feels real, but it's not the truth* is a helpful concept (and often-used mantra) in understanding the space where TIMBo is most useful. The feelings in Dolores's body felt very real when she discovered the flood mud in the heating ducts of her new home, but the message her body was sending to her about her life being in danger was not the truth. All our healing begins with understanding this concept so we can begin to have kindness for ourselves when we feel these abnormal stress responses to normal experiences in our lives.

It is only when we can create space in these moments, have a compassionate awareness for what is happening, and sit in this place of things feeling real but not true, that we can begin that perspective change. From here, new learning and memories take root in our bodies and minds so we can begin to live a happy and free life.

CHAPTER 4

The True Self

When I was struggling with depression and suicidal ideation, I took a drive out to the Kripalu Center for Yoga and Health in western Massachusetts. I was looking for a workshop or gift certificate for Mitch (we were separated at the time), and I popped into the bookstore out of curiosity.

A book called *Yoga and the Quest for the True Self* by Stephen Cope, a therapist and longtime Kripalu resident and teacher, caught my eye, and I bought a copy without hesitation. I don't think it's an exaggeration to say that this book changed my life. At that time I was struggling to figure out who I had become and how I got there. I knew my life was not what I wanted, and I knew a large part of the reason was because I had lost sight of who I was outside of being a wife and mother. I had lost connection with my true self.

I could blame my parents, my husband or any other external circumstance as much as I wanted, but until I understood what happened inside of me, I knew I could never begin the journey back to myself. Stephen Cope's book was the beginning of that journey. Through the sharing of his own journey and the stories of several of his clients, I began to understand that there was indeed an authentic me in there somewhere, and perhaps yoga could help me uncover her.

I bought that book more than a decade ago, and since that time, my work has led to the solid conviction that the majority of human beings eventually land in this same place. It's been called the quarter-life crisis or the midlife crisis, and sometimes it's referred to as hitting bottom. This can happen anytime. It is a moment of reckoning—an awakening to the fact that you are not who you know you are deep in your soul. You have journeyed far from your true self. The question is, How do you journey back?

First, you must compassionately understand how you got there and how linked it is to our unconscious survival responses. It took more than a decade of personal and professional investigation, growth, research, self-study, and study of the women who came to my programs and trainings, to codify a theory. This theory could change people's understanding of how they have become who they have become, as well as offer a pathway for the journey back.

TIMBO'S THEORY OF ADAPTATION

There is one often unrecognized yet universally perceived threat to our survival. This perceived threat informs much of our survival wiring from the earliest moments in life. It is also the basis of much of the pain and suffering we experience in our later lives. It's what led me away from myself and toward Mitch, locking onto him so tightly that I didn't recognize that I was eroding away inside. This perceived threat is the loss of human connection.[1]

Of all the animal infants, humans are among the most vulnerable for the longest period of time. Basic needs like being fed, staying protected and warm, and staying clean and free from infection are all a matter of survival, yet human infants are completely dependent on the adults around them to do these things.[2] It takes years for human infants to learn important gross and fine motor functions, basic language for communication, and more-complex social skills. Since we are so vulnerable and dependent, there is a single survival need that underlies every basic need we have as infants—the need for connection.[3]

Remember how we are all hardwired to remember any perceived threat to our survival? This need for connection is biologically programmed into us from the beginning as the foundation of our safety and survival. In fact, human physical, psychological and behavioral health depends on the connection we experience as infants and children.[4]

In his book, *Social: Why Our Brains Are Wired to Connect*, Dr. Matthew Lieberman explores how this intense need for connection drives us and causes us suffering: "Staying connected to a caregiver is the number one goal of an infant. The price for our species' success at connecting to a caregiver is a lifelong need to be liked and loved, and all the social pains that we experience that go along with this need."[5]

Because mothers are often the primary caregivers for infants, American psychologist Louis Cozolino explains, "It is our earliest interactions with our mothers that form the foundation for our emotional and sensory memories. These are our *earliest implicit memories* and serve as the core of our self-esteem, sense of well-being and ability to self-soothe. These implicit memories are at the root of *how we experience relationships in our adult lives*. This relationship and the implicit memories surrounding them establish the biological, behavioral and psychological expectations about the world and our hopes for the future."[6]

In a primitive society, mothers stay connected to their infants and young children for years, compared to three months, which is the typical length of maternity leave in the United States.[7] Biologically speaking, mothers' bodies produce natural opioids in support of their compulsion to nurture, and infants, in turn, feel safe and nurtured.[8] Ideally, children will later feel an inherent sense of worthiness due to the physical and emotional connection with their mother.

Unfortunately, a separation from the mother, even briefly, causes dysregulations with the fear response.[9] And rightly so. A lack of connection in infancy can lead to brain damage and even death.[10] The most startling evidence of this is the case of the Romanian orphanage. In the early 1990s, Mary Carlson, a researcher from Harvard Medical School, observed an overcrowded Romanian orphanage where multiple rows of babies were lying neglected in their cribs. The babies were rarely touched, even at mealtime, because the staff were hopelessly overworked. As infants, we register connection through physical touch, yet the staff of this orphanage were only able to provide what they thought were the basic survival needs: food, shelter, water and rudimentary hygiene. Although these four needs were being met, the babies were dying at an alarming rate.

What struck Carlson was the silence in the nursery. There was no crying or babbling, not even whimpers. Upon physical examination of the babies at the age of two, Carlson found that, collectively, they had unusually high amounts of a stress hormone known to cause brain damage and, in some cases, death. The orphanage staff were instructed to pick the babies up, hold them and soothe them physically, not to solely focus on feeding them or changing their soiled diapers. The death rates decreased drastically once the children began receiving physical nurturing from the orphanage staff.[11]

In the United States there are cases of gross abuse and neglect that cause dire physical and psychological harm to children, but maternal connection is an unrecognized and pervasive evolutionary need that has become commonly and unwittingly removed from our sophisticated social fabric.

I see, feel and hear the impact of this in every woman I meet in my training, regardless of their social or professional status. No matter our profession, age or level of trauma, more often than not we all touch into the pain surrounding our relationship (or lack of) with mothers or fathers. These are wounds that most of us thought we had dealt with but live on in our bodies.

In the book *Neurobehavioral Disorders of Childhood: An Evolutionary Perspective*, neurologist and author Robert Melillo and his coauthor, researcher Gerry Leisman, describe how physically separating rat pups from their mothers led to a substantial increase in the number of rat pups' brain cells that died: "The untouched, unloved organism had twice the rate of dead neurons than those who were stroked by their mothers."[12]

Remember: sensory memory occurs not just when we experience danger, but also when we *perceive* danger, which means that we can have extreme responses to seemingly benign circumstances simply because our bodies have been coded to perceive the situation to be dangerous. So, as infants, we often perceive danger that may not actually be a threat to life. Our bodies create implicit (unconscious) memories, which correlate with visceral sensations in our bodies. As we develop, these visceral memories and responses repeat and are strengthened with any sensory reminder of the danger, all without much consciousness.[13]

I have to assert here that I am in no way suggesting that we reverse the advances of our society and go back to strapping our babies to our backs while working in our villages or the fields. Nor am I suggesting that mothers are neglectful or abusive if they put their children in childcare after three months of maternity leave—this is the society in which we live. I am simply presenting the theory that our primitive biological systems are not caught up to the sophisticated society in which we live, thereby potentially creating stress and fear circuits in response to everyday accepted societal norms.

If you're a parent and you're feeling some anger or defense in reading this, you're not alone. I am a parent and, as such, I understand that the majority of parents make every decision in what they truly believe is the best interest of their children. We can never know what circumstances the biological survival systems of our children perceive as dangerous, and therefore we cannot completely control the development of any fear wiring in our children, no matter what we do. What we *can* do is understand this reality, and in learning simple tools and practices to rewire our body's responses (via TIMBo), we can also teach them to our children.

In this vein, we may not ever know what threats to survival we perceived in our own early life. My body still sends me messages that my life is in danger. It takes time and patience to override these messages. But without the knowledge and tools that I possess now, I would just wonder what was wrong with me and continue to believe I was somehow broken and unfixable, as I had for most of my life.

CONNECTION: A LIFELONG NEED

The need for connection doesn't abate as we age. But our response to perceived disconnection moves from visceral body sensations to more-sophisticated survival strategies that shape our personalities and our relationship to the world around us. This happens as our brains develop the capacity for language, thought and reason.[14]

As early as toddlerhood we are capable of understanding the basic cause-and-effect principle of life.[15] Much like how a gazelle, after a near miss with a predator, will remember where the vulnerable (dangerous) areas of the plains are, we also can develop rudimentary cognitive strategies to avoid danger.

In the case of humans, our sense of danger (or a risk to survival) often remains relegated to our perception of disconnection. But the mind of a child is not capable of seeing outside of the self to the parent or caregiver. For example, if we spill a glass of milk, and the person we are depending on for connection (survival) becomes angry and loses their temper, we are not capable of considering that perhaps they just had a bad day at work and are overreacting. When we are children, our bodies and minds register a risk of disconnection as caused by something we said or did. In response to this perceived threat to survival, we adapt.

I was told on many occasions throughout my childhood, "Stop crying, or I'll give you something to cry about," which might sound familiar to you from your own childhood or perhaps as a parent yourself. This may not seem like an overtly traumatic experience, but that is not the point. The point is that young humans are incredibly adaptive. If a toddler is yelled at or hit, or in any other way perceives that crying will mean disconnection, they will remember and adapt, putting great effort into remembering not to cry.

Young children will almost always take responsibility for any situation in which they perceive disapproval or rejection from their parent; this is a natural emotional survival response that has visceral sensations of fear as its foundation.[16]

In early childhood, when we begin to adapt our behavior in favor of connection, we are already starting to sacrifice our authenticity—to move away from our true selves. Over time, we learn the way we need to be in order to gain the love and connection of our caregivers. Ironically, children need two things to develop into healthy human beings: attachment and authenticity.[17] But from a young age we sacrifice one in favor of the other. This moves us further away from our authentic selves as the years pass.

Tragically, the same is true for abuse, neglect and trauma. A young child takes responsibility for the hurtful and confusing things that befall them and adapts in ways that don't actually help in the short run and are the root of great suffering in the long run. This can have devastating results later in life.[18]

IF WE'RE HUMAN, WE ADAPT

Adapting in favor of connection is a universal human experience. It ensures the survival of our species, and it starts in the earliest moments of life. In the best-case scenario, we adapt into successful, achieving adults because our parents valued achievement, so that is what we did. Perhaps we became the jokester of the family because we learned that being funny kept spirits high (and potential rejection low).

Adaptive responses are not caused by anyone—we can all stop blaming our parents. Instead, it is a natural survival development that goes unchecked, informs who we become and influences how we respond to the world around us.

As we mature, our need for connection continues, but the individuals or groups we look to for connection and acceptance shift. Unfortunately, this doesn't always work out so well, as we've all experienced the crushing pain of social rejection. Dr. Matthew Lieberman speaks to this when he explains that all pain has a corresponding physical sensation that is an evolutionary survival design.[19] It is meant to draw our attention to a danger—a vulnerability—whether that is an injury that needs our attention or the uncomfortable sensation of thirst or hunger.

A less acknowledged physical pain is our response to social rejection—pain we feel as sensations. We use phrases like *They broke my heart* and *I feel crushed* to describe the pain we feel when we are rejected by someone to whom we are attached. Being brokenhearted is feeling the physical sensation of the loss of an important connection, as it is registered by our brains and felt in our bodies.

Lieberman goes on to explain that the regions of our brain that register physical pain are the very same regions that light up when we experience the loss of connection or a social rejection.[20] Being connected to other human beings is so important to our survival that some studies suggest a correlation between a decrease in social connection and an increase in mortality.[21]

Of course, as we are growing up, we don't need to know the science behind the pain of rejection to tell us that it is real. I hear stories of rejection in every training and program that are so etched into sensory memory that all the feelings of that moment come back to the present.

Jessica

Jessica is in her early sixties, a retired psychotherapist and now the owner of a day spa. I first met Jessica in our initial training in January of 2012, and since then, she has been a friend and colleague with whom I have shared several training experiences.

In most of those trainings, something reminds Jessica of her grade-school trauma.

When she was eight years old, a group of boys started bullying her. When she could manage to escape them during the school day, they would be waiting for her on her walk home. Though this experience is almost a half century in the past, each time I have witnessed her telling of it, Jessica's tears tell me that the wound is still unhealed. The experience shaped who Jessica became as a person and likely had some influence on her chosen work as a psychotherapist working with troubled youth.

Jessica's insights include recognizing that trying to be invisible every day during the time of her bullying led to adaptive thoughts and behaviors that became her personality. She learned that staying out of sight, remaining quiet, not taking up any space and not taking social risks would reduce her vulnerability and, therefore, reduce her likelihood of being hurt. As is the case for most of us, each time we feel rejected, hurt, like we don't fit in or like we aren't good enough, those old body memories come to the surface and may be more uncomfortable each time. Why? The body is trying to alert us to danger.

Remember: the physical and physiological pain of rejection is a protective neurobiological mechanism that, when not resolved, will resurface whenever our body perceives danger. This is why, more than fifty years later, Jessica found herself tormented over what to do with a colleague who was verbally abusive to her.

Jessica's experience when she was eight years old had formed such deeply rooted body memories and adaptations that her body wasn't able to separate the past experience of childhood with the present-day experience. She needed to hear that she was an adult, she didn't need to accept the treatment of her colleague, and she could make any number of choices. Similar to when I couldn't conceive of leaving my marriage, my sister needed to remind me that I was an adult, and I had options. Jessica needed to hear the same.

Like most of us, Jessica's experience as an eight-year-old was just one experience in a lifetime of experiences that reinforced her particular adaptive personality. As a kid, adaptations continue to develop subconsciously, and by the time we reach adolescence we fully believe that we are who we have become.

THE NEED FOR CONNECTION IS A FACT OF (HUMAN) LIFE

The adaptive development of human beings is inescapable. It is perpetuated by the fact that our primitive biological need to connect is very often unmet in the sophisticated society in which we are living. Early unremembered and unconscious threats to connection set the foundation for continued neurological body responses. We've all experienced some form of social rejection at school or with friends (perceived or real). These experiences further fuel the fire of our primitive survival response and the associated pain of rejection.

The tremendous recent uptick in the use of social media among teens compounds this problem, as criticizing or bullying others (over Snapchat or Instagram, for example) involves nothing more than typing a hurtful comment from the comfort of your bedroom and sending it over the network with the push of a button. On the receiving end, the pain is no less than the pain of any other rejection.

Today, cries for connection are also sent digitally to anyone who will hear them, and we have a (false) sense of connection with anyone who will listen—no matter who they are or are pretending to be. Parents of teens in this digital age are struggling to understand how and why their young children are getting involved with inappropriate or dangerous people or being groomed by pedophiles. Implicit memories (biological fear responses) boomerang kids from feeling rejected to reaching for connection in an age when both are experienced any moment of the day just by picking up their smartphones.

These scenarios are present in the fabric of families everywhere, and it is the new normal for practically every kid to get a smartphone as a rite of passage, from dependent child to semi-independent teen or tween. Smartphones can give parents false comfort with the promise of twenty-four-hour connectivity with their tweens and teens, but they are also providing an increasing supply of painful or unhealthy social experiences for their kids. This new world conundrum results in drastic adaptations. I myself am guilty of using the fact that my kid has a smartphone as a false sense of "keeping my child safe," because I can track his location or communicate with him anytime. It's not outside the realm of reason to consider wraparound digital connectivity as a contributing factor to the rising rates of addiction and teen suicide we are seeing today.[22]

The reward of feeling connected online is at least equal to the anxiety associated with being "liked" and "followed." Exclusion or bullying online is just as painful, if not more so than in-person experiences. Strangers feel emboldened by the anonymity social media provides, allowing them to be cruel toward others with no accountability. With smartphones and social media, this happens twenty-four hours a day, seven days a week, all year long and all over the world.

Even without smartphones to warp speed the process of adaptation, by the time we are adolescents, all our experiences and subsequent adaptations have created an adapted false self—not an authentic true self. The continued search for connection reinforces our adapted selves. The false self becomes who we are.[23]

The drive to be connected, to fit in and to belong can override our sense of reason, because the wound of being rejected in early life is so deep, and the need to heal that wound is so great. This is especially dangerous during adolescence, when brain development is not complete, and decision-making is often ruled by impulse and emotion.[24]

THE PRICE WE'LL PAY FOR CONNECTION

I have heard many stories of shame or regret over choices women have made in their lives, but when we understand this biological need for attachment and connection as a matter of our survival biology, we can have compassion for those choices. The risk of being disconnected feels far more terrifying and threatening than the painful choices we make to stay connected to others.

This can help explain the example of staying in an abusive relationship. In my quest to understand how I came to stay in an abusive marriage and lose sight of my sense of self, this recognition began to explain things for me. By the time I became isolated, a mother of two and financially dependent on Mitch, I had also come to believe (through continued adaptive development) that my husband was the only man who would ever love a woman like me. The thought of losing my attachment with him felt inconceivable, because my unconscious hardwiring was perceiving this as life-threatening, and my mind had become convinced I could never be loved by anyone else. I chose to stay because his love was better than no love. What I did not recognize was that the fear, guilt and shame I experienced through my early development, teen and young adult years had led me to adapt into a woman who felt that the manner in which Mitch "loved" me was the best I was going to find.

I once had a participant pose a question in a training. Upon reviewing this theory, she raised her hand and asked, "Don't we all want to be our most authentic selves? Why is it so hard for so many of us?"

The simple answer is that when we adapt away from our authentic selves, it is in response to a real or perceived danger. We will unwittingly change ourselves in favor of maintaining connection with those who are responsible for us when we are children. This means after decades or more of solidifying these adaptations, to let go of them would be tantamount to death to our bodies.

Take the story of Dolores, for example. The flood mud in her heating ducts was a somatic marker (or trigger) to a time when she had zero control over her life—the flood of 1972. However, her adapted self began long before the flood, when she was a young child living with a violent alcoholic father. Her development of equating controlled perfection with safety was well entrenched by the time the flood destroyed her home.

ADAPTATION IS *NOT* TRAUMA-DEPENDENT

My childhood growing up in the sixties and seventies always seemed normal and typical. Yes, there was that one incident of my father flying into a rage and assaulting me when I was twelve, but it was just the one time. In my mind, this did not constitute abuse. Surely, my whole life trajectory didn't turn down the road to inauthenticity, depression and suffering because of this one incident?

The answer is yes and no. Sometimes there is just one incident in developing years that spurs a belief in oneself that changes the path of your life forever. Sometimes it is a slow and steady buildup of false ideas and beliefs that develop over time and land us in a place that creates pain, suffering, disconnection and (if we're lucky) eventually some version of rock bottom from which we can start rebuilding ourselves and our lives.

By understanding the TIMBo Theory of Adaptation we can begin to piece together how we took this journey. We can understand it compassionately, because it is a matter of biology turning to emotion turning to cognitive/behavioral ingenuity. It is no one's fault—not our parents', our families', the system's or ours.

The best news is that the journey is reversible, regardless of the degree of trauma we have experienced and whether any identifiable incidents are remembered or not.

To journey back to our true selves we must gain an understanding of the journey we have been on. In TIMBo we call this journey the development of emotional anatomy. As we delve into the specific layers of emotional-anatomy disruption in subsequent chapters, you will have an opportunity to discover for yourself how you may have adapted to keep yourself connected, and you will change your relationship to this self.

ADAPTIVE PROCESS THROUGH THE LIFESPAN

Primitive survival responses lead to neurobiological rewiring	Thoughts and behaviors are informed by survival adaptations	Adaptations become outdated and maladaptive	Adaptations lead to mental health issues, pathologies and social dysfunction

Birth — Conneciton is a primal survival need

Toddler + Primary — Perceived disconnetion underpins cognitive/behavioral survival adaptations

Adolescent — Neurological, Cognitive + Behavioral adaptations reinforce inauthenticity

Adult — Survival adaptations become maladaptive. inauthentic self limits true connection

70% of the brain is still undeveloped. Experience influences the development of the self.	Child sacrifices authenticity in favor of connection. Begins to lose connection with true self.	Adaptations define false self. Disconnection with true self is reinforced. Fear of vulnerability limits authentic connection with others.	End of life regrets involved loss of connection with self, family and friends (Ware, 2012).

PART 2

Emotional Anatomy

CHAPTER 5

It's Not About What Happened

As humans it's easy to get stuck in the quicksand of self-analysis. We struggle to understand why we are how we are, why we react the way we do and why we think the way we think. What I've come to learn and teach to countless women is that it's not what happened to us that matters as much as how we adapted as a result.

The Emotional Anatomy Theory you're about to learn explores this question of how we adapted by revealing the typical adaptations we all develop through the different stages of our lives. You might even think of these adaptations as characteristics or personality habits that originated from our bodies' natural responses to life's stressors—responses that ultimately influenced our emotional responses to ourselves and to the world around us.

By focusing first on how our bodies are responding to any given event and understanding that this may be a case of outdated survival wiring, we can empower ourselves with tools to change our responses. The important insights for which we search tend to naturally come as a result.

Start by thinking of the responses in your body (emotions) as having a variety of settings, like the flame on a gas stove. Now imagine that the dial on the stove that controls the flame is all the way on high when your body perceives a threat. Your flame can move from simmer to medium heat when your system is in homeostasis (balance), which can allow you to appropriately adjust and respond to events and people in your life.

When things are overwhelming or feel inescapably dangerous for an extended period of time, such as in the case of developmental trauma or trauma that spans decades (like abusive relationships), the flame can shut completely off. These two extreme settings (all the way high and all the way low) are where our bodies go when we feel threatened, and they can get stuck there. This is how we come to live our lives with our flame all the way high or completely off.

The emotional tags that we assign to these states tend to be connected with thoughts and feelings that we resist and judge. This is how I came to try every intervention in the book to lift me out of my dissociated fog when I was married—I hated it and wanted it to just go away.

But because of how our bodies remember experiences that feel dangerous, and kick into auto-response when reminders show up in present reality, judging or resisting our feelings only fuels more stress and keeps us locked in the place that we are desperately trying to escape. The key to changing our experience (and therefore our life) is to shift our relationship to these auto-responses.

WE REMEMBER THROUGH OUR SENSES

TIMBo works through the sensory system of the body, which is one of the earliest systems to develop—along with the survival system.[1] We think of memory as thought-based and narrative—a story we can tell from the past. But from the moment we are born, our memory is shaped through our experiences, and we experience things through our senses.[2]

So for a young child who might not have any conscious memory of abuse, a particular smell (frying bacon, for example) or sound or feeling can trigger an implicit trauma response. What's more, these responses can be triggered by an internal stimulus, meaning that a feeling inside the body can trigger a stress or trauma response.[3] For example, we can be triggered by the feeling of fear in our bodies. Or the feeling of being trapped or helpless. Just the internal sensory feeling is enough to initiate a constant state of anxiety so many of us experience. Anxiety begets anxiety begets anxiety and so on. This is made even more maddening by the inability to have a specific event or trigger to tag it back to.

In the case of profoundly traumatic experiences, this means that every sensory aspect of the experience can invade our present moment. It can feel inescapable, excruciatingly real, and just as devastating and life-threatening as the original traumatic event or events. Without awareness or tools to use in the moment, options for relief or escape feel impossible.

PAYING ATTENTION IS THE FOUNDATION FOR CHANGE

There is a popular saying with an unclear origin: "Pay attention to your thoughts, they become your words. Pay attention to your words, they become your actions. Pay attention to your actions, they become your habits. Pay attention to your habits, they become your character. Pay attention to your character, because it is your fate."[4]

The root of this entire process is in body sensations. The sensations of your body inform your thoughts; they are the root of all thoughts, emotions, behaviors, habits and character. Every single one of us has had moments in our lives when we did not notice the sensations in our bodies and automatically responded from fear.

Don't think this is you? Perhaps you can recall a time when you received an email that triggered an uncontrollable urge to respond immediately. Or perhaps you said something that hurt someone's feelings and became consumed with fixing things right away. Maybe you got cut off or cussed out by a fellow driver and found yourself shouting obscenities barely fit for a locker room. All of these responses are informed by the survival response, because even though your mind is completely aware that your physical life is not in imminent danger, your body is not.

Whether this response comes from a buried trauma or a code in your childhood survival wiring, it doesn't actually matter. It's not necessary for anyone to know, including you, what the historic trigger might be for these responses. The most important thing to acknowledge is that your response is out of proportion to the actual circumstance and is informed by the sensations in your body, which are alerting you to a threat to your life—like an alarm bell with a supersensitive trip wire.[5]

THE IMPORTANCE OF LISTENING TO THE BODY

Many of us lack the ability to stop and pay attention to any given experience without reacting, especially if it is a distressing experience. Before exploring your personal adaptations in the emotional-anatomy chapters to come, the first and most critical skill to learn is the practice of noticing the experience as it feels in the body. This is called interoceptive awareness.

Ideally, all regions of our brain should work together to help us make decisions based on all the information we have from both outside and inside our bodies. This is why interoceptive awareness is critical. It's likely you have had a time in your life when you had a feeling that something was probably a bad idea, and you made a decision based on that. In some cases, our minds override the feelings in our bodies, and we make decisions that way. Ever eat too much on Thanksgiving? That is a decision you made from your mind and not your body, which was likely giving you the signal you'd had enough!

There is a small region of the brain called the insula. The insula is the area that governs interoceptive awareness.[6] The trouble is that it's located in an important brain region called the prefrontal cortex. This part of our brain is essential for things like impulse control, emotional regulation, discernment in decision-making, error detection, empathy and healthy social emotional functioning.[7] But the prefrontal cortex is a region of the brain bypassed as nonessential when our bodies perceive danger and need all available resources for survival. Even mild acute stress can lead to a loss of prefrontal function. Once long-term stress or traumatic stress sets in, this brain area experiences significant dysfunction and even structural changes.[8]

The insula works closely with its brain neighbor, the cingulate cortex, which is also a part of the prefrontal cortex. The cingulate cortex is equally important for restoring health and healing. It is highly influential in functions such as reward anticipation, willpower, emotion formation, and processing, learning and memory.[9] The good news is that consciously choosing to pay attention to our body sensations (along with other activities that we'll explore later) strengthens the prefrontal cortex and restores its function in ways that can override our adaptations and drastically improve our lives.[10]

The ability to stop and pay attention to what we are feeling in order to teach our body new responses is difficult in the best circumstances. When our bodies (and then emotions and thoughts) are telling us we are in danger, it feels nearly impossible to pause and not react. But it's not impossible. Like anything, it takes practice at first. The key skill we have to learn is to create space between our body's response and the actions we take. The most accessible way to create this space in the midst of a stressful situation is to consciously breathe. But breathing helps us do more than just take a pause.

WHY THE BREATH IS CRUCIAL

Not only does conscious breathing help us pause instead of succumb to triggered reactions, but it also helps us repair and create new neurons. Just this simple act helps replenish our brains and bodies with healthy learning materials.[11] Amazing, right?

New and healthier neurons make learning and remembering new responses more accessible and successful. This resupply of neurons happens naturally through the stimulation of the vagus nerve, which has been linked to the production of brain-derived neurotrophic factor, or BDNF. This BDNF is known as superfertilizer for our neurons, responsible for creating new neurons and repairing old and damaged neurons.[12] The production of BDNF allows us to renovate our brain. You can't renovate a house with old and damaged building materials, and you can't renovate your brain (make new neural connections) very well with outdated and damaged learning materials. Breathing is the miracle of healing because in the most severe cases of traumatic stress, a breath is sometimes the only thing we can choose. This choice can be the difference between making a dangerous choice (like using a drug) or taking the first step in healing.

Paying attention to your internal body states takes focus, and the brain cannot focus on breathing, paying attention and creating thoughts and judgements at the same time. Perhaps you've already noticed that, while reading, your mind sometimes becomes preoccupied by your own thoughts, lessening your reading comprehension and forcing you to reread a section. When this happens, we have to return to where we began to drift, recalibrate our intention on focusing and comprehending the written word, and actively refrain from thinking of other things.

The process of paying attention to internal body states works much the same way: we notice our internal feeling states and suspend our thoughts, which are the source of our suffering. Then we can choose to breathe.[13] It's perfectly fine if our focus gets interrupted by thoughts, because the process of reorienting our attention also helps strengthen those important brain networks. So every time you catch yourself wandering off in thought, simply notice it and bring your focus back to the sensations in your body, and breathe. It does eventually get easier, and in the space we create with breath, we are eventually able to make a mindful choice.

The following chapters will take you through a step-by-step description of how and why we might develop fear-based body memories. You will understand how these memories impact our emotional development. You will have the opportunity to do some internal investigation and understand how your personal hierarchy of emotions may have developed. You will be given exercises to understand these sensations and emotions as survival strategies (or superpowers) that are out of date.

Having a basic breathing tool will empower you to create space for yourself and increase your healthy learning neurons. Through this process you will then be provided with one small but new experience. This is important, because new experiences are crucial to our current experience-dependent learning. We don't stop learning by way of experiences, but when our reactions are outdated, we are learning only to be more reactive. When we breathe and create space in response to stress, our new, healthy neurons allow us to replace old and out-of-date body experiences (which become memories) with new ones.[14]

It is not easy to do, especially during a flashback or body memory when the sensory system and cognitive tapes are all making us think the memory is real and happening now, which it's not. It's important to practice in times when you haven't been hijacked by your survival response so you're ready when the situation arises. Perhaps the time to practice is now.

FOG-THE-MIRROR BREATH

Before you begin to unravel your adaptive tendencies through the Emotional Anatomy Pyramid, I invite you to experience a fundamental breathing exercise we use in all my TIMBo trainings. This breathing exercise has the power to override the body's fear-based survival response. Again, through activation of the vagus nerve, this breath encourages the body to move from feeling agitated and alert to feeling calm and relaxed and can be used in any situation when you start to feel an uptick of anxiety.

If you feel more anxious after one or two tries, don't give up! There is a good explanation for this. When our bodies have learned to be hyperalert or run on a steady stream of anxiety (alertness) to stay safe, they will fight moving into a relaxed state. At first, some people experience an uptick of anxiety after trying the fog-the-mirror breath or other conscious-breathing techniques, because the body doesn't trust what the breath is telling it (yet). Stick with it. The more you respond with breath, the more your body will begin to trust and respond with feelings of spaciousness, peace and calm.

I suggest you first practice this in a low-stress, non-triggered situation. Before you start, take a scan of your body and note how you are feeling.

Place your hand in front of your face as if it were a handheld mirror.
Inhale deeply through your nose.

As you exhale, open your mouth and breathe into your hand as if you were trying to fog the mirror.

You will know you are doing this correctly when you feel heat on your hand.

You will notice that to do this, your whisper muscles will contract to create the heat from your breath. This activates the vagus nerve.

Do this for at least ten deep inhales and exhales.

Take another scan of your body, and notice how it feels after those breaths.

Make some notes about your experience.

The fog-the-mirror breath is a fundamental tool for bringing space and perspective into your life whenever you are triggered. It is my hope that, after reading this book, you will make this choice over and over.

CHAPTER 6

Fear

We humans are like any other biological organism. We have two basic biological drives in life—to stay alive and to procreate. This ensures the survival of our species. But the fear (survival response) we feel in response to our complex emotional and social environment is often mislabeled and misunderstood. Still, fear is at the root of our disrupted emotional development. While our individual life experiences vary, the development of our hierarchy of emotions follows the same basic trajectory for all of us; fear (the biological survival response) is always at its base. It is helpful to envision emotional-anatomy development as a pyramid, with fear at the base and subsequent emotions building up from there.

You can refer back to this pyramid and be reminded that all of our difficult emotions, as well as the thoughts and behaviors that follow, are rooted in fear (neurobiologically speaking). The following chapters will help you understand how unresolved fear leads to the development of guilt, shame, resentment, denial and feeling stuck, and provide you with a compassionate lens through which to view these things in yourself and others.

STOP TO LOOK FEAR IN THE FACE

The TIMBo manual includes a quotation from Eleanor Roosevelt: "You gain strength, courage and confidence by every experience in which you really stop to look fear in the face. You must do the thing you think you cannot do."[1] This is precisely what we are doing when we sit with uncomfortable body sensations. We are stopping and sitting with the fear (survival) response in our bodies, using the tools we learn in TIMBo to allow us to be there and get to the other side.

Fear is at the foundation of all other emotions, because it is a primitive response in our body. That does not mean that we always translate the visceral feeling of fear as *I am afraid*. However, when we are feeling things like guilt or responsibility, shame and resentment, the mechanism underpinning these emotions is the neurobiological activation of the survival response—fear.[2]

If you've ever felt anxiety in response to things like a sudden shift in mood from your partner or spouse, or not hearing from someone you are anxious to hear from (such as a romantic interest or a work colleague), know that this reaction is rooted in the survival response. Feelings of anxiety in regard to relationships can track back to the primal survival fears, because to survive meant to be connected.

EXPERIENCES THAT LEAD TO FEAR IN THE BODY

There are a number of early life experiences that contribute to the development of fear in the body, including but not limited to the following:

- Birth trauma
- Abandonment or neglect
- Poor physical bonding with mother
- Malnourishment
- Major illness/surgery
- Physical abuse or violent environment
- Inherited traumas/parents' survival fears (Holocaust survivors, war veterans, poverty conditions, etc.)[3]

As I mentioned earlier, our society is often unwittingly contributing to this development in a myriad of ways we wouldn't necessarily label as traumatic. Because this development takes root at such an early age (even in utero), we grow up understanding this feeling as our normal, unconsciously developing through the Emotional Anatomy Pyramid and gaining characteristics in personality (adaptations) that carry through into our adult lives. These characteristics of an overabundance of fear in the body include, but are not limited to, the following:

- Feelings of abandonment
- Feeling unseen
- Distrust of one's own body
- Feeling ungrounded
- Fear of change
- Poor or rigid boundaries[4]

EMOTIONS IN THE BODY

Most of the time we don't think about our emotions, let alone correlate them with the things we feel in our bodies. The emotions we experience, however, are as much a part of our physical bodies as our nervous system, hormones, musculature and immune system—in fact, they are all of these things working together. Every emotion is rooted in our autonomic nervous system, and what we feel depends on the particular hormones and neurotransmitters being produced and utilized in any given action or response to an experience or stimulus.[5]

For example, when we are falling in love, our brain signals the release of oxytocin and vasopressin, which are the feel-good hormones that also act as neurotransmitters and correlate with visceral sensations in our bodies. These visceral sensations travel back through areas of the brain that allow us to identify them as feeling states or emotions and trigger any number of physical, mental or behavioral responses.[6] If we take our thinking mind out of the picture and focus on the biological and physiological experience of "emotions," we get to the essence of how emotions present in our bodies and, over time, impact our physical and psychological health.[7]

Viscera is a term used for the internal organs of the body—the single tense is *viscus*, Latin for *an organ in the body*. These organs include the heart, lungs and all the organs in the gut, including the pancreas, intestines and liver. We can often feel (via visceral sensation) in and around the major organs and muscle groups of our bodies, and because of our capacity for language to label experiences, we have descriptive words for visceral feelings, such as *elated* or *crushed*, as well as body-associated words and phrases, such as *heartbroken, taking my breath away* or *gut feeling.* The only reason that emotions are thought to be a mechanism of the mind is because we have labeled them as such.[8]

In reality, emotions are experience-triggered sensory responses that we feel (in the short term) in our body. When we resist or judge our emotional experience, we are not allowing our bodies to return to balance—we remain in a state of stress.[9] This directly impacts our immune system in three ways: suppressing immune function, turning our immune system against our own cellular bodies (as in the case of cancer and other autoimmune diseases) and creating inflammation that becomes chronic. Over time, this leads to both physical and emotional problems and is even linked to premature death.[10]

HOW FEAR LIVES IN THE BODY

The lists below (and in subsequent chapters) provide a brief description of how unresolved fear in the body shows up in the short term and impacts our physical and psychological health in the long term. This is not an exhaustive list, but it is meant to help you identify fear in your body.

SHORT-TERM INDICATORS OF FEAR AND ANXIETY IN THE BODY

- Feelings of helplessness (chest)
- Shortness of breath/racing heart (chest)
- Diarrhea (abdomen)
- Restless legs[11]

LONG-TERM INDICATORS OF FEAR
AND ANXIETY IN THE BODY

- Weight problems (eating disorders, obesity, etc.)
- Low-back problems
- Tightness in the hips, groin and hamstrings[12]

RECOGNIZING FEAR FOR WHAT IT IS

To truly heal and change our lives, it's more useful to focus on how we feel fear now in the present moment—in our bodies—and to recognize those feelings as early primitive survival responses rooted in a perceived threat to life. It took me several years to recognize that in the time I was married to my husband, I had many moments when I sat with the question of whether to leave. Each time I put this question up against what I believed I would feel like if I left (alone, a failure, a disappointment to my family and the potential loss of my children—in other words, disconnection), I made the choice to stay.

I wasn't making a choice based on what was best for the healthy-adult-woman me—I was making a choice based on the antiquated-yet-present-moment fear of rejection or abandonment. While my mind may have known that I would survive the breakup of my marriage, my body did not. Looking back now, it seems inconceivable that I actually felt that I could not leave, and at the same time, I have a heartbreaking understanding of why so many women remain in abusive relationships.

The abuse never felt acceptable, but in my original quest to understand why I stayed in that relationship it became clear to me that I was subconsciously choosing connection—albeit a toxic connection—over disconnection.

The body holds the key to updating our survival wiring. Remembering specific stories is not necessary, and often in the case of women who have experienced complex trauma, it is too excruciating a thought. Healing can and does happen without telling anyone any details of your life—remembered or not.

Alexa

Alexa is a soft-spoken middle-aged woman whom I first met in a TIMBo foundations training—an introduction to the TIMBo program that interweaves lectures, videos and exercises demonstrating the science, theory and practice of the TIMBo principles.

Alexa was referred to TIMBo by a close friend she had come to trust. When I first met Alexa, the fear that ran through her body was palpable. She talked very softly, couldn't maintain eye contact and had difficulty stringing words together without apologizing after every other one. Her trauma was so evident that I was skeptical that she would be able to complete the one-hundred-hour training; in fact, I wasn't sure if she would make it through the four days of the training.

Alexa has a history of long-term complex trauma. She is a survivor of incest, physical abuse, emotional abuse, neglect and, later in life, long-term sexual trauma. She had been in and out of psychiatric hospitals her whole life and was told she would never get better. She was given a cocktail of medications that she was told she could never come off of.

Alexa was also an esteemed professional who could focus on her work life with enough presence to get from one day to the next, but barely. What struck me most about Alexa was her clear desire to disappear. Her voice was almost a whisper, she sank into the background whenever she could, and her constant apologizing sent a clear message that she felt like a mistake. Alexa had attempted suicide several times over the course of her life, starting with her first attempt at the age of eight.

Having been in and out of intensive treatment most of her life, Alexa was relieved to know she was not required to once again tell the story of her many traumas in order to experience healing. She was not required, in fact, to talk *at all*, which helped her feel in control of her choices and her experience. That does not mean the experience was easy, but her ability to be in the experience of whatever implicit body memories arose, use the tools she was learning in the training and bit by bit teach her body new ways to respond gave her a new experience of empowerment and unconditional acceptance.

During the training, she barely spoke; when she left, though, she thanked me and said she got more out of those four days than she had from all her years of therapy. I saw her next at the second training module, and after that, the third.

Alexa, like many other women I have worked with, has since told me she never thought life could be like this. She described how different she feels, making sure to tell me that she still has her difficult moments. Prior to TIMBo, Alexa was always running, never able to hold down a job for very long or even live in the same place for very long. All of that has changed. She loves the job she has had for several years now. She is off almost all of her medications and feels a sense of freedom she never thought possible.

When survivors like Alexa can recognize what they are feeling inside their body in any given moment, accept it for what it is (a neurobiological survival response) and use a simple tool (like fog-the-mirror breath) to create space, they can navigate through the experience with full consciousness and choice. Without these three crucial elements (awareness, acceptance and space), the experience is retraumatizing, and the feedback loop of traumatic stress further inhibits a survivor's ability to find language.

By working directly with sensations in the body, I've seen numerous women shift experiences of fear, helplessness, panic and self-judgement into experiences of awareness, choice and empowerment. It takes time to help your brain and body learn and remember new responses and have new experiences. Over time you string enough of these new experiences together, and you gradually begin to learn and remember how to do this by way of creating new neural connections. Amazingly, your body begins to learn a new way of being. A way of being that can lead to true happiness.

DOING THIS WORK SOLO

Nothing can compare to learning the powerful TIMBo skills in a live group or training. This is because so many of our real or perceived traumas involve early-life (and then later-life) relationships, which means many of our early fear reactions are going to kick up when we are in a relationship or in a social situation—like a TIMBo group or training.

This is an amazing opportunity, because we get to practice our awareness and the use of these tools in real time, together. And in doing so, we recognize that we are no different than anyone else in the group, we can teach our bodies new ways of responding, and we can do it in our own time and by our own moment-to-moment choice every step of the way. We get to back off and step forth as we feel we can, being witnessed and being a witness to others—including the trainers and facilitators (who are human beings with survival adaptations just like anyone else).

All this happens in a safely held container that provides a sense of grounding, predictability and structure, which is inherent in the curriculum design. The reason that this is so valuable is that when our bodies *do* tell us that our lives are in danger, we have a flesh-and-blood mentor and guide to help us recognize what's happening in our body, guide us through a breath and encourage us to have compassionate understanding for the fact that our bodies are misinterpreting the present moment. Our bodies have been working very hard all of our lives to protect us, when most of the time it hasn't been necessary.

The tendency of group members or trainees is to (at first) try to engage the mind in ways that it is accustomed to. Trying to think your way into feeling different is not possible at first. Facilitators and trainers are tasked with consistently guiding their group back to an awareness of their body sensations until participants begin doing it for themselves.

Because reading a book is normally a solo venture, you will have to take on the role of guide and participant simultaneously. As you encounter the many suggested exercises in the pages to come, I invite you to calmly task yourself with returning to your body whenever your habitual thinking mind kicks in. Be your own self-facilitator, consistently reminding yourself to pay attention to the sensations in your body and shifting your emotional experience from there.

EXERCISES FOR HEALING FEAR

The following exercises are intended to help you bring the practice of awareness, acceptance and space into your life in a way that is relevant to you. You might choose to skip these exercises and return to them at a later time. If you choose to skip any of these exercises for the moment, I recommend skipping all of them and returning to them when you are ready to give them a try, moving through them sequentially at your own pace.

   You may write directly into this book using the lines provided. You can also dedicate a journal or notebook to all of these exercises. I have had many women return to workshops a year or two or three later. When they look back at their writing from their first time through TIMBo, they recognize how much healing they have experienced!

WRITING EXERCISE #1: IDENTIFYING FEAR

Take a moment to think of some of your fears. Write them down and notice any sensations (or lack thereof) you are feeling in your body. This is just a time for noticing without judgment or trying to solve or fix anything.

Being alone forever
Hurting people
Disappointing people I love
Mismanaging money
Not being able to take care of myself
Being a bad person

....

_____

....

_____

....

_____

....

CREATING SPACE

When you use the tool of breath, you create space between the sensation of fear in your body and your response to that sensation. In that space, you can begin to think of new perspectives. While it helps to practice the fog-the-mirror breath you learned in the previous chapter whenever you want to create space, here is another one to add to your tool kit. Practice the following breathing technique before continuing on to the next exercise:

BALLOON BREATH

Lie on your back or sit up straight. Place one hand on your belly and one hand on your chest. Breathe in through your nose and let your whole belly inflate like a balloon. Feel your chest and belly rise beneath your hands. Exhale through your nose (or mouth, using the fog-the-mirror technique), and feel your chest and belly empty completely. Repeat five to ten times.

Notice, without judgment, how you feel in your body. Move on to writing exercise #2.

WRITING EXERCISE #2: NEW PERSPECTIVES

Now that you have used breath to create some space for yourself, write down some different ways of looking at your fears. Making the effort to notice new perspectives is the most important thing right now. You don't have to do anything other than notice possibilities, such as "I can breathe through this feeling of fear and get to the other side" or "I cannot control this situation, but I can breathe into my body to find a calm space." There is no way to think of new perspectives without giving yourself space.

If you've skipped the previous writing exercises, don't worry. Just pay attention to when you might feel ready to engage in the writing and come back to the exercises. Remember, you can practice the breath techniques you have learned even if you haven't done the writing exercises yet.

I can learn to create space to make decisions and to be patient with myself to let myself learn new ways to handle things.

I've come really far. I've learned so much. I can keep learning.

CHAPTER 7

Guilt

The next development of emotional anatomy is guilt. The concept of guilt can be thought of in various ways. When we make a mistake or do something that we know is wrong, we feel culpable. Guilt is sometimes thought of as feeling remorseful for our actions, which can lead to making reparations and learning from the experience. Guilt can be the admission of wrongdoing, even one as benign as shaving a few pounds off the weight listed on a driver's license. In fact, there are a lot of insignificant things that nearly all of us are guilty of. And in many ways, guilt serves a valuable purpose in helping us know when we've done something hurtful or damaging, and the feelings of remorse inspire us to make amends and do better next time.

When it comes to the development of emotional anatomy, this is not the type of guilt I am referring to. A more descriptive name for this type of guilt is *responsibility*. When our young brains are just developing the capacity to couple our survival responses with rudimentary reasoning, we end up correlating everything that feels threatening with something that we did. In other words, we feel responsible for the outcome of the experience.[1]

In healthy circumstances, this is also an important part of our development. If a toddler pulls the pet cat's tail and gets a swat to the arm, the rudimentary understanding in the mind of the toddler is *I pulled the tail, I got hurt, and I shouldn't pull the cat's tail again.*

Where this starts to become problematic and unhealthy is when our younger selves register perceived rejection—such as anger or punitive action by the parent—as a threat to our lives, and our developmental capacities at the time (six months to two years) understand the experience as something that we caused. In response to the guilt/responsibility we feel about this, we adapt our behavior. In terms of survival, this makes sense. If we believe we are doing or saying something that creates a threat to our survival, we are programmed to stop doing or saying that thing to prevent the threat from happening again.

Self-blame (a.k.a. guilt) becomes an extension of our biological fear response at an early age because young children do not have the capacity to consider that perhaps the adults around them are dysregulated and behaving in ways that might not be healthy. In essence, it is the young mind's way of protecting us as an organism. The alarm systems of our body signal rejection or disconnection. Our biology tells us to change something about ourselves in response in order to ensure connection and survival.[2]

This feeling of being responsible for parental rejection is impossibly futile, because as young children, we do not have the power to make things right, stop maltreatment or take care of our parents' emotional needs, though not for lack of trying.

As toddlers, the development of disproportionate feelings of responsibility have already begun.

Erin

When I first met Erin at a weekend TIMBo training, her reputation as a trauma survivor turned yoga teacher preceded her. At the time of our first meeting, that was all I knew of Erin. I vividly recall placing my hands on her head during Savasana (also known as corpse pose—lying flat on your back in stillness for several minutes) as Erin began softly crying. Tears streamed from her eyes and down the sides of her head while another trainer read a guided meditation.

As the weekend progressed, I came to learn more about Erin and how her personal relationship to guilt and responsibility set the conditions for the traumas she would later endure. When Erin and her sister were very young children, their parents divorced. Because she was so young, she doesn't recall the events of the split, but Erin recalls with sparkling clarity the constant ache of wanting to feel loved, cherished and connected with her father.

Erin's father was a retired air force pilot and lived a self-absorbed life. He moved out of her childhood home before Erin can remember. What she does remember is how he would regularly remark that the divorce was not his fault. In Erin's young mind she perceived that her father was telling her it was *her* fault. She felt responsible.

As a young child this feeling of responsibility began laying a foundation of feeling responsible as a matter of survival. As she grew, Erin increased her efforts to be connected, loved and even forgiven by a man who was (unbeknownst to her at the time) not capable of the emotional attunement and connection a child needs. Consistent feelings of rejection and not getting it right continued through Erin's developmental years. Each time she felt rejected or unlovable, she felt personally responsible for the feeling of disconnection with her father. She began to seek other ways to feel a sense of worthiness.

In high school, Erin became involved in organized sports and began to feel a fierce longing to be good enough for her team and her male coach. These familiar feelings would inform her decisions and actions, even as she endured experiences of abuse at the hands of a male physical therapist she was sent to see.

Through the confusion, abuse and increasing feelings of not getting it right, she blamed herself (took responsibility) for her traumatic experiences. She stopped speaking and began starving herself. Her parents were confused, frustrated and exasperated; they admitted Erin for her first inpatient treatment.

After the years of abuse in high school, which included physical abuse, weight shaming and emotional abuse from men in positions of power, she went to college on a full athletic scholarship. Again her team was headed by another abusive coach, and again Erin felt that she was somehow responsible. Erin tried to tell her father about the abuse. He responded curtly, saying, "Guys wouldn't put up with that crap." Once again Erin felt that she had disappointed her father.

Through college, her athletic coach continued to abuse team members, including Erin. She became more ill with increasing depression and worsening anorexia and bulimia. What began as Erin's survival adaptation for feeling responsible for disconnection from her father evolved through the years into feeling a sense of guilt and responsibility for anything happening around her. This included the physical, emotional and sexual abuse that she and her high-school and college teammates suffered, as well as her own sexual assault in college.

In time, Erin could not tolerate the excruciating physiological sensations that accompanied what had become a constant, persistent and debilitating critical voice that told her she would never be right. She began cutting herself and attempted suicide several times, with one attempt nearly successful. It was only then that Erin got a semblance of the attention she had sought from her father all those years ago. As a result, she unconsciously became afraid to get well for fear he would lose interest in her. To her it seemed she had figured out the key to being seen and loved by her father.

By the time Erin came to us she was years away from those traumatic events, enjoying a healthy and stable relationship and teaching yoga around the city. Her feelings of guilt and responsibility were still running the show, though. She hadn't succeeded in erasing herself via starvation or suicide, but she still felt like her very presence hurt people.

After that weekend workshop with us, Erin decided to take the TIMBo teacher training in the spring of 2013. When it was time for her to practice teach, her voice was so soft it was barely audible. We explained how a soft teaching voice can feel stressful to students since they have to strain to hear. Because of this, Erin was challenged to use her voice in a way that her body's survival response correlated with being vulnerable to a threat. Faced with the choice to step into that place of vulnerability, Erin was both excruciatingly uncomfortable and empowered through the weekend.

It took courage for her to look fear in the face and choose to do the thing she thought she could not do—use her voice, take up space and reteach her body and mind that her presence was not damaging to others. None of us could have predicted then that Erin would become one of the most vivid examples of the healing power of TIMBo. Because she was willing to face the vulnerability of getting well and even risk the guilt of taking up space, she would go on to help hundreds of other women heal their trauma via her own community programs and as a lead TIMBo trainer.

EXPERIENCES THAT LEAD TO GUILT IN THE BODY

There are a number of early life experiences that contribute to the development of guilt in the body, including but not limited to the following:

- Sexual traumas
- Emotional abuse
- Neglect or rejection
- Enmeshment
- Emotional manipulation
- Physical abuse
- Alcoholic families
- Inherited issues (e.g., parents who have not worked out their own issues around sexuality)[3]

Most of the contributing factors listed above can be considered what we refer to as *big-T trauma*. The development of responsibility works the same way when we are being abused or experiencing traumatic events as young children. We don't know that what adults are doing is wrong or abusive. Our ingenious little bodies and brains take responsibility and make all kinds of adjustments that affect our environment and experiences. Of course, they never do the job.

But all children develop survival adaptations in response to situations or events, even ones we would consider normal or benign. For example, my own two children are deeply loved by me, Mitch and both of their stepparents, yet both of them (now in their late teens and early twenties) struggle with feelings of inadequacy, guilt and shame and have needed significant psychiatric support. I no longer feel the crushing guilt in my chest that was my constant companion for the last ten years, but in letting go of that weight I also had to accept that my children internalized parts of their life experiences in the family as a rejection of themselves.

No matter how much we tell our kids we love them and that the fracturing of the family was not their fault, young children take it as simply a matter of survival to assume responsibility for things that are happening around them and do anything they can to fix the unfixable. As a result, there are characteristics in personality (adaptations) that carry into our adult lives.

These characteristics that signal an overabundance of guilt in the body include but are not limited to the following:

- Fear of sex
- Poor social skills
- Denial of pleasure
- Fear of change
- Lack of desire, passion, excitement
- Sexual acting out
- Hysteria/crisis junkie
- Mood swings
- Seductive manipulation
- Emotional dependency[4]

As an adult, the overabundance of guilt in my body left me feeling that merely existing caused pain and misery in the lives of those I loved the most. It did not occur to me to question Mitch's accusations. I had already fully adapted to accepting blame in favor of connection, moving me far from my authentic self by the time I met him when I was twenty-five. Spending over a decade in our marriage rocketed me further down that path. Years after my marriage ended, I began to understand that I held this feeling of responsibility in my body. This is what we develop as children without really knowing it.

HOW GUILT LIVES IN THE BODY

The lists below provide a brief description of how the emotions of unresolved guilt and responsibility in the body show up in the short term and impact our physical and psychological health in the long term.

This is not an exhaustive list, but it is meant to help you identify these emotions in your body.

SHORT-TERM INDICATORS OF GUILT AND RESPONSIBILITY IN THE BODY

- Trouble making eye contact (eyes)
- Heaviness in the upper chest (chest/shoulders)
- Worry (chest and abdomen)[5]

LONG-TERM INDICATORS OF GUILT AND RESPONSIBILITY IN THE BODY

- Problems with reproductive organs
- Tension in the hips
- Problems in the pelvis
- Bladder/urinary tract infections[6]

GUILT IN ADULTHOOD

When we are children, we connect the response we receive to things we say and do with our worthiness for love and connection. As a result, all sorts of wires get crossed. We then continue to adapt and develop into adults who take responsibility for the health and well-being of those around us. A very common manifestation of this can be seen in the communities of social workers and human service personnel that I cross paths with in my work and trainings.

The epidemic of burnout in so many helping professions is often a result of staff feeling overly responsible for the health, well-being and life circumstances of their clients. By the time professionals find TIMBo they are resentful, feel like failures in their jobs or are over-whelmed by the weight of all the suffering they see daily.

Through TIMBo, staff members find a way to express authenticity and empathy to clients and patients, empowering them with tools and practices to change their lives and circumstances; these same tools and practices remove the burden of being responsible for the outcome from the staff. This can apply to parents and teachers as well. Fear drives an attachment to a particular outcome. Guilt drives judgment when we feel responsible for failing to ensure that outcome.

When guilt and responsibility become the core of who we believe we are, it leads to a lifetime of suffering. It is the belief that drove my suicidal thoughts, the belief that drove Erin's suicide attempts, eating disorders and self-harm, and the belief that keeps individuals in abusive relationships. Abusers don't have to convince us that we are the problem; they only have to *remind* us, which they do regularly, because the belief is already there.

The reality is that developing guilt as an adaptive response is unavoidable. It is intrinsically connected with the survival (fear) response of our body. At the time it develops we are far too dependent on caregivers to consider anything other than the fact that we are responsible. But as adults, we can recognize its existence and use the tools and practices of TIMBo to heal the suffering these adaptations have brought us. Without this awareness we continue to feel responsible for things that we have no business feeling responsible for.

"IT WAS MY FAULT"

In the winter of 1987, I was walking home to my college apartment one night after a late dinner with a friend. I turned down my street and saw the figure of a man walking about fifteen yards ahead of me. He turned around and asked me if I knew what time it was. I felt an instant surge of fear in my body and snapped "NO!" and he turned around and kept walking. Then I felt like a bitch for snapping at him. I felt guilty. I told myself I didn't have to assume people were bad, and I second-guessed myself and regretted how I had responded to him, all in a matter of seconds. As I got closer to my apartment and the distance between us reduced, I shouted out to him, "I think it's around midnight, actually."

He turned around and started walking toward me. I stopped in my tracks (the freeze response). He held his hands out, palms face up, and began curling his fingers toward himself, saying to me, "Come here."

I began walking backward, continuing to face him, and repeated the word *no* as he kept curling his fingers and saying, "Come here." Finally, he put his hand in his coat pocket and said, "I have a gun in my pocket, and I am going to shoot you if you don't do what I tell you."

One thousand options crossed through my mind in that moment, and in the end, I screamed as loud as I could and hoped someone would open their door for me to run through before he could shoot me (flight). I ran up the hill with a speed I don't think I've experienced before or since. It was like my feet levitated off the ground. I was jet-propelled straight to the top of the hill. My screams were alarming enough to cause some concerned neighbors (a group of upperclassmen who were sharing an apartment in a house much like all the other houses in the area) to open their doors to see what was going on. I didn't even think. I saw an open door and ran through, collapsed to the floor and dissolved into tears.

I can tell you that calling the police was not the first thing on my mind. I remember crying, retelling my saviors what had happened and feeling scared to leave their house so I could walk back to my own. After about an hour one of the boys offered to walk me home.

Even then I didn't think to call the police. I experienced firsthand the reality of the rational brain taking a back seat in the moments before, during and immediately after a life-threatening experience. It wasn't until my roommates suggested I call the police that I finally picked up the phone. Sadly, I remember feeling that it was likely to be a useless gesture. This man would continue walking the streets and threatening more women.

What remained with me for years after that incident was not a sense of relief that I got away from that guy or even regret that, despite filing a police report, nothing happened to him. It was that it wouldn't have happened if I didn't tell myself to trust, to be nicer or to stop being a bitch. In other words, I felt responsible for what happened to me because I had made the mistake of allowing myself to be vulnerable.

THE FIRST AND SECOND
DARTS OF EMOTIONS

My response to this near-miss assault—and the way I ruminated on what I did wrong that led to the terrifying encounter—is a classic example of how feelings of responsibility become maladaptive. Ideally, as a healthy adult, we can feel responsible for something and take accountability. Saying *I'm sorry* and taking steps to repair any hurt, damage or misunderstanding is adaptive and helps us mend relationships and develop a strong moral code. We can learn from an experience and appreciate that learning, and we can become better people as a result.

When we feel a sense of responsibility that is rooted in fear (the survival response) and followed up with self-judgment, it causes us to suffer. This feeling of suffering is created by our mind, and this is where we differ from the antelope on the plains.

Back to our animal survival hardwiring: the antelope remembers the near miss, makes an adjustment in behavior and stays alive—as simple as that. If a cat takes a swipe at a dog, the dog moves away, and that is the end of it. The dog doesn't ruminate on all the ways he upset the cat and wallow in feeling like a terrible canine, telling himself that he's stupid and wondering why that always happens to him or why he always does this.

We humans, on the other hand, do exactly this, creating additional suffering with our minds, our thoughts and our tendency to get stuck in self-judgment, worry and panic. This is known in Buddhism as the second dart.

The primitive survival (fear) response is the first dart. The discomfort, or first dart, created in our body is a necessary part of being a living organism. The first dart keeps us alive by alerting us to real or perceived danger and preparing our body to respond. The second dart is the way in which we respond to the first dart.

The second dart (our self-judgment, effort to escape sensations we are experiencing, fear over what we are feeling in our bodies, etc.) is unique to humans and the basis of the emotional and cognitive survival development of young humans. Rick Hanson, American psychologist and author of *Buddha's Brain*, describes this tendency as Velcro for negative experiences and Teflon for positive experiences.[7]

For example, when we have decades of accumulated guilt and responsibility in our bodies, a first dart can be triggered by any sensory reminder (meaning an activation of an early fear-based memory, like spilling milk). The first dart reproduces the uncomfortable survival responses we felt viscerally at the time of the initial experience—responses that have become encoded in our body. The second dart reproduces the self-condemning emotions we felt at the time, as well as self-judgment and panic. This can lead to a tendency to catastrophize as adults. It is so hard to let go of the second dart because it is intrinsically linked in our body to the first dart (survival response) and has become our normal. It is what we have learned and remembered through our experiences. Let's explore my example of learning not to cry.

While perceiving rejection from my caregiver when they scolded, "Don't cry or I'll give you something to cry about," I would have experienced a cascade of responses. First, my body response would create immediate fear and shut down the tears. Since I was so young, the sense I made out of this experience was less conscious and more body-based; nonetheless, it would be something like the following: *Daddy doesn't like when you cry. Don't cry ever again. If you cry, you will make Daddy mad.*

The next time I cried, I would get the same message from my father. The survival response will be more pronounced each time, because the body will amp up the response if it deems you need a more forceful reminder. This makes encoding (learning and remembering) more likely. Additionally, a layer of self-judgment will be added on: *You did it again. You know you're not supposed to cry. You're so stupid.*

Then, maybe more perceptions of rejection occur—with siblings, cousins, classmates, teachers or some other social situation. It's likely your body responses increase in intensity, which fuels your conclusions about both yourself and the world around you. *Why am I such a baby? Am I too sensitive? No one likes me. I don't fit in. I should just shut my mouth. Who needs them? I'm fine by myself.* There is no one prescriptive development of cognitive adaptations, but they are often judgmental, informed by the first dart (survival response) and intended to keep you safe (connected).

EXERCISES FOR HEALING GUILT

As a reminder, I recommend doing the exercises in this book sequentially, starting at the base of the pyramid in chapter 6 (fear).

WRITING EXERCISE #1: IDENTIFYING GUILT

Take a few moments to think about some of the things you feel guilty about or responsible for. Just make a note down below (or in a notebook or journal) of these things without judgment, and notice what you might be feeling in your body as you write.

CREATING SPACE

You can use the tool of breath to create space between the sensations of guilt and responsibility in your body and your response to those sensations. In that space, you can begin to see the feelings of guilt and responsibility you have carried throughout your life as a survival strategy, not a character flaw. Practice this breathing technique (or any from the previous chapters) before continuing on to the next exercise.

SHRUG-SHOULDER BREATH

Sit up straight. Take a deep breath in through your nose, and hunch your shoulders up toward your ears. Open your mouth, exhale with a sigh, and either let your shoulders drop straight down or roll them back and down. Repeat at least ten times.

Notice how you feel in your body without judgment. Move on to writing exercise #2.

WRITING EXERCISE #2: MEET YOUR INNER CRITIC

Take a few moments to think of your feelings of guilt or responsibility as a voice separate from your own. Contemplate if this voice may have a specific shape or color or sound. Consider that this voice formed at a time when seeing things as your fault was a way to keep you safe. Is it scared and small? Or is it mean and nasty? Use a pen, pencil or marker to draw an image or two of your inner critic.

_____

YOUR INNER CRITIC: REBREAKING THE BONE

Remember when my sister told me that sometimes you have to rebreak the bone for it to heal properly? Well, this is exactly what is necessary when it comes to healing. Think of your relationship with your inner critic as an actual relationship. You are your true and authentic self, and your inner critic is not you, but an adaptation (like a hologram) that is telling you negative things about yourself.

The first step in the healing process is to recognize that these internal critical voices ride in on the coattails of body sensations. They tell you all the ways that you are flawed, not good enough, inadequate or at fault because they are informed by the visceral sensations of fear.

By using breath to create space between the sensations of your body and the voices of your inner critic, you can choose not to believe what he/she/it is saying. Let them say whatever they say for now! Just like my experience with Mitch, when I rebroke the bone I could see that he was emotionally abusive, and I had time and space to build my strength and not take everything he said as the truth.

Creating space and seeing your inner critic as not the real you are all you need to do right now. Later, in part 3, we will work more creatively with the inner critic. For now it's enough to see him/her/it as separate from you and create space between what they are saying and what you believe.

CHAPTER 8

Shame

Somewhere along the way we develop shame. Most every one of us knows all too well the sickening feeling of shame, yet because we are loath to speak of it, shame becomes the very thing that drives our disconnection from one another. And this disconnection ultimately erodes our health and well-being.

Shame does not discriminate. It begins in childhood and can drive the development of personality disorders, social dysfunctions and addictions.[1] When we remain silent about shame, we begin to lose our capacity for empathy or compassion—for ourselves and one another. We move further and further away from our humanness.[2]

Without an understanding of shame, we blame ourselves and feel broken. If we're not blaming ourselves for feeling unworthy, then we blame others. This carries us further into a place of resentment and denial. We become locked in a prison cell of self-loathing.

The shared feeling of shame is what connects me to you. It is what connects me and you to *any* human, no matter how rich or poor. No matter what country or circumstance they live in. Whether they live next door or are an uber-celebrity. Shame is a universal human survival adaptation, and almost no one is spared.

Diana

Anyone who grew up in the early eighties remembers the fairy-tale wedding of Princess Diana and Prince Charles.[3] She, a shy but beautiful kindergarten teacher. He, a long-eligible royal bachelor who had finally found his bride.

At just nineteen years old, Diana had the perfect pedigree for marrying into the royal family. Raised in an aristocratic family and having attended finishing school in Switzerland, Diana (known as Lady Diana Spencer) had never had a boyfriend and was barely of legal age when she began her courtship with Prince Charles, some thirteen years her senior. People everywhere were enthralled with this unlikely match, but for teenage girls like me it was the most magical event imaginable! We woke in the early hours of the morning to watch the magnificence of the wedding and dreamed at night of being in Princess Diana's shoes. The jewels, the fashion, the royal functions and the fairy-tale castles were the stuff that dreams were made of. It seemed like a life right out of the pages of a storybook.

But the truth is that Lady Diana Spencer, the girl who became the Princess of Wales, was a human being, just like you. And just like any human being, she had experienced the development of shame in her childhood and carried it through her adult life in adaptive ways that expounded her suffering.

Diana was raised by an emotionally unavailable mother, whom Diana remembered as "crying all the time." At the age of six her mother left Diana and her siblings, giving full custody of the children to Diana's father.[4] Prior to her mother's departure, her parents' arguments came to blows. These fights were witnessed by Diana, and she was extremely frightened by them.

After her parents' divorce Diana felt that she was used as a pawn between the households, often being forced to choose one parent over the other. This caused her extreme anxiety, and she became fraught with worry. She called her childhood "very unhappy" and identified many of her childhood memories as traumatic. From as early as she could remember and through her childhood years Diana felt the consistent feeling of being an utter disappointment. This feeling was strong fuel for the development of Diana's deeply rooted shame.

Shame has been described by some as feeling unworthy of love and connection.[5] Diana couldn't help but feel this way due to her mother having lost a baby boy just one year before Diana was born. She knew her parents were desperate to have a son and heir, but the baby lived only a few hours after his birth before passing away.

It was clear that her parents were disappointed that they had another girl. For as long as Diana could remember, she felt she was just born wrong. Her young life continued this way, increasing her feelings of being unworthy of love, which were made worse by the fact that she only received material things from her parents—never the love, care or nurturing that she craved so badly. Her father paraded nannies in and out of the household, which felt extremely disruptive. No matter how many people around her or gifts bestowed upon her, Diana felt alone, unloved and unsafe.

She was just a teenager when Prince Charles came along and took an interest in her. Diana could barely believe what was happening. How could someone like the Prince of Wales take an interest in someone as fundamentally flawed as her? It was beyond anything she could possibly imagine. Diana felt she would finally experience feeling loved, cherished, cared for and safe. The couple became engaged, and the wedding date was set. The public was ecstatic. Diana's every move was followed by a growing pack of journalistic hounds.

Before long, Diana's dreams were dashed as she quickly realized her husband-to-be had been and continued to be in love with another woman. This was crystal clear once she overheard him professing his love for this other woman on the phone. By this time, Diana didn't feel she had any choice but to go ahead with the marriage. After all, what would people think of a girl who turned away from the most sought-after suitor in the world?

One day her husband-to-be gave her a pinch at the waist and made a comment about her being a little chubby. Diana remembers that day as the start of her years-long battle with bulimia nervosa, a serious and potentially life-threatening eating disorder involving bingeing on food followed by purging. Diana's rapid weight loss was seen by the press and the public as a typical bride getting ready to look her best on her wedding day. But in fact, it was Diana's only way to feel in charge of her worthiness. Bulimia gave her a sense of relief from the crushing feelings of not being good enough—feelings that took root far before her engagement.

Diana spent the day before her wedding in tears. She referred to her wedding day as the "worst day of my life." She vowed to stay silent and kept to that vow, yet her suffering and her eating disorder grew worse and worse as time went on. When she was pregnant with her first child, she attempted to end her life by throwing herself down a flight of stairs. Before her untimely death in 1997, she would attempt suicide four additional times.

Diana, just like her own mother, spent day after day crying. Her two children were constantly worried about her. She withdrew into herself and became tortured by her thoughts. Her eating disorder became so acute she was binging and purging up to four times a day. She was in ill health and fainted in public when it was at its worst. Nothing she did would ease her suffering, and still she remained silent as her husband continued his love affair with another woman.

Finally after years of suffering in silence, she reached a breaking point. She sought the help of a therapist to recover from her long-term eating disorder and depression. After years of keeping everything on the inside, the traumatic existence she was living in was taking its toll. She felt like a trapped animal in a loveless relationship, and no amount of adoring fans changed the fact that she felt no different than she did when she was a child. Broken, unlovable and worthless.

One day, Diana was invited to a function where her husband's mistress would be in attendance. She planned to be present at the function so that she could confront the other woman face to face. Charles was belligerent when he discovered Diana's plans to go. Nevertheless, she did attend the event, and there she faced her husband's mistress, pronouncing with a strength she hadn't possessed until now that she wasn't a fool and knew exactly what was going on.

That evening she cried like she had never cried before. It was like a tidal wave of stored-up grief and pain had suddenly found an opening and was taking the opportunity for expression. After that evening she felt different. Stronger. Clearer about who she was and how she wanted to live her life. It was like a fog had cleared. After more than a decade of living in what felt like the captivity of a loveless marriage and being hunted by the press, she knew she didn't have to feel like a victim. She could feel like a victor.

For the rest of her short life, Diana tapped into her true passion and engaged deeply in the humanitarian work that called to her. She shocked the world by shaking the hands of AIDS patients without gloves, crusading for the end of land mine use and connecting once again to the work she had always loved—caring for children. The rest of the story is known, and Diana's life was tragically cut short in a car accident.

On the outside I have nothing in common with the Princess of Wales, and it's likely to be the same with you. But we are all the same in how we develop, internalize, feel and suffer via our emotional development. I used Diana as an example to make a point. I just as easily could have told the story of Oprah, Lady Gaga or Elizabeth Taylor. Or you.

I have sat in circles with women that you think would have nothing in common with me or with one another. From educated, professional and wealthy women in the U.S. to inmates, homeless women and women recovering from addiction. From women in the poorest regions of Haiti to Maasai tribe women in Kenya. Women of all races, ages and religions.

What I know in the fabric of my being to be true is that the feelings that we think separate us, actually connect us. And no feeling is more isolating (when shrouded in silence) and more connecting (when spoken about and resonated with) than the feeling of shame.

THE QUEEN OF SHAME

Years ago I happened upon a TED Talk by a woman whom I now consider to be the Queen of Shame. I found the talk just a few weeks before I offered my first TIMBo facilitator training in early 2012. The talk was called "The Power of Vulnerability," and the woman was the then unknown (to me anyway) Dr. Brené Brown. As of this writing, the talk has been viewed more than thirty-seven million times and has helped bring a global awareness to the subject of shame. Brené Brown has since catapulted to fame, inspired millions of people around the world and launched her very own television special on Netflix.

Brown's talk describes her search to uncover the mysterious thing that sabotages our ability to feel worthy of love and connection. Not surprisingly, her research identified that thing as shame. She goes on to say that in order to feel worthy of love and connection we simply need to believe that we are *worthy* of love and connection. Easy, right?

Here's the hitch: the key to believing we are worthy of love and connections is embracing vulnerability. To Dr. Brown's surprise (and dismay) her research uncovered the truth that having the courage to be imperfect, to let go of predictability and certainty, to stop trying to fit in and to risk being truly seen (in other words, vulnerable) was absolutely and unequivocally required for feeling worthy.[6]

But there is a catch-22. Shame (feeling unworthy of love and belonging) is the stonewalling force behind our reluctance to being vulnerable. In the example of my teacher training, it was shame that drove me to run into the bathroom and cry in private. Crying meant that I was imperfect, flawed and broken. I did not want to make myself vulnerable to the criticism of others. I didn't want people to see that I was a hot mess.

Vulnerability is the willingness to be seen, to be imperfect and to stand in the not-knowing of life. I couldn't have stood on that stage and broken down without the willingness to be truly vulnerable and have no certainty around the outcome of what I was about to step into. That one act changed my life entirely.

So the answer to living a happy, free and connected life is as simple as embracing vulnerability. But why is it so hard to do?

VULNERABILITY FEELS DANGEROUS

Vulnerability is where we got the most hurt as young humans. We are encouraged to be our authentic selves, to be seen, to be *vulnerably* seen, and yet in the body (and mind) of the majority of us, it feels like a huge risk. A life-threatening risk. Most of us have spent our entire lives using all manner of coping mechanisms to avoid vulnerability. It can feel tantamount to certain death.

Here's why: as children we are mostly powerless in the world. But what we do have is the ingenious ability to adapt in order to protect and predict our precious access to connection. By the time we have started moving up the emotional pyramid we have already equated safety with *not* being vulnerable. We try to make every moment of our lives predictable. Predictability and certainty are the opposite of vulnerability. It is control, and control feels like safety.

It doesn't stop there. Since we inevitably discover we can't control or predict the actions and responses of the adults around us when we are children, our adaptation response is to conclude that there is just something about us that makes us unlovable. This is what Diana felt. This is what many of us learned to feel as children. This is shame. Brown defines the difference between guilt and shame in the following way: Guilt is "I made a mistake." Shame is "I *am* a mistake."[7]

SHAME HELPS US BE IN CONTROL OF REJECTION

Shame is what makes us all more alike than different. It is the universal human connector. We all adapt in favor of connection, because we all need connection to survive. Similarly, we all have moments in our young lives where our efforts to adapt to feel worthy of love and connection cross over into shame in order to be in control of our rejection.

I'll repeat some of that. The development of shame and the underlying belief that "I am the problem" is an adaptive strategy to provide certainty over our rejection. Why? Because having a sense of control, predictability and certainty—even if it is centered around feeling like no one could really love us—feels better than leaving ourselves vulnerable (i.e., allowing ourselves to feel worthy of love and connection) and getting hurt or feeling repeatedly broadsided by rejection.[8]

DON'T EXILE SHAME

Shame is universal. As Dr. Brown shares in both of her TED Talks, the only people who don't have shame are sociopaths and psychopaths, so by having shame you are actually in pretty good company.

The healing journey of TIMBo is not a journey to leave shame (or any other emotion) behind, condemn it or get rid of it. The truth is that shame developed in us because it had a very good reason for doing so. It had a purpose that made all the sense in the world for us at the time we developed it. But for the majority of the women that have come through our trainings and programs, and I suspect for every other human being in the world, changing our relationship with shame is no small task.

We are accustomed to our shame condemning our worth, as it tells us we are not lovable. In turn, we condemn the shame. Instead, the key to healing through TIMBo is to cease all of our habitual efforts to escape our emotional experience, including the experience of shame. It is a practice of understanding what is happening in our bodies and what it is trying to tell us, and then talking back to it.

It's not necessary to have a specific memory to connect with feelings of shame, though most of us can think of at least one incident in our young lives when we felt crushed by the comment or actions of a caregiver, family member or peer. It doesn't have to be a traumatic event. It can simply be a comment that carried the sting of rejection or an action that we perceived as rejection.

Unfortunately, the most well-intentioned parents can't predict how their comments or even their emotional responses will be perceived by their little ones. However, if we compassionately understand the development of shame as a survival strategy in both ourselves and the human population at large, we can help our children as they grow.

CHILDREN, PEERS AND THE RISKS OF SHAME

As we grow and spend more time in school environments, shame continues to develop. Our priorities for connection begin to include peer groups. Our already adaptive survival responses make us susceptible to further shame at even the slightest feeling of rejection.

Schoolyard bullying, like the experience of Jessica, leaves lifelong, invisible scars that often fuel existing feelings of shame and unworthiness and drive kids to keep the incidents secret from parents or other caregivers. We either try to fit in or predict our rejection by telling ourselves we never will.

Today, social media has created an environment for spewing judgmental and hate-filled comments that leave the same (or worse) lifelong scars as abuse and bullying in the schoolyard. Suicide rates among young people are on the rise, and I do not think it is a stretch to attribute this to the bullying environment that is so easily created over the internet and social media.[9] These experiences are common among kids of all ages.

Worse still, traumas such as sexual abuse, physical abuse and living with a mentally ill parent create a childhood of secrecy, which fuels shame even further. Remember: shame needs three things to survive: secrecy, silence and judgment.[10] When these experiences are part of our developmental years, we feel we have to keep these secrets to try to maintain our worthiness or to protect others.

As caregivers, it's not our job to stop the development of shame (a nearly impossible task). Rather, it is to help our children or anyone else in our lives recognize shame and use tools to compassionately *be with* it—but we must do this for ourselves first. This can be tricky since the more we deny our shame the more of it we have, and the more of it we have the more we deny it. I have witnessed at least a few TIMBo participants eventually exclaim, "At first I denied having any shame. Then I realized I have so much shame that I am ashamed of my shame!"

Herein lies the unparalleled value of recognizing how shame feels in our body. It allows us to willingly and courageously reside in the deep underbelly of the emotion, using tools to notice yet not obey the self-annihilating thoughts that often accompany our deeply ingrained messages of *You are not good enough.*

EXPERIENCES THAT LEAD TO SHAME IN THE BODY

As we've covered, there are a number of early life experiences that contribute to the development of shame in the body, which include but are not limited to the following:

- Abuse (dangerous or punitive environment)

- Age-inappropriate responsibilities
- Shame from parent
- Authoritarianism
- Bullying[11]

The shame that develops from these experiences contributes to certain characteristics in personality later in our adult lives. These characteristics include but are not limited to the following:

- Poor self-discipline
- Low self-esteem
- Emotionally cold
- Victim mentality
- Unreliable
- Dominating
- Need to be right/have last word
- Manipulative
- Stubborn
- Type A tendencies
- Arrogant
- Competitive[12]

SHAME IN THE BODY

The lists below provide a brief description of how the emotion of unresolved shame in the body shows up in the short term, as well as the impacts it has on our physical and psychological health in the long term. This is not an exhaustive list, but it is meant to help you identify shame in your body.

SHORT-TERM INDICATORS OF SHAME IN THE BODY

- Sweating
- A bad feeling in the pit of your stomach
- Digestive issues[13]

LONG-TERM INDICATORS OF
SHAME IN THE BODY

- Indigestion
- Ulcers
- Abdominal problems[14]

EXERCISES FOR HEALING SHAME

I have full confidence that every human being has internal or embodied resources they can access for their own healing. But using these resources is difficult when we can't create the space to help us access them. Our survival system is too busy fueling shame-filled thoughts that cause us to either withdraw from others or create an onslaught of thoughts telling us we aren't worthy. These thoughts create a world of silent suffering that makes considering what tools are available to us difficult, if not impossible.

The learning that is needed to change these thoughts takes time, but the most important thing to remember is your built-in superpower—just by breathing and moving, you are creating changes in your brain that will get you there. You will notice little changes and tiny triumphs. You can share these simple practices with friends and family, and that will lead to more feelings of confidence and competence. One step at a time, you will notice small changes, and with commitment and faith in the practice, your relationship to yourself will change.

WRITING EXERCISE #1: IDENTIFYING SHAME

Take a few moments to think of some of the things that you feel shameful about or that sometimes make you feel unworthy or not good enough. It's not necessary to get into detail. Instead, keep it simple with words like *dishonesty*, *selfish*, *ugly* or *hurtful*. You are the only one who needs to know what you are referring to. As you think and write about these things, notice how you are feeling in your body.

_____

_____

_____

_____

_____

_____

_____

_____

_____

_____

_____

_____

_____

_____

_____

_____

CREATING SPACE

When you use the tool of breath, you create space between the sensation of shame and unworthiness in your body and your response to that sensation. In that space, you can begin to gain knowledge of your body sensations and confidently help yourself and others.

SUN BREATH

Come to a standing position or sit up straight. (Be sure you have room to move your arms.) Start with your arms by your sides, palms open and facing forward. Take a deep breath in through your nose while you raise your arms out to the sides and up over your head. Pause for a moment at the top of the breath, with your arms up.

Exhale through your nose as you bring your hands down and into a prayer position in front of your chest. Pause again at the bottom of the breath, with your hands still in front of you. Repeat by inhaling as you swing your arms out to the sides and up above your head once again, then bringing your hands together at your heart as you exhale, pausing at the top and bottom of each breath. Repeat at least ten times.

THE HEALING POWER OF CONFIDENCE

Relying solely on our thoughts and intellect to heal our emotional pain is like trying to move an object by picking up its shadow. That is not where the source is. It is in our body; therefore, we must first interface with the sensations in the body in order to heal.

By using tools as simple as breath and movement to put space between our body sensations, thoughts, feelings and actions, we can feel empowered. Change happens because our new sense of empowerment, and new body responses, eventually become part of our implicit memory. Our thoughts and actions follow suit.

It took courage for me to get up on the stage when I was in Hawaii. Crying in front of anyone felt like a death sentence. But I can tell you that I have cried on stage in front of people at least a dozen times since then, because that first experience in 2006 gave me the confidence to trust that I would be OK. Not only that, every time the outcome was the same—it helped people.

I promise you that one day you will experience something that previously would have sent you into a tailspin of fear or self-loathing, but that feeling won't be there. You might find yourself looking around for your old familiar friends (stress, anxiety, guilt, shame) and be slightly confused that you are feeling the absence of something you have lived with for as long as you can remember. You will develop confidence in these tools (confidence can also be understood as trust or reliability), which will help you turn to them more readily.

With confidence in the tools comes the willingness to share them with the people you care about. I have heard reports from women in all of the countries where I have worked describing how they shared simple breath or movement tools with their friends, children or family members. They beam with pride when they describe how what they shared has helped others, and I know in my heart that their feelings of worth increase each time they experience helping another human.

This is the start of a life-changing journey back to the place that all of our survival adaptations have been working so hard to find (yet unfortunately have marched us steadily in the opposite direction)— the place of feeling worthy and connected.

WRITING EXERCISE #2: CONFIDENCE

Take a few moments to think of some of your personal assets. Keep in mind that a personal asset you could name is curiosity, because curiosity is perhaps what is driving your interest in reading this book. As you did before, think less about details and more about words, such as *willing, caring* or *intuitive.*

POWER POSING: BUILDING CONFIDENCE

In our second module training (out of three modules), we show a video by Amy Cuddy called "Your Body Language May Shape Who You Are." Dr. Cuddy is a social psychologist who describes the manner in which our posture can actually influence how we think and feel about ourselves. Most fascinating is the experiments she conducted involving power poses.

Power poses involve making yourself large, most often by lifting the arms over the head and holding them there for a short period of time. Dr. Cuddy describes staging a job interview—the stressful experience she and her colleagues felt that most people were familiar with. They gave human research subjects either a high-power pose or a low-power pose (hunching in and making oneself small) and instructed them to hold the pose for two minutes, then head in for the job interview.

Prior to posing they all took saliva samples to measure specific hormones (cortisol and testosterone). During the interview the interviewer was instructed to show no social emotional response on his face. For the person being interviewed, Dr. Cuddy describes this as standing in social quicksand.

After the interview finished, the subjects were given an opportunity to gamble, and researchers took a second saliva sample. What they found was quite astonishing. Research subjects who took the high-power poses experienced a 20 percent increase in testosterone (the confidence hormone), while subjects who took low-power poses experienced a 10 percent decrease. In regard to cortisol (the stress hormone), high-power posers experienced a 25 percent decrease, and low-power posers experienced a 15 percent increase. In addition to that, about 80 percent of high-power posers were willing to gamble, as compared to only 60 percent of low-power posers.[15]

The significance of Dr. Cuddy's experiment is that the very simple act of taking a physical posture with arms in the air for only two minutes created hormonal changes that were recognizable behavior changes. Specifically, high-power-posing people were more tolerant of stress (as evidenced by the drop in cortisol) and were more willing to take risks (as evidenced by a rise in testosterone).

Dr. Cuddy's experiment also involved a group of evaluators who were tasked with watching tapes of the job interviews. Without any knowledge of which individuals were high-power posers and which individuals were low-power posers, they chose all the high-power posers for hire after watching the tapes. When asked further why the evaluators chose the high-power people, they cited things like presence, authenticity, confidence, comfort and passion. To me this speaks to the phenomenon of physical posturing driving an unconscious stripping off of adaptive behavior, which can thwart authenticity and presence. This is astonishing considering that situations that involve social evaluation (like a job interview) can feel extremely vulnerable, so in response, our survival adaptations often become turbocharged.

Regardless of what is at stake, feeling confident enough to be one's true authentic (and even messy) self may sound simple, but after a lifetime of survival adaptations, the choice to put them aside can feel exceedingly dangerous. Hormonal changes that occur in the body as a result of breath and movement that involves power poses nudge individuals toward taking the risk to be vulnerable.

Breath work and movement are some of the most effective ways for being with our difficult body sensations and emotions while creating space to think and do something *other* than our habitual reaction (which feels like a risk). Learning how to *be with* the difficult sensations can be the difference between life and death. For example, individuals who rely on substances to keep from feeling pain but inadvertently put their lives in danger many times.

WARRIOR POSE

The following movement is from the TIMBo yoga portion of our program. It is a stand-alone option anytime you feel you need something more than a simple breath or something more energetic than a sun breath. When I first introduced this posture to our trainees in Haiti, it was a traditional warrior one posture held in stillness. When we returned to Haiti, the women had put their own twist on it, transforming it into a posture with movement and power, to my delight. I brought the new improved posture back to the States, and I now offer this to you:

Stand facing forward, with one leg forward and one leg back (about two to three feet apart). With your legs straight, bring your arms up over your head, and take a deep breath in. As you exhale, bend your front knee to about ninety degrees and bend your elbows, bringing your arms down and your elbows in toward your ribs. On the exhale, straighten the legs once more while raising your arms up overhead. Repeat at least ten times, with an option to eventually keep the knee bent and the arms overhead for several breaths (traditional warrior one pose).

CHAPTER 9

Grief and Resentment

Our survival adaptations travel up the Emotional Anatomy Pyramid in response to experiences when we perceive the absence of being seen, heard or loved. We move from the early and unconscious development of fear in our bodies, to developing guilt and responsibility in an effort to figure it out, to resigning ourselves to the fact that there is just something wrong with us (shame). We begin to resist or distrust expressions of love and affection from anyone. We've learned that trusting we are worthy of love made us vulnerable to hurt and pain. All this emotional development happens before we are through our primary ages.

Through no fault of our own we continue to develop protective adaptations. By the time we have developed shame (not feeling worthy of love, connection and belonging), we begin reaching outside of our family of origin in search of someplace we can feel a sense of belonging, most often among peer groups.

Unfortunately, the experience of trusting enough to connect, then feeling rejected (and of course I am including the *perception* of rejection) not only by our caregivers but now by classmates, teachers and coaches is painfully repeated throughout childhood. Every painful rejection further fuels our commitment to protect ourselves from similar experiences in the future. This is when we begin to unconsciously close off our heart—because the heart has to be open to embrace vulnerability.

It would be great if we could head this off at the pass when we are young. But in our developing years we don't connect vulnerability with the capacity for love, creativity, growth and authenticity. We only know we had an experience in which we felt betrayed and powerless, and we often turn to an emotion that makes us feel in power and gives us a sense of control. Resentment.

Molly

When I first met Molly at a foundations training, she was a rock-solid feminist using her voice to speak out against gender-based violence, sexual violence and any and all injustices that women across the globe face. She had a natural empathy for the world's downtrodden and had spent the better part of the previous decade advocating for vulnerable populations of all kinds. Addicts, asylum seekers, the homeless, the mentally ill and the sexually abused all could find a soft place to land in Molly, as she intently listened and validated the feelings of injustice and powerlessness that were inherent in the thousands of traumatic stories they told her. Molly had firsthand experiences with these painful feelings, and she was willing to fight for others. Like many other people I know who find themselves in professions of healing, Molly became an advocate and crusader for justice because of the experiences she herself had lived through.

At the age of seven, Molly was sexually abused regularly by some neighborhood teenage boys. Feeling alone and unsafe, she was not able to turn to her mother or her violent father for refuge, so she remained silent. Molly and her older sister didn't feel protected by their mother, who was herself the target of abuse and violence. All three cowered in fear when they sensed a violent rage brewing in their volatile and unpredictable father. Home was not a refuge.

Witnessing her father's brutal beating of her mother at home and experiencing sexual abuse in the neighborhood left Molly with no safe place to go. At the age of eleven she eventually found refuge in a relationship (and I use this term with a nauseating feeling) with an eighteen-year-old man. Sex became the price she had to pay for his "love," and the union lasted a number of months. Already having experienced so much trauma, Molly was constantly afraid, confused and utterly voiceless. Why mention anything to anyone if nothing was ever going to be different?

Molly began to die inside, walking around the world in a state of numbness. When she was fifteen, she and her older sister began to be repeatedly sexually assaulted by a married man (and distant nonblood relative) who maintained a veneer of respectability in the local church community. When Molly told me her story she remarked on this abuse as being the most heinous and sadistic of all of her abuses, while simultaneously emphasizing that it was the abuse of her sister by this man that made it all the more painful and horrific.

As she continued in life, Molly's journey took her to the deep underbelly of drugs, mental illness and prostitution, where she experienced even more sexual trauma. Having discovered drugs as a useful way to numb her pain, Molly walked through life in a haze that kept her from coming face to face with the pain and trauma of what had now become her normal. When Molly's sister died by suicide, a rage ignited in Molly. A rage that fueled her commitment to getting help for herself and then helping others.

Molly sought psychiatric inpatient treatment and discovered yoga. After a few years she decided to become an expressive arts therapist and a yoga teacher, feeling committed to work with drug addicts, prostitutes and sexual assault survivors. She felt driven to help these people with whom she could deeply empathize by offering them that which she never had—someone who could see, hear, feel and validate their pain.

She became involved in a seven-year relationship with a woman she loved deeply. But Molly felt she needed some time away from the relationship. Just after she finished her yoga teacher training, her girlfriend died by suicide.

Molly felt herself shut down completely. Once again, she went through life in a state of numbness. It was as if her body had made the decision that feeling anything was just too dangerous, and she even found herself struggling to find the tears of grief she knew were there but couldn't access and so desperately wanted to feel.

Molly felt like the walking dead. It took several years for her to approach her yoga mat again. About five years after her girlfriend's suicide, Molly found herself in a TIMBo foundations training, sitting in a circle with a dozen strange women and tapping into the red-hot rage that had been building in her body since the time she was seven years old.

RAGE: A TRAUMA TRAPPED IN THE BODY

No one would deny that Molly's life handed her plenty to feel rage over, and it would be no surprise if you felt some rage while reading her story. Rage is a natural part of the healing process. It is an unresolved survival response that has become stuck in the body. Silence and secrecy compound this feeling of stuckness. Our continued feelings of something being wrong with us compound it further. It is not a surprise to me that so many trauma survivors turn to quick yet unhealthy coping mechanisms to numb the feelings of rage. They are confusing and often unbearable.

Traumatic events during childhood rob us of the ability to fight or flee. Molly's body needed to mobilize when she was being abused as a child. Her survival response jet-propelled hormones and biochemicals through her body for an intense expression of motor response (fight or flight).[1]

These biochemicals are what gave me the ability to levitate up the hill that night I was threatened with a gun. They are what would be behind the ability of a mother to lift a car to save her nearly crushed baby. But as children, very often our only option is to freeze. The flood of biochemicals has nowhere to go and stays trapped in our bodies.[2] Trauma is feeling trapped. Traumatic stress is rooted in that same feeling. This cocktail of biochemicals is what survivors like Molly find so intolerable.

What we think of as anger and rage is actually the body's way of signaling the need to mobilize or otherwise discharge the survival biochemicals. But rage is only useful when it leads to discharging energy in a healthy way.[3] When survivors are unaware of their bodies, let alone the body's need to discharge long-built-up survival chemicals, they often make poor choices in response.[4] Sex, violence or self-harm can all be understood as an ill-fated attempt to discharge long-held trauma. It doesn't work because it keeps us in a shame spiral.

Instead, healthy mobilization can discharge energy by moving the body in a way it was unable to during an original traumatic event, as Peter Levine describes in his book *Waking the Tiger: Healing Trauma*.[5] Dr. Levine's book was the first I heard of the impact of trauma on the human organism. He describes the immobilization or freeze response as useful to an animal when fight or flight is unavailable (think a floppy mouse in the jaws of a cat), and it is normally a last-ditch effort that leaves the animal's body like a shaken-up champagne bottle with the lid still on.[6]

To bring the body back to a sense of balance or homeostasis, the animal must shake, run around or discharge the energy in some way— and animals almost always do (with the exception of domestic animals that are abused but trapped). Because the freeze response is often the only option available to us in childhood, we can't mobilize and instead engage in the ingenious process of adaptation.

RESENTMENT: A MASK FOR GRIEF

Until we understand our rage as the neurobiological runoff of lifelong feelings of powerlessness, we will misunderstand and fear it. Rage is an extreme form of feeling powerless in the body, but there is another, even more toxic emotion that keeps the lid on the volcano, creating more pressure and thus more distress. That emotion is resentment.

Moving our body helps give it what it didn't have a chance to do— mobilize. This can help diminish feelings of rage. But the sublayer of rage is resentment. And resentment is a diversion from the grief we need to feel in order to heal.

The illusion of resentment is that it makes us feel in control. We misunderstand grief as weakness. But as Peter Levine posits in his book, grief is one of the most accessible ways to discharge the neurobiological buildup inside of us. When our body presents us with distressing body memories, it is handing us an opportunity to grieve and begin healing. But we fear that if we open that door, our grief will swallow us whole, and we continue to hang on to resentment.[7]

It's not uncommon for me to see a woman begin to cry simply because she has given her body an opportunity to move and breathe in a TIMBo session. During her training to become a licensed TIMBo facilitator, Molly had many opportunities to take the lid off her long-held anger and grieve many of the experiences of her life. Like letting the pressure out of a pressure cooker bit by bit, grief can be discharged at a pace that is manageable.

At times our body hands us more grief than we bargained for, but I've never seen anyone, myself included, return from the experience not feeling a sense of having peeled off a layer of pain. Grief is not a one-and-done experience—once you begin grieving, you'll find it necessary for the maintenance of your emotional well-being. And at times your body will present you with opportunities to grieve past traumas that you may not have known were there or that you thought you had dealt with.

For years after the end of my marriage I actively refused to grieve the loss, because it felt like doing that would mean that Mitch would win. *What's there to grieve?* I would tell myself. *None of it was real anyway.* But not grieving the powerlessness I felt around all that had happened and continued to happen made me cling to anger and resentment. It was my only feeling of power.

Brené Brown reminds us that blame is a way to discharge pain and discomfort, but it only provides the illusion of relief in the short term and causes us harm in the long term.[8] Blame and resentment create a toxic feedback loop of stress in the body. And we now know how a lifetime of toxic stress can impact our health.[9]

THE PHYSICAL HAZARDS OF RESENTMENT

In the book *When the Body Says No: Understanding the Stress-Disease Connection*, Dr. Gabor Maté shines a fascinating light on what stress in the body really is. We think of stress as the panic to meet a deadline or the moment when life throws us a curveball, and we need to suddenly switch to crisis-control mode to get through the difficult time. Sure, those are stressful situations, but it's not the same as chronic or toxic stress.[10]

As Dr. Maté describes, stress is consistently coursing through our body via the development of emotional anatomy. As we move through the adaptive process, we move further away from our true and authentic selves. We develop a false self-belief system, a specific worldview and even a personality that is unconsciously based in survival.[11]

We rarely stop to think about what emotions are at the basis of people who are perfectionists or habitual caregivers or chronically cheery, for example. But more often than not these are unrecognized survival adaptations that are no different (neurobiologically speaking) than being a chronic complainer or someone with martyr syndrome.

We don't have to have drastically traumatic experiences in life like those survived by Molly to have lived with unrecognized stress running through our systems over the course of our lifetimes. As Dr. Maté boldly states, stress runs through our body every time we say *yes* when we would rather say *no* or every time we do something out of a feeling of obligation (responsibility) instead of it being our choice. When we are unaware of or feel justified in resentments about our past or present life circumstances, we are missing an opportunity to reverse the effects of long-term stress—effects that include physical ailments, autoimmune diseases and even early death.[12]

Feeling resentment is not something to judge yourself over, but it is something to recognize as a cover for emotional pain. Resentment is more than likely to be rooted in feelings of powerlessness; not being seen, heard or recognized; being treated unfairly or unjustly and so on. This is where the grief and sadness can become accessible, but it cannot be forced.

I have had many times in my life when I recognized that I was not ready to grieve. Simply knowing this fact and creating awareness around it without judgment or forcing myself to get to the grief is enough. Staying constantly busy and constantly complaining or blaming prohibits grief from accessing the space it needs to be felt. The ability to *create space* and nonjudgmental awareness around our moment-to-moment experience will eventually open the body enough for grief to present itself, even when we least expect it.

GRIEF FINDS A WAY

Just a year or two after my divorce I had developed a friendship with a woman about thirteen years my junior. She had been a yoga student of mine, and after joining me on one of my yoga retreats to Italy, we became close friends. Looking back on this friendship I can see that it was one of convenience (mostly mine). She had been willing to come to my house when I wanted and stay away when my kids were around. We enjoyed traveling together and taking road trips to New York City and Maine. She even spent a few holidays with my family in Pennsylvania. I felt disproportionately attached to her, but not in a romantic way at all. In fact, during our three-year friendship she had at least one boyfriend, during which time we often hung out together as a threesome.

One July she began dating a fellow yogi that we both knew well. It happened to be a woman, and for some inexplicable reason I was hit with a tsunami of anger, resentment and grief. To this day I am still unsure of why my feelings were so disproportionate, but there was no denying that something was triggered, and my body was not going to let the opportunity go, regardless of what my head wanted to do.

I spent days on my couch, collapsed in a ball of tears and snot, wondering what the hell was happening to me. I felt panic at the thought of losing her, anger that she was "betraying" me, and the deepest sorrow I could possibly imagine. All the while I knew that this had little to do with her. Even so, I wanted to know why this grief was consuming me.

Each day I was plagued with a memory of me and my sister at around three and four years old. My sister was born almost a year to the day before me, and we were extremely close. In fact, when I think back to my youngest years, I recall feeling almost in love with her, and having that feeling of closeness as a part of my young life is something that I am able to look back on and cherish. However, this particular memory involved the first moment when I felt the risk of our bond being threatened.

My sister had started preschool (being three years old, I was still at home with my mother). One day she was playing on the backyard swing set with me and a newly made school friend. They began singing "My Country Tis of Thee," a song they were learning at preschool. I felt left out. Discarded.

That's it. That was the memory that kept invading my consciousness during those gut-wrenching moments of grief, and it left me very confused. What a benign memory to be accompanying this intense and almost unbearable grieving process that, like it or not, I was clearly going to have to ride through.

In the end, our friendship did not survive—which left me feeling confused, discarded and misunderstood—just like when I was three. Just like when I learned the truth about Mitch. I had cried more at the loss of that friendship than I did when my marriage collapsed. There are times when I consider that clinging to resentment toward Mitch just circumvented the grief (a grief that is necessary to heal) to the first available opening. In the end it doesn't matter what it was about or why it happened then. What I do recognize is that the body will take an opportunity to grieve and heal where it can, and now that I understand that, I see grief as a necessary part of emotional maintenance.

TO AVOID GRIEF IS TO AVOID JOY

In the words of the wise Brené Brown, you cannot selectively numb emotions. When you spend life holding tight to resentment and avoiding grief, you cut yourself off from feeling the full palette of human emotions that creates an authentic and fully lived life.[13] Worse still, you are harming yourself in ways that become silent contributors to mental, emotional and physical suffering—and possibly early death.[14]

While the inexplicable grief I experienced in response to my friend's new relationship was excruciating and eventually cost me the friendship, I am grateful that I was able to at least recognize that my body was taking an opportunity that my head simply wasn't aligning with. It would by no stretch be the last time I cycled through grief, but so far, I haven't been brought to my knees in quite the same way. And I believe with all my heart if I hadn't lost that friendship, I would not have had the space in my life for many of the new relationships and opportunities that have come my way since that time.

Grief is scary. Rare is the person who shouts, "Bring on the grief!" but the more you experience grief and then recognize how it opens you up to feeling alive, the more you will welcome grief. It is a necessary part of the healing path and a sign that sustained healing in the body, mind and spirit is actually happening. Until you allow the grief to come and flow, the grip of resentment will continue to provide a false illusion of control when it actually causes further pain and suffering.

EXPERIENCES THAT LEAD TO RESENTMENT (GRIEF) IN THE BODY

I know as well as anyone that letting go of resentment is not as easy as just deciding to do that. Nor is it at all possible to simply replace resentment with forgiveness, gratitude or joy. Instead we must non-judgmentally become aware of our resentment, feel the sensations in our bodies that accompany it and consider that it is a by-product of the pain and sadness we have held in our bodies from the time we were very young.

This loss of authentic connection with ourselves, caregivers and peers is a very real grief that begins to build up in our bodies from an early age. Below are some of the causes of the development of grief in the body.

- Rejection
- Abandonment
- Loss
- Shaming
- Abuses to any other emotional development
- Divorce/death
- Loveless environment
- Betrayal[15]

Without the ability to recognize and express our grief, we continue to develop personality characteristics that shape who we believe we are and determine the forward path of our lives. Below are some of the ways that the emotional-anatomy development of unexpressed grief manifests in adults. These characteristics include but are not limited to the following:

- Withdrawn
- Critical

- Judgmental
- Depressed
- Fearful of intimacy/relationships
- Lack of empathy
- Narcissism
- Demanding
- Jealous
- Overly sacrificing[16]

By the time we are developing resentment, we have already experienced a buildup of fear, guilt and shame in the body. These emotions all stem from the very real (or even perceived) loss of connection.

Because we are still in early development, we are very much prioritizing finding a place of unconditional acceptance and a feeling of belonging, which means that awareness of these emotions is secondary at best. Our ability to express them feels like a threat to the connections we seek. Resentment begins to take form, not as an emotion but as a means to keep our painful emotions locked away inside of us as we continue our search for worthiness.

In the lists provided below you can see a brief description of how the emotion of unresolved grief in the body shows up in the short term and how it impacts our physical and psychological health in the long term. This is not an exhaustive list, but it is meant to help you identify grief in your body.

SHORT-TERM INDICATORS OF HOLDING ON TO GRIEF AND RESENTMENT

- Crying
- Heavy feeling in the heart
- Sudden rise in temperature[17]

LONG-TERM INDICATORS OF HOLDING ON TO GRIEF AND RESENTMENT IN THE BODY

- Heart problems
- Respiratory problems
- Problems with the inner arms, wrists and hands*[18]

* Biologically speaking, the repression of grief impacts the viscera of the heart. The viscera surrounding the heart extends out through the arms, wrists and hands.[19]

REPRESSED EMOTION AND DISEASE

In my opinion, our culture encourages us to keep it together, holding emotion at bay so we can be strong or present a brave face. As parents we tell our children to stop crying, or we say "You're OK" when they are scared and tears begin to fall. We are trying to help but instead are invalidating our children's experience of fear and their natural discharge of that energy.

Boys are told to man up, implying that to show emotion is not "being a man" or is considered weak. These messages and the subsequent adaptation of keeping emotions on lockdown take a terrible toll on our physical bodies. There is some science behind this, which is fascinating.[20]

In *When the Body Says No*, Dr. Maté describes a longitudinal study conducted in former Yugoslavia. Researchers wished to discover what, in addition to smoking, was the chief contributor to the development of lung cancer. Not that smoking isn't a contributor to lung cancer, but if smoking alone caused it, 100 percent of smokers would develop lung cancer. As Dr. Maté states, to say smoking causes lung cancer is like saying jumping in the deep end causes drowning.

The study followed about fourteen hundred men and women over the course of ten years or so. This group was made up of both smokers and nonsmokers. In the end what they discovered was that of the individuals who developed lung cancer, repression of emotions was the common denominator.[21]

Resentment is the lid that keeps the wide array of all emotions (including positive ones) locked tight inside of us. Grief is the opening of the dam that can allow the full array of human emotions to ebb and flow from one moment to the next. This keeps us balanced, healthy and free.

The importance of identifying resentment to arrive at the underlying emotion of grief cannot be overstated. Resentment impacts not only the immune system in a potentially life-threatening way but also our ability to be effective parents, friends and professionals. With no awareness or acknowledgment of our resentment (and therefore no ability to step into the vulnerability of grief), we are unable to see the world through a clear and nonjudgmental lens.

What we see, think and feel will be through a lens of animosity—creating an us-and-them or kill-or-be-killed worldview. In parents, this creates stress in children. In friendships, it creates blocks to authentic connection. And in professionals, it creates ineffective leadership styles, which in turn contribute to secondary trauma or compassion fatigue in direct-service or lower-tier workers.

Resentment keeps us stuck stewing over the past and inhibits our ability to trust in the future. It drives blame and complaints. Without grieving we run the risk of putting Band-Aids on our resentment in any number of ways, ranging from grabbing drinks and bashing the boss after work to engaging in what is known as spiritual bypass: the ineffective practice of grasping for joy and gratitude in place of anger and resentment.

These stopgap measures perpetuate emotional repression. Continued stress reactivity in the face of non-life-threatening circumstances (such as ones we face every day in our personal and professional lives) inhibits our ability to bring a sense of curiosity, innovation and faith to moments of uncertainty. And what is life if not uncertain and unpredictable?

I prefer to leave it up to the growing community of brilliant physicians in the world to continue providing scientific evidence showing links between early childhood experiences, emotional repression and premature morbidity and mortality. What I can emphatically support is the very real link between grieving and healing, and to get to that pivotal place, we must recognize our held resentments with no judgment and perhaps even a sense of curiosity.

EXERCISES FOR HEALING GRIEF

WRITING EXERCISE #1: IDENTIFYING RESENTMENT

Take a few moments to think about some of the things you feel resentful about. Don't get into the why of things—just notice who or what. It can be a person, a group of people, a system, an organization or anything else. It's important to write down anything you feel resentful of without judging yourself. As you think about the things you feel resentful of, notice what you feel in your body.

_____

_____

_____

_____

_____

_____

_____

_____

_____

_____

_____

_____

_____

CREATING SPACE

When you use these tools and techniques, you create space between the sensation of resentment (grief) in your body and your response to that sensation. In that space you can begin to gain knowledge over your body sensations and find compassion for yourself and others.

The breath described below is one of my favorites because (for me) it is immediately effective for creating space. Inhaling and exhaling through alternate nostrils has the same effect on the brain as things like tapping (using your fingertips to tap the right and left side of your body) and other exercises that can immediately integrate right- and left-brain activity. It is not for everyone, so give it a try, and if it does not feel like a good fit, simply replace it with another breath you have learned.

ALTERNATE NOSTRIL BREATH

Sit up straight. Dent the right nostril (you do not have to plug it completely) with the thumb of your right hand and inhale through your left nostril. Release the right nostril, dent the left nostril with your index finger, and exhale through your right nostril. Keep the left nostril dented, and this time inhale through your *right* nostril. Release the left nostril, dent the right nostril, and exhale through your left nostril. Continue like this, alternating left and right nostrils for at least ten rounds of inhales and exhales. Notice how you feel after these breaths.

WRITING EXERCISE #2: COMPASSION

Take a few moments to think of some of the things that you have grief over losing. It can be the loss of a pet, the loss of a person, the loss of a childhood experience you never got to have or the loss of the nurturing you never received. Without acknowledging grief, it is not possible to find compassion for ourselves or compassion for others. Keep in mind that you do not need to do anything about these feelings. Naming them is the most important step and can often give rise to tears. This exercise may feel a little frightening or even slightly overwhelming. Just notice how you experience whatever comes up for you. You don't need to do anything about what you feel. But without naming our grief and sadness, we will always hold resentment in our bodies.

CHAPTER 10

Feeling Stuck

In TIMBo we refer to grief as the tollbooth to healing. It's an unavoidable process that moves us down a path of healing, much like a tugboat moves a large ship out of the harbor. It is not the entire process, nor is it finite, but without allowing ourselves to experience grief we continue moving up the Emotional Anatomy Pyramid into feeling stuck.

The experience of feeling stuck in our developmental years is rarely understood by us as such. As we've covered, a cumulative repression of and resistance to our basic human emotions leads to the unexpressed development of grief. Grief needs to be expressed in order to recalibrate our bodies. It is a discharge of built-up energy that is a by-product of the continual stress we experience during our lifelong adaptive process. If grief hasn't been discharged by the time we've reached this stage of development (and for most humans it rarely has), the emotional-anatomy development of feeling stuck takes hold.

Feeling stuck happens when we have spent years living with survival adaptations that have, over time, become our identity. In other words, feeling stuck happens when we feel the discomfort of not being who we truly are, but we don't know how to change things. We are trapped, and we feel cornered.[1]

As we've been discussing, developing children are hyperaware of every comment or response they receive from their parents. This is to ensure love and approval. Comments from siblings, peers, educators and coaches have just as potent an impact. We become determined to fit into the mold we believe is being crafted for us so we will feel worthy of love. But *we* are the ones crafting the mold.

For instance, I have seen commitments to one version of this mold—one learned through the traditional education structure— manifested in more than half of the women who complete the one hundred hours of intense training to become a TIMBo facilitator. It's common to witness trainees with an accumulation of stress in their bodies via our education system that (in my opinion) is antiquated and often itself traumatizing. These women completely freeze up when faced with taking the licensing exam necessary to deliver TIMBo to the populace.

It may not seem like a traumatic situation, but years of being judged as either worthy or not good enough based on a letter grade can fuel a self-belief system that can be detrimental in either direction. Those who receive recognition and praise from parents and teachers alike are often filled with anxiety at the thought of not performing well on the exam. I've seen this manifested in women feeling a crushing fear of making mistakes or not doing things perfectly.

Those who consistently struggled in school, were reprimanded by parents for below-average grades and were told by teachers that they weren't meeting their potential often feel completely frozen (stuck) and let all of their training go to the wayside simply because the thought of an exam creates such discomfort. They already feel like a failure, so why bother?

As we continue to grow older, our neurobiology vigilantly scans for all signs of "getting it right" and makes adjustments to prioritize feeling worthy (of being loved, fitting in, etc.). Our emotional development continues up the pyramid, with feeling worthy of connection and belonging as the top priority. As this continues we also experience a continued erosion of our true spirit (our true selves).

FROM GLAMOROUS TO STUPID:
A MEMORY OF ADAPTATION

I recall a memory from my own life when, as a burgeoning teenager, I had saved up enough money to buy myself a pair of shoes. They were a wooden wedge–heeled pair of sandals that I thought were the coolest and most sophisticated foot adornments I had ever seen. I was extremely proud to have purchased them with my own money. I was jumping out of my skin with excitement to show them to my mother.

I imagined wearing these beauties with summer dresses to one social event or another, feeling grown-up and independent and letting people know (because of course they would ask me where I got my gorgeous shoes) that I had purchased them with my own money, not to mention that they were, in fact, designer.

I fantasized all the many ways that these shoes could and would change my life and catapult me into a life of sophisticated fashion and style. So when my mother returned home I excitedly called her up to my room, took out the shoebox, peeled back the tissue and with a huge smile proudly stated, "Look what I bought today!"

I don't even remember her words—I only remember the feeling I had in that moment. It was clear beyond a doubt that she did not like those shoes one bit. My heart sank. My enthusiasm immediately deflated. In my memory she looked at the contents of the box as if it were filled with slimy slugs. I felt stupid and like an utter disappointment. I put the box of shoes in my closet, and I never wore them. Not once. I never forgot that feeling—a feeling that revisited me over and over in my first marriage.

These little moments are not traumatic, nor are they in any way outside any normal parent-child interaction. I'm sure my mother has no memory of this little exchange, just as I am sure I (as a parent) have no memory of some of my children's most stinging memories. And as a parent, it pains me to know that my own children have very likely adapted in ways that have eroded their spirit. I have seen evidence of this in both of my boys, and like all of you reading this book right now, it will be up to them to decide to recover the authentic spirit that still lives inside of them.

The hard part is that to do that, we must develop an inner compassionate strength. In the face of criticism or rejection, that inner strength does not take it personally. The only way to do that is to compassionately understand that *we* are taking it personally (making it mean something about us) because at one time it was important to do so. Consciously or unconsciously, we connected our worthiness (survival) with doing or saying the right thing or being the right way.

To truly feel the freedom to be our authentic selves we have to stop and look within. We think changing our jobs, our partners or our homes will help us feel better, but looking outside of ourselves has short-term impact. We have to recognize that we are the ones who chose (for very good reasons) to believe the things we have come to believe about ourselves. We must look in the face at our tendency to blame and feel resentful and recognize that these feelings are a cover for feeling deep sadness over not being seen, understood or worthy of love and belonging. Healing is an inside job.

Maya

Maya is one of the most fantastic dancers I have ever seen. When the music comes on she floats around the dance floor, grabs the hand of any available dance partner, looks them square in the eye and begins wordlessly twirling. She spins and dips with her partner with ease, grace and confidence. Dancing with Maya feels like riding a roller coaster; at some point you recognize you have to let go of control, trust that you are belted in, and resolve to enjoy the ride, because you are in good hands.

Off the dance floor Maya is like a wounded bird. Shy and soft-spoken, she is unassertive. She punctuates most sentences with a question mark, as if she doesn't trust herself to know her mind. She has trouble looking people in the eye.

Maya will tell you that she had a good childhood but that her family did not demonstrate love or affection—it was just intellectually understood but not necessarily expressed. Regardless of no identifiable overt trauma, abuse or neglect, the absence of nurturing touch or demonstrations of love and affection leave children like Maya at a loss for understanding how to both receive and express authentic and unconditional love.

Like all other children in the emotional-development process, Maya had her own version of adaptations that left her fumbling around in a void without any helpful modeling. She was left to figure things out for herself. This obviously put her square in the crosshairs of some individuals who see girls like Maya as easy prey to take advantage of.

In her early twenties Maya was sexually assaulted, after which she sought the help of a therapist. When she began to talk about the rape, she was told, "You think *that's* bad? My daughter was raped at knifepoint!" After that appointment Maya didn't speak of her rape for decades.

Eventually Maya married a man whom she knew to be a philanderer, but he professed his love to her. By now she had a diminished sense of self; she figured it was the best love she'd be able to find. For over thirty years Maya was the victim of her husband's narcissism, gaslighting and emotional abuse—not to mention more infidelities than she could count. Those decades of Maya's life left her feeling like a trapped animal, and her body became her enemy—creating both sickness, pain and dissociation.

When the body has no escape from abuse, the unease it experiences in a lifetime will lead to disease on a physical level, as well as adaptive behavior that leaves one feeling isolated, stigmatized and utterly stuck. Maya, like any other victim of emotional and domestic abuse, could not see a way out of her abusive marriage. Like me, Maya was absolutely convinced (the intention of most abusers) that the only person on the face of the earth who would love such a broken woman like her was her current husband.

It takes a Herculean act of strength to extract oneself from the only love you believe you will ever find—even if that love is killing your body, mind and spirit. By the time I met Maya at a TIMBo foundations training, she had left her marriage, but the scars of abuse were apparent in the way she communicated as well as her physical response in the training.

Maya was silent for nearly all four days of the first training she took with us. During some of the more emotionally intense exercises, I observed Maya clutching her stomach, as if experiencing physical pain.

She was confused and scared but still never said a word. It took Maya just over three years to pluck up enough courage to step back into the TIMBo community. She joined a service trip to Haiti, where she was able to see firsthand the healing power of TIMBo and its impact on communities of women who, in her mind, had it much worse than her.

But while in Haiti, Maya recognized that regardless of what that therapist said to her all those years ago (and the message she internalized that led to her silencing herself), there is a healing experience waiting for women when they connect and resonate with the basic human emotions we all feel—not the day-to-day details of our life experience.

While sitting in a circle in Port-au-Prince, Haiti, sharing feelings of guilt, shame, and feeling stuck and witnessing the tears of one another, Maya begin to consider that she had the right to feel all that she was feeling. She had that right as much as any other woman in the circle. She felt a small glimmer of hope in the connection she felt to these women—women with whom she would never have imagined having such strong connections!

It was during this trip to Haiti that I got to see the exuberance of Maya, her fantastic moves on the dance floor and her subtle yet brilliant humor. Maya's light began to shine, and I was thrilled when she signed up for the following two training modules once back in the U.S. But becoming unstuck has been a challenge for Maya, because the physical sensations in her body (which involve some actual pain) keep her wanting to fast-track her healing. She has expressed on more than one occasion that she just wants to "get there" and would like the instruction manual to know how to do that.

Unfortunately, there is no step-by-step instruction manual, but there is a way to change the relationship to the sensations in your body, the thoughts in your mind, and the actions and reactions you take. This eventually changes your belief about yourself. All this takes courage, work and faith, and becoming unstuck will not happen simply because you will it to be so. You cannot become unstuck just by thinking differently, because your neurobiological response to the events in your life have become implicit memory.[2]

This is why the very basic tool of noticing the sensations in your body, choosing a tool to create space and noticing without judgment how these moments feel will begin to loosen the binds of your body and guide you to a place where you are willing to continue down the path. A path paved with little and gradual changes.

FEELING STUCK AFFECTS OUR VOICE

When the engine of a car is not running properly, the impact is often noticed in the symptom of the problem, not the root. Lights might falter, acceleration might feel sluggish, or any other number of things might start us fishing for a fix. Until we understand that the operating nexus of the car needs tending to, the symptoms will keep showing up.

Feeling stuck has some similar symptoms, most often showing up in our ability to communicate clearly, calmly and firmly. This includes communicating to others, to ourselves *and* to our bodies. When we have gotten to this place in our emotional development we often feel confused about or fearful of expressing ourselves. We become reactive or defensive in response to others and feel misunderstood. This compounds our existing adaptations and fuels further adaptations in how we communicate.[3] But just like the example of the car, the root of the problem is in our operating nexus—our body.

Feeling-stuck adaptations can range from becoming terrified to say anything for fear that it will be wrong and you will be rejected, to incessant talking for fear that you will not be seen, heard or understood. They meet the same fate of feeling invisible or rejected. In either case, there is an internal current of fear running through our bodies; the manner in which we communicate is the by-product of this fear. This is why returning to basic tools like breath and the exercises in the fear chapter is so important for lasting healing.

THE PATH TO WELL-BEING

We feel a sense of well-being when we feel seen or heard. We feel it when we feel a sense of belonging and being worthy of love. And we feel it when our life has meaning and purpose. Feeling stuck can be understood as a years-long culmination of the absence, lack or loss of these things.

When we are stuck, we have come to know our survival adaptations as our normal, or who we are. When we don't speak for fear of being criticized or talk incessantly for fear of not being seen or recognized, we sabotage our chance of making truly authentic connections, because we either can't listen or can't be heard. True authenticity or intimacy relies on the willingness to be vulnerable, to take emotional risks and to make mistakes. When we operate from our adaptations, we are doing anything to avoid being vulnerable.

Reversing the impact of our adaptations is very difficult. Remember: these adaptations are linked with the survival response that tells us our life is in danger and creates significant discomfort in our body. This discomfort is given a label like anxiety, fear, depression, guilt, shame, etc.

So for women like Maya, the discomfort of *not* speaking is far less than the excruciating thoughts and subsequent sensations associated *with* speaking. All of our adaptations are there to help us predict an outcome. Healing means letting go of the need to predict any outcome. The first step to letting go is to communicate directly with the sensations in your body and remind yourself that you can take a risk and do something that is nonhabitual—such as speaking when you have a strong adaptive response telling you not to do so.

This can be just as challenging to someone who takes up a lot of space with chatter. This is an adaptation I know personally, and I can attest to the work it takes to recognize the fear associated with *not* chiming in and instead remaining grounded and spacious, which allows me to be present for others—in silence. The practice of TIMBo-ing myself when I feel this particular adaptive response has made me a more compassionate and present listener. It helps me communicate to people so they feel seen and heard. My ability to resonate with the people in my professional and personal life communicates a sense of belonging—belonging to the collective human experience.

I hold a core belief that anyone, even the most traumatized women, can experience healing with TIMBo and in turn share something that has changed their lives with other women or people they care about. This is the very thing that has given me, the facilitators I train and anyone who uses TIMBo for their own well-being a sense of purpose and meaning. Because at the core of things, making a difference in even the smallest of ways is a basic human craving that is one of the foundations of well-being.

EXPERIENCES THAT LEAD TO FEELING STUCK IN THE BODY

We can't reverse feeling stuck if we can't communicate first *through* and then *without* survival-associated body sensations. If we continue on with no awareness and no tools to *be with* these sensations, our life experiences fuel an erosion of well-being that culminates in feeling further stuck, trapped or powerless to change our life circumstances.

Whether it is an unhealthy relationship, the hamster wheel of a professional career, debilitating behaviors (like addiction or eating disorders) or even a truly unchangeable situation like incarceration, the origins of feeling stuck are in the disruption of our childhood emotional development. Below are some of the common contributing factors to developing feeling stuck in the body.

- Verbal abuse
- Secrets
- Authoritarian parents (no talking back)
- Alcoholic or addicted family[4]

Feeling stuck has its roots in early experiences in which we actually were powerless or helpless. Remember: in our developmental years our primitive neurobiology often perceives what would be considered acceptable practices in our society as a threat to survival. It is the sole job of that system to be on the alert for any sensory reminder of threat.

Over time, those sensory reminders often emanate from inside the body, yet we have no knowledge of it. This phenomenon creates more feelings of being stuck, helpless and powerless to change our lives or our relationships.[5] Many of the women that come to the TIMBo program and training are in this place. Feeling stuck can manifest in some of the following ways once we become adults:

- Fear of speaking
- Small, weak voice
- Can't communicate clearly

- Difficulty putting feelings into words
- Shy
- Excessive talking
- Poor listener
- Interrupts
- Gossips[6]

We've all been that friend that tries to give advice when someone close to us comes to us with complaints, frustrations or advice for current life circumstances that just feel bad. Often we feel that our advice falls on deaf ears. We can feel frustrated when we seem to be having the same conversation over and over while watching our friend stay put in the circumstance we have offered (what we feel is) sage advice for changing.

It is not that our advice falls on deaf ears. It's because when people feel stuck, it's difficult to put advice into action. The sensation of being trapped is not changeable by way of advice. We attend to the sensations in our body first.

Dr. Bessel van der Kolk is one of the pioneers in trauma adaptation, traumatic memory in the body and the use of body-based interventions in recovery. He is also the founder of The Trauma Center here in Boston. In his brilliant book *The Body Keeps the Score: Brain, Mind, and Body in the Healing of Trauma*, Dr. van der Kolk states, "Long after the actual event has passed, the brain may keep sending signals to the body to escape a threat that no longer exists."[7]

This has been seen in experiments with rats that are given an electric shock in response to an action like pushing a lever for food, for example.[8] Once the animals are neurologically conditioned to respond to that activity with fear, their behavior changes, informing all of their actions from a place of fear. But when the electric shock has been removed from the activity of pushing the lever for food, the rats' behavior remains as if the threat is still there, meaning that the perceived threat of danger is still felt in their bodies even when the actual threat has been removed. This is the neurobiological basis of feeling stuck.[9]

HOW FEELING STUCK LIVES IN THE BODY

In the lists below you can see how the emotion of feeling stuck shows up in the body in the short term and how it impacts our physical and psychological health in the long term. This is not an exhaustive list, but it is meant to help you identify feeling hopeless or stuck in your body.

SHORT-TERM INDICATORS OF FEELING STUCK

- Hearing loss
- Stuttering
- Clenching jaw/gnashing teeth
- Lump in your throat[10]

LONG-TERM INDICATORS OF FEELING STUCK

- Ear infections and hearing loss
- TMJ
- Chronic fatigue[11]

PAY ATTENTION TO THE SENSATIONS IN YOUR BODY

On my thirty-ninth birthday I sat on the edge of a sea cliff in Acadia National Park on the coast of Maine. This was before I first stepped into my local Boston yoga studio, before I met Daniel and before my sister helped me realize I could separate from Mitch. But that day was the start of feeling like something wasn't right. I couldn't shake the feeling that I wasn't living the life I wanted to live. I wasn't the person I wanted to be.

I didn't know why I was feeling this way (this was before I found out about Mitch's life of secrets and lies), especially considering that on a superficial level I had it all. A devoted and adoring (or so I thought) husband, two beautiful kids, a house in one of the most coveted neighborhoods in Boston, a summer home in Maine, no financial issues and so on. Why was I so desperately unhappy? If I had known then what I know now, I am quite sure that I would have been less likely to descend into a tailspin of depression and suicidality.

Years later, once I began to breathe and move my body in the Boston yoga classes, I began to move from the mental feeling of being stuck to the physiological feeling of being stuck. I felt trapped, and I felt desperate. My sister's insistence in reminding me that I wasn't trapped and I could take space from my marriage if I wanted to sparked something in me. It was a new consideration of reality.

Still, I could not fathom that I could extract myself from my marriage. I couldn't put the suggestion into action because I had become immobilized (feeling stuck)—a result of years of emotional and psychological abuse. Thus, my life felt physically inescapable, even though it wasn't.

If I had the ability to know that the sensations in my body were screaming that my life was in danger (even though it wasn't), I believe I would have had a different experience. Not to say that it wouldn't have been painful, but staying stuck increased the suffering I experienced. Eventually, the practice of yoga gave my body the mobilization it was desperately crying out for, but I had to move through the emotional pain. This created enough space for me to realize that I needed to get unstuck.

Without the knowledge of my survival adaptations and body sensations, I had been convinced there was no way out. With the help of my sister I found a way out, but again, without my embodied resources, leaving the physical place of feeling trapped didn't change the fact that I still felt trapped in my own body.

It has taken years to repair that survival wiring. It wasn't until at least five years after the destruction of my marriage that I realized I was still stuck to some degree—I wasn't healing. In fact, my fear-based feelings were getting worse, and I began to retreat from the world. Isolation gave me the illusion of being unstuck, but really I just went from one prison to another.

To heal I needed to enter the very place where I had been so hurt and traumatized—relationships. To do that I needed to gain knowledge and compassion for my survival wiring and subsequent adaptive development. Without the courage to feel the excruciating sensations of trusting, taking risks and being vulnerable, I doubt any sustained healing would have happened at all.

EXERCISES FOR HEALING FEELING STUCK

WRITING EXERCISE #1: IDENTIFYING FEELING STUCK

Take a few moments to think of some of the times you've felt hopeless or stuck. You don't need to get into the why of things—just notice what or how. It can be a conversation that you had, a person in your life or a moment when you felt trapped. As you think about these experiences, notice what you feel in your body.

_____

_____

_____

_____

_____

_____

_____

_____

_____

_____

_____

_____

_____

CREATING SPACE

When you use the tool of breath, you create space between the sensation of feeling hopeless or stuck in your body and your response to that sensation. In that space you can begin to understand your body sensations, clearly and compassionately listen to your body and begin to allow communication between your body and your mind.

LION'S BREATH

Lion's breath is one of the most powerful breaths we teach in TIMBo, but it has to be said that it is not for everyone. It is the absolute antithesis of feeling stuck in that it asks you to open your throat in ways that can feel very uncomfortable and scary in the face of survival adaptations that involve keeping your voice small and your expressions repressed.

I personally was very averse to using lion's breath when I first came upon it, and I had to work my way into it over time. If you are finding yourself feeling uncomfortable in the use of this breath, simply back off a bit and express yourself as you are able. Over time you will find you feel more and more comfortable with opening your throat, using your voice and expressing yourself in bigger and bolder ways. Once you realize you have the right to take up some space, it will feel empowering—let it be a step-by-step, level-by-level choice.

Start by sitting up straight. Take a deep breath in through your nose. Exhale according to your comfort level, choosing one of the following:

Level 1: Open your mouth, and forcefully exhale your breath.

Level 2: Open your mouth as wide as you can, and forcefully exhale all of your breath.

Level 3: Open your mouth as wide as you can, stick out your tongue a bit, and exhale all of your breath.

Level 4: Open your mouth as wide as you can, stick out your tongue as much as you can, and exhale with an audible growl (like a lion) as you exhale all of your breath.

WRITING EXERCISE #2: COMMUNICATION

Take a few moments to think of some conversations you can have with your body during times of overwhelm, hopelessness or feeling stuck. If you like, you can just think of single words or ideas that you would like to remember. For instance, *calm, breath, space, nurture, peace*, etc. You can also think of easy short statements, such as *I breathe into my body, I remind my body that I am not in immediate danger, I calm my body's panic.*

CHAPTER 11

Denial

Near the end of the TIMBo program we introduce a quote by Tenzin Gyatso, the fourteenth Dalai Lama. It reads, "To be aware of a single shortcoming in oneself is more useful than to be aware of a thousand in someone else."[1] By the time we arrive at this quote we can all understand how this feels true, especially when we replace the word *shortcoming* with *body sensations* or *adaptations*.

But when we are in adolescence (the age when this stage of emotional development happens), we have little to no awareness of the sensations we feel in response to things. We just want to belong. The last thing we want to address is the emotions, thoughts and reactions that inform who we are in the world. In fact, as teenagers our brains are yet to be fully developed. We can't easily consider the perspective of others. We have little impulse control and don't consider the impact of our actions.[2] As teens we just want to feel good, and we want it now. For teen survivors of trauma this can have devastating short- and long-term impacts.

In the context of TIMBo, denial can be understood as having developed a false or adapted self, which culminates in an unconscious denial of our true and authentic self. Think of it this way: each time we operate from a survival adaptation, we are refusing vulnerability. As a reminder, fear, guilt, shame, resentment and feeling stuck are the emotional impacts of resisting vulnerability. To stay alive, our bodies have learned we must mitigate all risks and stay in control (no to vulnerability, yes to predictability). But living as our true and authentic selves requires vulnerability. So the denial of the true self is not conscious so much as it is also a survival mechanism. By this point in life it has often (but not always) turned from adaptive to maladaptive.

TO BE OUR TRUE SELVES FEELS RISKY

By the time we are adults, connecting with our true and authentic self feels profoundly risky and dangerous. The day I had my epiphany on the cliffs by the sea was the day that my false self collided with the faint memory of my true self. I had spent more than a decade becoming more like Mitch than my old self (without the lies and infidelities). Mitch was a negative, skeptical, sarcastic and critical man, and I was becoming his female counterpart. It is not and never was who I am at my core. But my realization that day was terrifying, because he loved the person I had become—not the person that I truly was. To be my true self meant risking losing everything.

One day I drove my son to his fencing lesson and plucked up the courage to call my mother from the parking lot while I waited for his lesson to end. I wanted to tell her what was happening with me, but I was intensely fearful. By that time, I believed that my family loved and accepted me because of who I was married to. I had made something of my life. I had finally gotten it right. To tell her the truth, I believed, would risk that connection too.

But my mother was supportive and understanding, and she shared a story of her own courage that was instrumental in helping me commit to living an authentic life. She told me that just after her fourth child (my younger sister) was born, she had a very similar epiphany to mine on the sea cliffs. Up until that point she was living in a role that was typical for women of the late fifties and early sixties—a stay-at-home housewife whose sole focus was the health and happiness of her husband and children.

But by this point it was the mid-seventies. Women's lib and the equal rights activists were blowing up current events. The flood of

1972 facilitated new friendships with modern women who went bra-less, wore macramé and had careers. She began to feel inside herself that the life she was living and the person that she'd become did not reflect the person she wanted to be. She was intelligent, passionate, strong and driven. She was getting encouragement from her new friends, who reminded her she could do anything she wanted to do. This was a new age—the age of women's empowerment. This created a conflict between who she wanted to be and who she felt she needed to be for her husband and family.

She told me that one day she wrote my father a letter, explaining that she was not the person she wanted to be. She laid out in great detail who she wanted to be in the world and what that would mean for their marriage. She did not want to leave my father, but she was aware that her commitment to living her life as her true self might throw a wrench into the spokes of their marriage and family. The letter concluded with a recognition that he might not want to be married to her anymore if she connected back to the woman she truly felt she was. She let him know in no uncertain terms that she would accept that if it was his choice, but she was not going back to living the way she had been for the last dozen years.

Like my realization on the cliffs of Maine, the day my mother gave my father that letter is etched in her memory as a turning point in her life. They had gone to a fast-food restaurant, ordered food and sat down, and she handed the letter to him while at the table. In the end they stayed together—my mother enrolled in college and became a nurse, and my father adjusted to living with a newly empowered and career-driven woman, wife and mother of four children.

THE JOURNEY AWAY FROM THE TRUE SELF

A good litmus test for determining if your adapted identity is linked to your survival wiring is to try *not* doing what you would habitually do. Choosing to live as your true self will feel like risking it all. For example, in the case of someone who has come to link their worth with their profession, being laid off or changing careers can feel tantamount to death. Our minds tell us that we must be a certain way or do a certain thing to fit in. But the stress of not being our true selves takes a toll on our bodies in the end.

The truth is that we are all worthy of unconditional acceptance, belonging and connection just for being human. Unfortunately, almost all of us have adapted out of that knowing, and have created conditions and expectations for ourselves that we hold ourselves to. Creating expectations for ourselves is not in itself a bad thing, but when those self-imposed expectations are tied to our very worthiness—that's a problem.

What's worse, regarding the experience of trauma, this place of denial can put us in dangerous life circumstances that can lead directly to things like overdose, incarceration or suicide. This may sound like an inflammatory statement, but by way of trauma, the self-concept becomes completely fractured.[3] Traumatic experiences, such as the ones experienced by Molly, whose early sexual abuse and violent household shaped the course of her life, lead us to believe that we are completely broken, unfit for love or connection and steeped in shame and self-hatred—all informing a false idea of who we are in the world.

This journey away from our true spirit informs the choices we make in life. These choices can be inauthentic at best and traumatizing or self-destructive at worst. As we continue, so does the reinforcement of our false self. But we eventually become completely stuck, because our body cannot continue this way—but our mind tells us that we must, in order to be loved or to belong. We can, in turn, feel trapped.

You'll recall my discovery of Stephen Cope's book *Yoga and the Quest for the True Self.* As I read through this book my mind was blown, because he had put words to what I had been experiencing that birthday on the cliffs of Maine. I just couldn't go on with life the way I had been living it. The day on the cliffs, the conversation with my mother and reading Mr. Cope's book are experiences I credit for changing the course of my life.

But not everyone is fortunate enough to discover a book like Mr. Cope's or to happen upon a yoga class that creates enough space in their body that they begin to question the life they are living. As humans, regardless of whether we consider ourselves trauma survivors or not, we feel the deep biological necessity for connection. We want to feel like we belong. We all wish to move out of feeling stuck and begin looking for our people out of the deep human craving for belonging.

The tragedy is that for those of us who have a destructive self-concept due to trauma, the people we bond with will be the people that help us reinforce it. This is likely one of the reasons young boys raised in poverty by parents that are addicts, abusive or neglectful so readily join gangs.

The traumatic experiences of childhood create a self-belief informed first by fear, then guilt and shame turned to resentment and anger, leading to becoming stuck in a firm false belief about the self—often as a "bad kid." It is from this place of a false self-belief that we look for belonging. This locks the denial of the true self in place. We can't believe anything different about ourselves because we have found a (false) sense of belonging.

When I met and married Mitch, I felt like I belonged. Every time I visited my family and spent time with my siblings and their spouses, I felt like I finally belonged. Later when we had children, I felt that sense of belonging increase and extend out to my children with the birth of their cousins. We all belonged. When they entered the school system I felt a sense of belonging, because we were a family—right along with those other families. Mom, dad and kids. We belonged. To risk my marriage meant to fracture that sense of belonging for not just myself but also my children. The feelings of guilt and responsibility were too much to bear.

LIVES AT RISK

Survival adaptations have a very good purpose when we are young but can be deadly, especially in adolescence, when the denial of the self becomes entrenched. I can very clearly see how and why teenagers whose emerging sexuality resides outside of the hetero model resist it so painfully. Already struggling with figuring out who they are and how to be in their family of origin, teens likely suppress any willing-ness to come out as anything other than hetero. But even in the most loving and accepting family, coming out in adolescence means risking a feeling of belonging in the larger societal context.

Because of a teenager's inability to engage in impulse control or consider long-term consequences to short-term actions, the risks become very high. Teenagers either lose complete touch with their true and authentic selves or deny their true selves in favor of fitting in. It's when teens feel that no matter what they do they will never belong that they often make irreversibly damaging choices, such as suicide or overdose.

THE ADDICTION RISKS OF DENIAL

Growing research shows us that addiction is a result of turning to something that effectively dulls the pain of feeling broken, unlovable and disconnected.[4] But it is less recognized that addicts surround themselves with other addicts because it satisfies a need for connection with a community that gets them. At the same time, it reinforces their false self-concept that they are unfixable, broken human beings that belong in one place and one place only—isolated from the larger society and hanging out with other addicts.

The reality is that all humans deserve unconditional love and acceptance just for being a human being, but the stigma around addiction keeps addicts in their cage. To consider moving out of the denied self means to risk disconnection with other addicts. Remember: it feels safer to feel unworthy of love than to risk feeling lovable only to be hurt. When we as survivors find a group that helps us feel we belong—no matter how toxic—we concede to taking what we can get.

To trust anything else will run an addict smack into the wall of implicit trauma memories that are the source of their shame and self-stigma to begin with. And the painful body sensations associated with those memories make reaching for a drug so much easier than feeling the discomfort necessary for true healing. And with a community of other addicts around them, strengthening their isolation from the larger community and normalizing their drug use, it makes absolute sense that reaching for a drug would be an easier choice than facing the pain associated with recovery (addiction and trauma recovery alike) all by themselves.

If we are fortunate enough to escape the entrapment of addiction, it may mean that we have constructed other cages for ourselves like compulsive eating, dieting, exercising or simply obsession with food and weight. Eating disorders of all kinds are rarely about weight or nutrition. At the root of the disorder is often a self-constructed and firmly held belief that what we weigh, how we look and what we eat are directly connected with our worth as human beings. We can become addicted, in a sense, to the control we feel when the scale steadily drops and conversely racked with anxiety when we have lost control and the needle creeps up. We commit to a strict eating regimen that can return our sense of control, which most often is unconsciously connected to our feelings of worth and our ability to belong.[5]

In extreme cases we may develop anorexia or bulimia, but it is rare that any of our efforts to meet the self-created criteria for worthiness ever result in a feeling of worthiness. The truth is we are worthy simply because we are an alive-and-breathing human miracle.

Wouldn't it be great if we could all read that previous sentence and realize, *Oh great! I've never thought of it that way. Thanks for that nugget, and now I feel worthy! I shall return to my true authentic self!* But it can't happen that way because our survival adaptations turned addictions, compulsions and behaviors are informed by our survival wiring.

THE EXTREMES OF SELF-DENIAL

When we speak of denial in the context of TIMBo, we can understand it in two senses. One form of denial is to deny that we are good enough—to fixate on the ways we are failing to be good enough and destroy our self-concept even further, which connects us with communities and partners who often help us reinforce this self-belief.

This is what my therapist meant when she said that I married the person who made sense for me at the time. Unconsciously, I was looking for someone who could help me feel good enough, and that had to be someone who could point out all of my flaws—and there were so many that I never even knew I had. This is how abusers become so powerful over others. These people aren't limited to romantic partners or spouses. They can be parents, siblings and even our own grown children.

In the end, if we always believe we are somehow broken and need fixing to be deserving of love, we can never find a strength inside of us to say to ourselves, the world and our abusers *I am 100 percent worthy, just as I am.* Instead we'll continue to look outside of ourselves to find a worthiness that has been inside of us since we were born.

The other way to think of denial is when we stop striving for that feeling of worthiness. This is often the impact of trauma and can have two extremes. One is to deflect all criticism outward in the direction of other people, systems and circumstances. There is no self-awareness, self-investigation or taking responsibility or accountability for anything. This is commonly seen in narcissists and sociopaths. Even when committing the most heinous atrocities against others, these individuals are in such denial of the self that they find a twisted justification in placing the responsibility of their actions anywhere but on themselves.[6]

But in less extreme cases, this form of denial is recognized in chronic blamers and complainers. The development of resentment has solidified into feeling stuck and landed them in a place of denial. Their own thoughts, actions and rationales maintain disconnection with themselves and with others, which fuels the resentment, driving further disconnection through outward criticism.

On the other end of the pendulum are survivors of trauma who come to loathe themselves. The trauma they have experienced and their failed efforts to find true connection and love leave them utterly convinced that they are not fit for society. The only way to feel safe is to believe they are so damaged they are bad for people. This is a way to keep the potential for further hurt, betrayal and trauma at bay.

Keeping yourself from being vulnerable by believing you're unfit for the world may have its roots in the need for survival, but the chronic isolation and disconnection that ensues often leaves these individuals turning to suicide for the ultimate control over being hurt or rejected by others (not belonging). After all, if you're not around anymore, you can't be hurt or hurt others. This form of denial is what brought me to the brink of suicide in 2005. It is common in many of the women

I see in TIMBo. Women like Erin, women like Molly and women like Ruthie.

Ruthie

I met Ruthie when she participated in a TIMBo program in 2014. Ruthie is a beautiful woman with fine features who projects a bohemian yet sophisticated air, complete with streaks of purple and pink running through her chin-length asymmetrical hair. She is a fierce activist for women's and LGBTQ rights, and a lover and protector of all creatures great and small. She is, of course, a vegan.

Ruthie grew up in a suburb outside of Cleveland, Ohio, and was the youngest child of three siblings. Her mother suffered from untreated bipolar disorder, which presented itself as severe and long-lasting depression that left her unable to provide any semblance of parenting for her children.

Ruthie's father was an abusive workaholic. He was rarely present in the household. When he was, he fought with Ruthie's mother and was emotionally abusive to the children. The fighting between her parents, emotional abuse by her father and chronic neglect by her mother left Ruthie devoid of any sense of safety or nurture.

She had few, but precious, memories of her mother singing to her. Those moments brought her fleeting feelings of love and security. But her mother's moods more regularly swung from depressed and nearly catatonic in bed to manic and frightening, which left Ruthie unable to trust that anything could be predictable or consistent.

When she was of preschool age she was sexually abused by a neighbor. Even at such a young age Ruthie remembers feeling somehow responsible for the abuse and told no one about it. Around age ten, Ruthie grew increasingly and disproportionately responsible for her mother's well-being and felt despondent when her mother was hospitalized for a period of weeks.

Ruthie's worry for her mother grew as she entered early adolescence. By the age of thirteen she felt like the only adult in the household. When her father began making inappropriate and uncomfortable comments about Ruthie's developing body, she had had enough. Ruthie ran away.

As a burgeoning teenager, Ruthie felt she had some street smarts (she didn't) and headed to a local hangout near the high school. Even though she was now homeless and without a plan, she still felt that she would rather be anywhere but home.

When a group of high-school boys began talking with her, she felt special and more grown-up. They lured her into a parked car and took turns sexually assaulting her. This horrific event is the experience that would change Ruthie's life forever.

She managed to escape the car, ran into the woods and vomited at the base of a tree. Somehow Ruthie got herself to the emergency room of a hospital, where she had to endure the horrendous process of the rape kit. She felt unsupported and ill-treated by hospital staff. Then and there she knew that there was no safe place in the world for her, and she completely withdrew into herself. She developed selective mutism and did not speak for a long time after the assault.

Through high school she stopped talking and stopped eating. She was disconnected from her body and lost large chunks of time. Her developing anorexia was the only place where she felt in control, as she lost her way through a haze of gratuitous alcohol consumption and sexual acting out. This gave her an allusory sense of control but was retraumatizing. A false self-concept began to set in. She was only good for one thing: sex. She was a loser and a troubled kid who drank. And she could only feel OK about herself if she continued to starve herself.

The one place of solace in Ruthie's high-school life was art class. There she could briefly forget her pain and escape into a world of color and creativity. Being creative then became a part of her new self-concept, and she enrolled in an art college.

But her traumatic experiences eroded her spirit more than art could revive it. Her false self turned completely self-condemning. She was damaged goods. Unlovable and broken. She would never belong. She attempted suicide by overdosing on a cocktail of drugs and alcohol just before college graduation, after which she was admitted as an inpatient at a local psychiatric hospital.

After her attempted suicide Ruthie began volunteering at a local animal shelter. She adopted a puppy. Her dog would become the provider of something Ruthie had never felt in her life: unconditional love. Her love for her dog sparked a desire to be a helper. She was accepted into an art therapy degree program at a university in Boston. Ruthie felt like her life was finally moving in a positive direction. Then the Boston Marathon bomb happened.

As a result of the terrorist attack in her new hometown and the ensuing fear that enveloped the city, Ruthie experienced an increase of PTSD. She began losing large chunks of time. Over that year, her belief that she was unlovable and broken and that she'd never belong became even more pronounced. This belief fueled a growing life of isolation, with just her dog and cat for company. Her resurgence of PTSD symptoms caused her to worry about her animals' well-being. She took herself to the psychiatric emergency room at a local hospital and experienced (for the first time) a positive and caring environment within the medical community.

She recalls sitting with a psychiatric nurse in the emergency room who spent hours by her side teaching her sudoku, a Japanese puzzle that works the memory using numerical items but requires no mathematical calculation. Sudoku uses the memory and logic areas of the brain simultaneously and is likely used with trauma patients to integrate left- and right-brain activity in crisis intervention (trauma activation and flashbacks are said to be a mechanism of right-hemispheric activity).[7]

Ruthie remembers this as her first experience with the medical community where she felt truly heard, seen and supported. She continued to live with her false self-concept of being broken, but she never forgot that nurse.

About a year after the bombing she decided to check out a local yoga studio. She had been searching for a trauma-informed yoga class and thought the little neighborhood studio she found might be just the place. When she walked through the door she felt cautious, but in response to asking for trauma-informed classes she was told about the once soft-spoken Erin, whom we met when exploring guilt and responsibility. By then Erin had finished her one-hundred-hour TIMBo training and was offering TIMBo privately to clients while employed at this studio.

Working with Erin helped Ruthie change her perspective to what was happening in her body, and she began learning how to use simple yet powerful tools like breath. Because Erin had credited TIMBo for her *own* continuing recovery, Ruthie trusted her and began to feel less broken. The perspective of seeing her body as a brilliant organism that protected her in ways that kept her alive was something new to Ruthie, and though her PTSD was still quite acute and distressing, she felt tiny changes that kept her continuing her work with Erin.

During that work and later in a public TIMBo group, Ruthie experienced what we call hands-on healing. While many schools of thought consider touching trauma survivors risky and dangerous, I have always felt that—when offered mindfully, after trusting relationships are formed in the group (about four to six weeks) and always with an option for choice—touch can be incredibly healing.

The touch we offer in TIMBo is not like it is normally experienced in a typical yoga class. It is focused on presence, not directing the body or correcting alignment in any way. The single most consistent comment we hear about the touch we offer is that it feels like a mother's touch—a quality of touch so many of the women we see have never felt in their lifetimes.

Because Ruthie had gained some very important tools in her work with Erin, she was able to accept this touch, even though it took her body some time to trust that it came without conditions. The TIMBo touch would eventually be one of the most important components in Ruthie's process of healing, helping her shift her false self-concept from *I am unlovable* to *I am worthy of love.*

After Ruthie participated in a few more public groups led by Erin, a benefactor came forward and offered to provide a scholarship for Ruthie to participate in our TIMBo training modules. During these trainings Ruthie found her most challenging and ultimately her most healing experiences.

Here, Ruthie began to feel safe and supported. She felt part of a community and found something she had never experienced in her life—unconditional acceptance. She belonged. She entered the training process feeling terrified to be seen or to speak up, but she trusted Erin, who by now was a trainer, and she trusted me. There were times when it was difficult, but Ruthie's body took care of her when she felt overwhelmed, and the training was contained in such a way that she never felt completely swept away by flashbacks.

Every step of the way she made choices that were new and sometimes terrifying, but on the other side of those choices (like speaking into the training circle), she recognized that she was not only still alive but also accepted, valued and even loved, just for being a living and breathing human being.

Ruthie is a beautiful young woman who, because of some horrific traumas in her life, developed a devastatingly repugnant view of herself. She couldn't just change how she felt about herself. Few of us can until we compassionately recognize that even the most damaging self-beliefs began as survival adaptations. It was only with the tools of TIMBo that Ruthie could consider walking the path toward her true self—a self that was worthy of unconditional love and belonging.

Ruthie now feels passionate about being a TIMBo leader and knows she can help women like her find healing and freedom through the program—not in spite of what she's been through but because of it. TIMBo has helped her feel seen and heard, and it has given her a feeling of belonging. And most miraculously she knows that she can truly help women who have been through trauma change their lives. Nothing feels more meaningful than that.

EXPERIENCES THAT LEAD TO DENIAL IN THE BODY

The emergence of the false self via the developmental path of resentment and feeling stuck brings us to a firm belief about who we are. Our need for connection and journey away from anything that feels uncertain, uncontrolled or vulnerable keeps us on this path away from realizing our true and authentic selves. The origins of this self-denial often coincide with our development during adolescence.

Below are some of the common contributing factors to developing denial in the body, including but not limited to the following:
  • What you see does not match what you're told
  • Invalidation of intuition
  • Ugly or frightening environment (war zone, violence)[8]

Any parent of a teenager will describe to you with sparkling clarity the time in their child's life when they noticed their child becoming a person they did not recognize. This normal part of development is shocking under the best of circumstances, as it is a teenager's job to try on different identities as they navigate who they want to be in the world.

Childhood experiences up to that point inform their journey toward their future selves, and often teens are influenced by places in which they excel, such as sports, academics or the arts. When traumatic experiences influence an adolescent's development, well-intentioned parents can be shocked by the choices their growing children make in who they believe they are in the world.

Regardless of any parent's best intentions, we all create expectations and conditions for ourselves that we feel ensure our worthiness. Below are some of the ways denial manifests in adults.

- Insensitivity
- Lack of imagination
- Difficulty visualizing
- Poor dream recall
- Can only see one right and true way
- Delusions
- Obsessions
- Nightmares
- Difficulty concentrating[9]

HOW DENIAL LIVES IN THE BODY

In the lists below you can see how the emotion of denial shows up in the body in the short term and how it impacts our physical and psychological health in the long term. This is not an exhaustive list, but it is meant to help you identify the symptoms of self-denial in your body.

SHORT-TERM INDICATORS OF DENIAL IN THE BODY

- Headache

- Sinusitis
- Problems sleeping[10]

LONG-TERM INDICATORS OF DENIAL IN THE BODY

- Hallucinations
- Eye and vision problems
- Recurring nightmares[11]

THE PATH TO HEALING DENIAL

There is a way to heal from trauma that has developed into the self-denial that, over time, fuels behavior disorders. It has to start with the most simple, basic and accessible practice of awareness. Every step of the way, the recovery process has to be the choice of the individual, and survivors will only be willing to engage in processes that carry the degree of risk they are willing to take.[12]

Awareness of sensations in the body, understanding of what they are (biologically speaking) to minimize judgment, and simple and accessible tools like a few deep breaths are often the only place to start for survivors. The good news is that these practices prepare the body for taking incrementally higher risks for recovery. Over time more awareness builds—and compassionate awareness is the scaffold that facilitates healing from trauma.

STAYING WITH THE BODY AND THE BREATH

It is my hope that by now you have participated in at least a few of the somatic awareness and breathing exercises described earlier in the book. The value of these earlier exercises is that they take you through a journey of awareness.

If you haven't done so already, now is a good time to go back to the beginning of the Emotional Anatomy Pyramid and begin the practice of body and breath awareness through the exercises. If you've already tried some of the exercises, let your intuition guide you to which one might help you pause and create more awareness when you are in the grips of denial. Practicing these skills on your own and sensing which ones will be the most helpful is a direct pathway back to the authentic self.

WRITING EXERCISE FOR DENIAL

We also emphasize journaling in TIMBo because writing helps you recognize how you may have adapted through your developmental years and how you might journey back to your true and authentic self. Take a moment to reflect on all the material you have read thus far. Notice if you found yourself thinking things like *Oh, that's me!* or *Things are starting to make sense!*

Write down some of the experiences you remember through your life and the adaptations you believe you developed as a result. The most important thing is that you don't judge yourself or anyone else for these experiences. Just notice what it feels like to put some pieces together for yourself.

CHAPTER 12

Doubt

Doubt keeps us stuck in the conviction that things will never change, that this is the hand we were dealt and that it's just the way life is. It prevents innovation, creativity, resilience, optimism and growth because it aims to protect us from the sensations we have in our body in response to failure, loss or unexpected change. If we understand the development of doubt as a long-term yet unconscious survival wiring, we can begin to see it as something that can be healed, rather than a permanent personality trait that keeps us from living a full and joyful life.

Doubt can be understood as the unilateral absence of trust. After decades of unconsciously responding from a place of fear (in our bodies) while experiencing all of the hurt, pain and disappointments that are an unavoidable part of life, it is inevitable that we will end up with a lack of trust and faith in ourselves, others or the world around us. It takes awareness, self-compassion and actual work to change how we feel in our lives, because feeling more trusting, resilient and satisfied in life is not dependent on anything or anyone outside of ourselves. It has everything to do with what is inside of us—starting with how we are wired to respond to the things and people that come our way. But to even begin that process we have to go back to the root of all emotional-anatomy development—fear.

One of the most useful notions I gained from reading Dr. Gabor Maté's book *When the Body Says No* is his identification of the three universal triggers of stress: lack of control, uncertainty and lack of information.[1] Think about these things for a moment. Think of some times in your life when you have experienced a lack of information, a lack of control or a lack of certainty.

You are likely to have at least a short list, right? Because the truth is that these three things are an unavoidable part of life. How our body (and then our mind) responds to them has more to do with how we experience life through our developmental years, always prioritizing survival via connection in the best-case scenario, and survival via avoiding vulnerability when our adaptations prove to be anything but foolproof.

Uncertainty, lack of control and lack of information are all places of extreme vulnerability. They are the unknown, a place of more questions than answers, and a place where we have a choice to trust and have faith or to fret. In this space we often respond to these things with worry, stress and anxiety, which, neurobiologically speaking, are rooted in fear in the body. Because the body has been wired to recognize vulnerability as dangerous. This is the neurological root of doubt. It is the ultimate in perceived self-protection.

We all know these people, and maybe we can recognize some of these traits in ourselves. The naysayers, the killjoys, the skeptics. The blamers and complainers. The procrastinators and those who always have big plans that never come to fruition. Because to have a negative view on life means that you'll never be unexpectedly disappointed.

To expect failure means that you'll never feel broadsided, and to never finish anything means that you can't be criticized—because no one can criticize something that you didn't put out there for others to see.

If we respond to any of life's uncertainties with doubt, we have the illusion of safety and control, even if it isn't conscious. The trap is that we end up criticizing ourselves, which fuels the doubt and fear we bring to life's uncertainties even more. Our false belief about ourselves strengthens. We get stuck in a trap that is damaging one person and one person only—ourselves.

HOW WE GROW INTO DOUBT

The trap of doubt can be untangled when we recognize that it has fear at its foundation. We can use the knowledge and tools presented through this book and the TIMBo program to stop when we feel anything other than trust and faith, and feel the sensations in our bodies, compassionately understand them as our survival response (fear), and create space. We simply cannot move from doubt to trust by just deciding to do that—the body will fight tooth and nail, because it is trying to keep us alive when we are in a vulnerable space.

We are not born with large doses of doubt, mistrust or skepticism—we grow into it. I would bet that everyone has felt the niggling voice of doubt trying to influence their actions and decisions. I myself have been told by many people "You should write a book!" But for many years, each time I began the process of putting words to paper, my voice of doubt (a.k.a. fear, a.k.a. my fierce protector from rejection) reminded me that no one would really have any interest in anything I had to say.

I have now come to recognize this part of me as a young (inner) child, trying to keep myself safe from the sting of rejection—the same sting that I felt when my mother did not like my fancy shoes. The sting that my body recognized as disconnection or rejection and translated to a threat to my survival. The truth is that these feelings aren't fun. In fact they sometimes downright suck, but the practice is in recognizing that our bodies are telling us that our lives are in danger—we have to use our minds to reassure it that we are not at risk of losing our lives.

THE LURE OF PREDICTABILITY

In 2009, when I began what eventually became years of researching everything related to trauma and trauma-informed programming, I learned that trauma survivors needed information, structure and predictability.[2] A lack of predictability is frightening to the system of a trauma survivor, because most traumas originally happen when they are unexpected. There is a feeling of being completely broadsided, along with feelings of fear, hurt, betrayal and confusion.

For instance, if we are living in a home with a parent who is sometimes loving but sometimes abusive, we are much more likely to develop a way to always be alert to danger so we can predict coming events and protect ourselves. We can then grow into hypervigilant adults who trust no one, always expecting danger and never putting our guard down, even if we want to. This is an exhausting way to live life.

What was lost on me at the time is that I myself was searching for information that would make eastern practices and theories—like yoga, meditation and chakra theory—make scientific sense in a way that I could understand them and explain them. My unhealthy relationship with doubt, which is not the same as discernment, was not willing to just believe that there was an energy center in the groin, let alone that it is called the *root chakra*, it's associated with the color red and it governs our feeling of being safe and grounded. That meant nothing to me. My need to make sense of things with information and my quest to connect what felt like mystical ideas with scientifically proven theories was, in fact, being driven by my trauma symptomology and the need for information.

I was not going to trust what I was being told simply because someone was telling it to me. But ultimately the result was this book, so sometimes a healthy dose of skepticism can be a good thing, because it can lead to innovation—but only when accompanied by some faith in oneself.

Doubt becomes crippling when the fear that drives it tells us that events and situations outside of ourselves can be controlled. If we are attached to a specific outcome, for example, we run the risk of sabotaging ourselves, because it becomes so easy to respond from fear and anxiety over an inability to predict or assure that outcome. The opposite of doubt is trust or faith, but the most important thing to understand is that well-being is not dependent on our ability to have faith that we will achieve a particular desired outcome—it is the faith that no matter what the outcome, we will be OK.

When we can't sleep at night because we don't know what's going to happen (in our relationships, in our jobs, with our children, etc.), it is because our antiquated wiring is alerting us to imminent danger. Having faith that things will turn out all right is not what I am suggesting—in fact, things don't always turn out all right, and our attachment to a particular outcome keeps us in a place of suffering. But having faith that you will survive however things turn out is the path to healing. In fact, it is often the path to thriving and becoming fully alive.

It is our lifelong emotional-anatomy disruption and ever-strengthened survival adaptations that create a false connection between our capacity to survive and a specific outcome. This is the exact dichotomy that kept me in an abusive relationship for seventeen long years. It is the dichotomy that underlies our inability to create healthy boundaries and make healthy decisions for ourselves. When we feel attached to staying connected in particular ways to the people, jobs or situations in our lives simply because they carry a degree of predictability, which feels safer than the unknown, we may not actually be making the decisions that are in our best interest.

The challenge is that by the time we are attached to fighting for a particular outcome to ensure predictability, we are adults, and considering that this anxiety is rooted in our earliest life experiences is not something readily in our scope of awareness. The only way to begin to unravel this is to become aware of our bodies, to use simple tools to create space, and to have faith that we will be OK, regardless of the outcome. This is simple—but it is by no means easy.

One of my most memorable experiences of this realization is during my period of depression and suicidality in 2005. I had fought to maintain the outcome of being a married mother of two for as long as I could manage it, but the emotional abuse I had endured brought me to my breaking point. I had attached every ounce of worth to being a wife and mother, but the years of being told by my husband that I was never doing a good enough job at either left me convinced that the only right course of action was to take my life. I know now that predicting an outcome—even if it was to wipe myself from existence—felt better than existing in a chasm of not knowing.

EXPERIENCES THAT LEAD TO
DOUBT IN THE BODY

The development of doubt in the body is directly connected to the fear we feel when things are unpredictable or uncertain. Our attachment to particular outcomes erodes our faith in our capacity to endure struggle and discomfort, and this erosion of faith negatively impacts our ability to be resilient.

Doubt is a by-product of all the emotional anatomy disruptions that have been accumulating in our body from the time of birth, which originated with our body's incredible capacity to keep us away from the threat of danger. By the time we have developed doubt, we rarely have this recognition and have become resistant to change and resigned to the way things are. Below are some of the common contributing factors to developing doubt in the body.

- Information withheld
- Education that thwarts curiosity
- Forced religion
- Invalidation of one's beliefs
- Blind obedience (no right to think for self)
- Misinformation/lies[3]

Below are some of the ways the development of doubt manifests in adults.

- Spiritual cynicism
- Learning difficulties
- Rigid belief systems
- Apathy
- Over-intellectualization
- Spiritual addiction
- Confusion
- Dissociates from body[4]

HOW DOUBT LIVES IN THE BODY

In the lists below you can see how the emotion of doubt shows up in the body in the short term and how it impacts our physical and psychological health in the long term. This is not an exhaustive list, but it is meant to help you identify how feelings of mistrust, skepticism and lack of trust live in your body.

SHORT-TERM INDICATORS OF DOUBT IN THE BODY

- Feeling jittery
- Depression
- Hopelessness[5]

LONG-TERM INDICATORS OF DOUBT IN THE BODY

- Addictive behavior (drugs, alcohol, sex)
- Eating disorders
- Suicidality
- Isolation[6]

SPIRITUAL BYPASS

The term *spiritual bypass* is gaining more and more visibility these days, and it speaks directly to the development of doubt. This can often be where an individual might turn once they have reached this apex of the Emotional Anatomy Pyramid. While some trauma survivors experience chronic hypervigilance and a lack of trust in anyone or anything around them (often accompanied by an onslaught of paranoid thoughts), there is another end of the spectrum—blind faith.

We all know stories of charismatic leaders of religious cults, and we may think *Who are these people?* These are people just like us who have emotional-anatomy disruption all the way up the pyramid to doubt. But where I (and maybe you) have a need for things to be proven before blindly believing what I am told, some people—like those who join cults—succumb to their self-doubt and choose to have blind faith in a person of power, while simultaneously feeling the sweet elixir of belonging. This holds true for the yoga world as well, and in recent years we have witnessed the fall of several yoga "gurus" who rose to a position of power and abused that position—preying on vulnerable people who just wanted a place to belong and for someone to give them the answer.[7]

We all want to belong—it is one of the pillars of well-being. But trauma and early adverse experiences can lead us to one of two extremes: controlling the feelings of being different and not belonging through self-isolation, or finding a place to belong while we give up our agency and blindly follow someone who we feel knows better than us.

This is ripe breeding ground for abusers, whether it is a spiritual cult or a marriage or relationship. Both are fueled by the same combination of one person (or people) in power and the other (or others) looking outside of themselves for what to do, what to believe and how to behave. The only way to break this pattern is to trust in the unknown, have faith in our ability to be OK no matter the outcome, and gain strength and knowledge each step of the way.

Kay

Kay came to TIMBo when we were offering our first online pilot training back in 2015. Kay is a smart and accomplished lawyer turned yoga teacher and a mother of two grown children. She grew up in a very large family of ten children, with six older siblings and three younger siblings, who were commonly referred to as *the three little girls* by the other family members. She speaks of her family and her upbringing with fondness but makes no bones about the fact that she had to figure things out from an early age.

With such a gaggle of kids in the house, Kay's parents couldn't dote on her or provide for her in the way that today's generation of parents with just one or two kids can. This may be part of the reason why, when Kay had children of her own, she committed to making them her priority and focus.

After about the age of eleven, Kay recalls very little parental supervision—no one was really telling her what to do. She became pro-active to get her needs met. If she wanted clothing, she figured it out herself. When applying to colleges, she was pretty much on her own. She developed the skill of identifying what she wanted, figuring out how to do it, following up on all tasks and going for it. All her life she felt more grown-up than she really was—she was not included in the group of the three little girls. If she wanted to feel noticed or paid attention to by her parents, she had to put herself into her parents' range of vision by continually volunteering to do something for them. She became a great helper.

Kay eventually went to college and on to law school, then fell in love and got married. When her kids were seven and nine, the family went on a beach vacation together. There was an approaching hurricane they weren't aware of, and when Kay's husband waded into the water with his back to the ocean so he could watch the kids play in the sand, he was knocked down twice. The second time, his head hit the hard seafloor, and he broke his neck, sending Kay and her family into crisis.

At this time in her life, Kay was practicing law at a firm that was handling a lot of medical malpractice cases. Because of her knowledge of the medical field, Kay knew of a neurosurgeon who was considered to be one of the best. The family consulted with this neurosurgeon and were advised that Kay's husband needed to have surgery immediately.

Twenty years later, Kay recalls feeling unease in her body, but she ignored her intuition in the face of the doctor's power and insistence. Despite Kay's reluctance, she agreed to the surgery.

As a result of the surgery, Kay's husband suffered a spinal cord injury that nearly permanently paralyzed him. When the neurosurgeon insisted to Kay that her husband was fine, she felt unseen, unheard and enraged that no action was being taken. True to her adapted nature, she acted herself. She called the on-call anesthesiologist, who recommended that she get her husband an immediate CAT scan, as any delay could cause permanent paralysis. As a result of the findings of the scans, Kay's husband required six subsequent neck and back surgeries over the next four years—leaving him disabled, depressed and disengaged. Kay tried her best to take care of her husband and tend to her kids, but over time, her husband withdrew from her more and more, and once again she felt completely invisible.

Kay's kids began to suffer, and try as she might, she couldn't help them in the way she yearned to. She stayed in the marriage for several more years for the sake of her kids, but ultimately the relationship was beyond repair. Kay and her husband parted ways.

Prior to the accident, Kay had discovered yoga, and now it had become her only refuge. Having grown up in a large family, she loved the feeling of community that her yoga studio created, and her desire to help people made yoga teacher training a natural choice for her. She fell in love with the hatha school of yoga. During this period, the founder rose to a position of yogic guru with thousands of devotees in his influence around the world. Kay felt like part of a community, and it brought her the feeling of comfort she remembered from her childhood in a large family.

During an advanced teacher training, Kay was publicly humiliated by the founder when she couldn't move from one yoga posture to another in the exact manner he directed. Kay was physically incapable of moving that way, due to injuries she had suffered prior to the training, but the founder publicly shamed her regardless, demanding that she heal her shoulder as soon as possible.

Kay had hoped the training could provide an experience of self-care and increase her well-being, but instead, the founder's treatment left her feeling invisible, unworthy and not good enough. Kay again ignored her intuition, because the founder provided her with something that had been missing from her family—guidance, counsel and direction from someone in power. Kay and her fellow yoga trainees continued to be pushed to do more, do better and be better.

After her public humiliation, Kay continued with this school of yoga for three more years. She did not recognize it at the time, but slowly and surely Kay was giving up her power, eventually losing all trust in herself, and feeling that she was never good enough.

In 2012 her guru and teacher fell from grace in an explosive power-abuse scandal, and Kay's world once again turned upside down. After her husband's injury in 1999, the demise of her marriage in 2004 (which she felt responsible for), her children's suffering that she couldn't take away and her feeling of being betrayed and broadsided by a person she trusted, she questioned everything. Signing up for the online TIMBo training three years later took a lot of courage, especially given her current lack of faith and trust in yoga communities. But she yearned to be part of a larger community and to find something that would allow her to help others, including her children, who were now grown. Her fear and doubt were evident from the start of the training. She wanted to know where all of this was coming from, what research had been done and on what basis it was built.

We gave her the information that she sought, and she slowly began to trust. Later she became focused on learning exactly what to do, how to do it and when to do it so that she wouldn't run the risk of hurting anyone. It was challenging for her, but there was something in TIMBo that she felt was changing her, and she began to have faith in the program first, before she had full faith in herself to use it to help others. In the years since 2015, Kay has become a confident leader of TIMBo who remains open to learning and growing and is connected to the TIMBo community in ways that enrich all of us. Her quest for information, details, answers and guarantees in the TIMBo training made absolute sense given what she had been through in her life.

Her traumatic experience in a yoga community run by an esteemed gurulike figure would naturally lead to doubt and skepticism when entering another. It is not unlike the doubt and mistrust I had after the abuse and betrayal of my marriage. Moving through and out of debilitating doubt takes work, because it has developed to protect you. Kay now knows that she may not be able to prevent difficult or even tragic things from happening in her life, but because of the tools and lessons of TIMBo, she knows that she has the strength to navigate her life with faith and confidence that she has what she needs inside of her to weather any storms that come her way.

The next section of this book will provide a framework for you to walk this path. Make no mistake; there are no answers for you here—only ways to ask the questions and practices for being in that place of not knowing. I can tell you with 100 percent certainty that if you commit to this path, your body will change, and as a result, your life will feel different because *you* will feel different. It is not easy, but it is simple. The most difficult part is letting go of judgment and expectations, but you will get help with that too.

If you haven't begun the exercises in this book, now is a good time to go back and review. Write in the space provided in this book or in your journal, practice the breath and movement, and maybe even put this book down while you try these things in the daily comings and goings of your life. It is very helpful for gaining awareness of your adaptive process, collecting and practicing tools for moments of distress, and building confidence in those tools.

I know just as well as anyone that life is unpredictable, and this is what TIMBo was made for—the times of darkness and the times of despair. Whatever you choose to do, I offer you my favorite quote from the TIMBo workbook and encourage you to take this with you from this moment forward:

> *"Faith is the bird that feels the light and sings while the dawn is still dark."*
>
> —Rabindranath Tagore

WRITING EXERCISE FOR DOUBT

Before you start this exercise, make sure you have completed the writing exercises for fear through denial. Once you've completed those exercises, read through your identified emotions, starting with the fear exercise. As you sit with these recognitions, notice if they correlate with one or more of the universal triggers of stress: uncertainty, lack of control and lack of information. Identify some tools that can help you change how you feel in your body.

Remember: doubt is a culmination of all of these emotional developments. To find freedom from doubt, we must find the courage to remain in the dark while feeling confident that we will be all right. The tools you have learned thus far will give you that confidence.

PART 3

The Healing Journey

CHAPTER 13

Our Emotional Fingerprint

Every human travels the same journey through the Emotional Anatomy Pyramid, from fear through doubt. But our unique life experiences influence what will become our adapted or false self. Our emotional-anatomy development is as individual as our fingerprints. We all have them, but they're all unique.

If we don't address imbalances and the consequences of the adapted self after traveling through the developmental process the first time, we will travel through it again. Likewise, our process of awareness and healing doesn't end by going through the stages of TIMBo one time. Each time I deliver a training or participate in a program, I gain new insights and awareness about my own process, and I heal a little more. Up to now, this is how I understand my own fingerprint of adaptation.

Fear developed very early in my life. Perhaps it was inherited from my mother, perhaps it was a result of something else. I felt *responsible* and *guilty* for receiving spankings as a toddler and grade-schooler.

As a tween, *shame* came next—feeling fundamentally flawed and inherently unlovable after that one fearful incident with my father. I developed anger and *resentment* toward my "perfect" older sister, who I felt betrayed my trust by consistently tattling on me, and angry that my parents loved her more than they loved me (my perception as a child). Around this time I developed an adaptation as a way to feel worthy and get the parental attention I craved—I became the joker, as in the funny one of the family.

But more and more I was getting unwanted attention as a result of my developing body. As I left adolescence, I moved into *feeling stuck* when I reached a place of not knowing who I was or my worth.

By the time I reached *denial* of my authentic self, I no longer believed in my innate value and only felt valuable as an object of desire. I had felt victimized enough times that I finally "took control" of my sexual life. I could seduce boys my age and feel powerful and in control, but I never felt the feelings of worth or worthiness I was looking for.

As a young woman, I wanted sex to be a pathway to love and connection. For the boys I was with, sex was a means to a different end. When I did find a nice boy to be in a relationship with in my third year of college, I lost interest in sex—with him. I acted out sexually, a continued effort for feelings of control and worthiness. My feelings of shame intensified.

I was unaware of my emotional development, adaptations and constant need to find a sense of worthiness outside of myself. I felt increasingly more disregarded and disposable, while unconsciously creating this feeling by choosing to engage with young men that were already in relationships. They (of course) never chose me. By the time I was twenty-five years old I was living in a place of *doubt*, not believing I would ever find a man who would love me for who I (thought) I was.

Then I met Mitch.

The whole process of emotional-anatomy development started all over again, starting with fear of abandonment once we arrived in Maine and ending in doubt when I was contemplating suicide. Through all of those years (from zero to forty-something) I never considered that I might have trauma. After all, I had made all of my own life choices, right? No one twisted my arm or held a gun to my head.

After my divorce I dove into the work of trauma and trauma recovery—for others. I did not connect trauma with my past or present life. I would spend five years unaware of the trauma that I held in my own body. I was stuck at the bottom of the pyramid, and there I stayed—consumed with fear but in denial of that fact. I still didn't recognize that I had any trauma to recover from.

Then I met Samantha.

Samantha

When I first met Samantha she was new to yoga and had signed up for a TIMBo training upon the recommendation of a yoga teacher. Eight months prior to the start of the training Samantha had overdosed on a cocktail of opioids and alcohol and nearly died. After trying everything, including years of Narcotics Anonymous and Alcoholics Anonymous groups, she began seeing a yoga teacher who specialized in working with people in recovery. It was this teacher who suggested Samantha take our TIMBo training.

During the training Samantha had many significant healing moments, including tracing her unique emotional-development fingerprint. She saw how the abuse she endured in childhood set her up for a soul-shattering traumatic experience in middle school, which would lead her down the path of self-destruction that culminated in her overdose.

Samantha's mother suffered with untreated bipolar disorder. This meant that Samantha's life was unpredictable, confusing and sometimes violent. To Samantha, it seemed that her tomboy tendencies enraged her mother, whose baby boy had died less than a year before Samantha was born. Samantha's earliest memories of her mother's rage are around age seven. But as often as her mother was inexplicably frightening to Samantha, she was also overtly loving. Samantha will tell anyone that her mother was like a proactive mother bear and would fight to the death to defend her children from anyone who threatened to hurt them. Samantha feels that same fierce protection toward her mother today. She will not allow a bad word to be spoken of her mother, explaining to anyone who dares to be angry about Samantha's childhood abuse that her mother was not well. Still, Samantha remains haunted by memories of her mother's bad days.

Day in and day out, Samantha was the helpless victim of an unpredictable environment that ranged from her mother's manic fits of singing and dancing about in the kitchen to being the target of physical and verbal abuse for no apparent reason and with no warning. While Samantha's father was a secure and loving presence, he was at work most of the day and in school at night, and he did not recognize Samantha's pleas for rescue. Instead, he tried to help Samantha discover what *she* had done to upset her mother so much. In the end, Samantha took herself to child protective services, asking to be removed from the home. Her request was denied.

By the age of twelve, Samantha had learned to study her mother's face for any twitch, twinkle or wince that might signify a coming assault. She learned not to trust the overflowing love her mother occasionally offered her. She was on alert twenty-four hours a day, trusted no one and felt fundamentally flawed. Through the course of her developmental years Samantha tried to change and adapt. Eventually she gave up on trying to be the kind of child she thought her mother would want or love and succumbed to the belief that she was damaged goods.

The activation of Samantha's biological survival response became her everyday normal, but her dependence on her caregivers for survival thwarted her ability to actually fight or flee. Day in and day out, she was in a place of profound unpredictability accompanied by fear, helplessness and powerlessness.

Adapting is the only resource a child has, and in this consistently unpredictable and abusive environment, the need to make herself lovable (and therefore connected and safe) was a matter of survival. Children feel inappropriately responsible for the abuse they are experiencing and try their best to affect their environment by changing their behavior. Young children cannot conceptualize things like mental illness, substance abuse or the fact that grown-ups have self-regulation issues.

When abuse continues, children give up trying to create safety and predictability in their lives by changing themselves, instead deciding that the reason they are subject to abuse and mistreatment is because they were somehow born bad. Samantha came to thoroughly believe that there was just something about her that made her unlovable. She felt she was rotten, unfixable and vile. She never felt safe and began carrying a knife in her sock to school each day.

Once Samantha developed the adaptive belief that she was fundamentally flawed, she steered herself toward connection anywhere she could find it. It is a common developmental path for emerging adolescents to travel: moving away from primary care providers and toward peers. But for adolescents who have environmental or developmental trauma (trauma lasting through the developmental ages), this shift in the search for connection and a feeling of belonging has profoundly damaging potential.

By this time, Samantha, like any child who experiences years of early-life trauma, had a severely altered self-concept. Believing that she was a fundamentally bad weapon-toting tough kid, Samantha found peers who reinforced this belief for her—yet she (like all adolescents in her position) could only recognize the connection she was desperately seeking. She finally felt a sense of belonging. As is often the case, these peers and this new connection put Samantha at risk. She began drinking and taking drugs by the time she was eleven.

At nearly thirteen years old she was lured into a field by a supposed friend and brutally raped by four boys, ranging in age from sixteen to nineteen. To this day Samantha maintains that she would have been killed were it not for the hidden knife in her sock, which she finally managed to reach and use. Samantha, covered in dirt and blood, ran home to her mother. Before Samantha even opened her mouth, her soiled appearance caused her mother to fly into a rage. Samantha received a brutal beating. She ran out of the house and found shelter in a storage shed, the only place that felt safe for her at the time. Over the next ten years Samantha developed an addiction to drugs and sex. She had fits of rage, would regularly pick fights, developed a consistent hypervigilance and eventually began sleeping with a loaded gun on her nightstand.

When Samantha talked about the rape to one of several therapists she cycled through, she told the story as if it had happened to someone else. There was no emotion and no visceral connection to the event. Her attempts to keep any and all body-based trauma memories at bay with drugs, alcohol and gratuitous sex were successful. By the time I met Samantha she was close to picking these up again but stayed committed to getting sober and began connecting with her body through yoga and breath.

Samantha had experienced profound relational trauma. Her early life was marred by profound mistreatment and made more confusing

by intermittent demonstrations of love by someone she needed for survival. Her experience of being the victim of a barbaric assault was the
start of a commitment to never be vulnerable again. But we can't truly
connect without vulnerability, and we need connection to live a full
and healthy life. But who would blame Samantha for distrusting all
humans after what she had lived through?

So here she sat in the TIMBo training circle. The safety of the circle was challenging all of her hard-earned survival adaptations. This
social/relational safety was something she never had in childhood, and
it allowed her to soften her defenses. During one particular exercise,
her body presented her with a memory of the sexual assault. It was
the space created and held in the training that allowed her to vulnerably feel and grieve—an experience she otherwise would surely have
reached for a bottle or a pill to avoid.

The tools of TIMBo (breath, talking to your body) began to help
Samantha soften the survival wiring that dated back to her earliest life
experiences. She recognizes that her body was re-creating an experience that happened some thirty-four years prior. With our guidance
she curled up on the floor and allowed us to place a blanket on her. She
cried hard, grieving and releasing some of the traumatic energy that
had been locked in her body and resisted for so long. It was that very
experience that presented Samantha with the new reference point.

Samantha's habitual response would have been to take a drug, find
someone to have sex with or barricade herself in the room with her
loaded gun. The experience of allowing herself to feel the excruciatingly uncomfortable memories and not dying was the start of teaching
her body a new way of being.

Without her awareness of how her body experienced, encoded
and remembered the sexual assault and her years of childhood abuse,
she would not have had the courage to move through the process of
healing in body, mind and spirit. In recognizing that everything she
thought and did in her life was an attempt (conscious or not) to survive, Samantha began to consider that she was not, in fact, a fundamentally flawed human being.

Samantha has shared with me on more than one occasion the pivotal moment for her in her first TIMBo training module. It was one
line of text in the TIMBo manual, which reads, "This does not mean

you are a bad person. It means that you did not have the tools." When Samantha read these words, it was the first time she had considered that maybe she wasn't actually a bad apple. Maybe she just didn't have the tools.

There were tools she could learn to change the course of her life, the beliefs she had about herself and the reactions she had to the world around her. She had to first recognize that the damaging beliefs she had about herself did, at one time, serve a very useful purpose. They were once her superpower. All of this began when she read those two little sentences in the TIMBo workbook.

CHAPTER 14

A Relationship of Healing

About a week after the training where I met Samantha, I received a phone call from her asking for advice on how to "walk around in the world" with the changes she was now feeling. She felt cracked open, vulnerable, loving and somewhat confused. I advised her to continue using her TIMBo tools—primarily the breath—and to trust them.

What she didn't know was that she was ahead of me in the process. I was teaching women how to use TIMBo tools to manage their trauma responses and encouraging them to allow themselves to feel vulnerable, yet I was not able to manage my own trauma responses. I was dissociated any time I wasn't actively working. At the time I wasn't even aware that I was experiencing PTSD symptoms.

Dissociation creates a feeling of numbness and a profound disconnection from the body. I existed in this state for at least a decade while I was married, which is the only way I was able to engage in intimacy (at least physically). When you feel nothing, you'd be amazed at the things you can endure. Dissociating is the body's way of protecting you from experiences that are inescapable.[1] It is not happening via a conscious choice; our bodies have learned to automatically cushion us in this way. In my marriage, I felt nothing but a soft and hazy insulation from everything, including myself.

Samantha called me a few months after that original call to ask if I wanted to hang out. I quickly made an excuse. When she tried again a few weeks later, I told her I didn't socialize much. She made a third attempt, suggesting she make an introduction to a potential funder, and I agreed. That was when our friendship began.

After nearly two decades of emotional abuse I was determined not to get close to anyone again. I had made a commitment to living and dying alone. As our friendship deepened, Samantha saw how wounded and guarded I was. She observed my deer-in-the-headlights behavior in response to my then raging sixteen-year-old. After the divorce Mitch refused to coparent with me, stonewalling my efforts at every turn. In fact, he and his family had swiftly made it clear that I was not recognized as a parent, let alone the mother of my children. My family lived far away—I was all alone.

Samantha wanted to help me in any way she knew how: by offering to take out the garbage or giving me rides to and from the airport. All of her efforts made me angry and incited a curt and rapid "No, thank you." Every one of Samantha's generous offers triggered a fear of being trapped. In response, I committed to maintaining tight control over my willingness to be vulnerable—at least I tried.

Back then I would often slip into a dissociated state. But Samantha, unlike Mitch, would notice. Each time she gently reminded me that my home was a safe place, and I was in charge of who came in and out. With the utmost care and compassion she would offer to leave me so that I could feel in control and safe (via isolation) in my house. She would give me a hug and a smile, walk out the door and drive one hour back to her house.

The process of being seen and given space allowed my body to feel, which meant I was becoming vulnerable. A couple of months after Samantha and I became friends, my body and mind were in conflict. My body was trusting, feeling safe and wanting further connection with her. My mind was not on board.

Finally one day I collapsed in a heap and broke down crying. I told Samantha that I didn't want to have any feelings for her. I was angry. I felt betrayed by my body and wanted to stay protected from hurt by controlling my vulnerability, but I was losing the battle. Ironically, this was the same conflict Samantha experienced in her first training when she finally let herself feel vulnerable and begin healing. At the time it felt excruciating. I wasn't aware I was winning my life and myself back.

WAS THIS ANOTHER LONG CON?

My healing journey started right after I was reduced to an angry, sniveling mess the day I told Samantha that I didn't want to fall in love with her. I fought my feelings with all the might I could muster, because I didn't want to trust. Trusting was dangerous. I didn't want to get trapped again, and the only guarantee I felt I had was to not trust. Especially people who were being nice to me.

Contrary to what some might believe, survivors of abusive relationships learn not to trust kindness. Abusers use kindness to gain the trust of those they are abusing. Kindness is a way that abusers reel you back into their world after they've hurt you. And in my case, an abuser's "kindness" is a direct link to the profound feelings of guilt and responsibility that kept me in the relationship.

Each and every time Mitch was abusive, he followed it with an expression or action of kindness. How could I turn away from such a kind and loving human being? Now faced with the kindness of Samantha, I was so angry with what was happening to me. How could I be falling into the same trap? Why would I be steering myself toward yet another life of (what I believed would be) captivity? How could I be falling in love? I wasn't a lesbian! Anger was accompanied by confusion and grief.

I eventually decided to dip my toe into the water. I was terrified, and Samantha knew it. I told her I was incapable of being in an intimate relationship. When she asked for more of an explanation, I could only tell her I was afraid, and it was complicated. Samantha promised that she wanted to meet me exactly where I was, and I half-believed her, since that is precisely what she had been doing since we met. But so had Mitch at first.

In the beginning, my body screamed at me that this new relationship was a trap. But even when my body began to loosen its defensive grip, my mind still felt distrustful of everything Samantha said and did. I felt resistant to every act of kindness and extremely angry when I realized I was falling in love with her. One day I called my mother and told her what was happening in my life. I told her about Samantha and the fear I was experiencing. I recall with sadness how I told her I was afraid I was getting involved in a long con. I wasn't being ridiculous. It had happened to me once, and it could happen to me again if I wasn't careful!

So when my relationship with Samantha went from just friends to something more, I knew I had to get my long-term therapist on the phone. I knew this relationship would crash and burn if I didn't call a time-out right away and get myself in front of Joan, whom I had been seeing for nearly ten years and whom I credit for saving my life.

SUPPORTING EACH OTHER THROUGH TRAUMA RECOVERY

Samantha found a therapist around this time too. She had been in and out of therapy for years but had never talked about her sexual assault in a way other than distantly reporting the facts. We both needed to engage in the intensely difficult work of trauma recovery, and we had to support one another in that. It was excruciating to witness Samantha's pain, yet most of the time supporting her was not difficult for me, because her memories were usually triggered by something that had nothing to do with me: the sound of a man clearing his throat, a smell or a feeling.

One day not too long after we had transitioned from being just friends, we decided to take my younger son (then eleven years old) to play minigolf at a popular summertime spot. The place had a couple minigolf courses, an ice cream stand famous for gigantic servings, an outdoor restaurant with plenty of picnic tables, a driving range and a petting zoo. It also had a little area where you could climb into a bumper boat (think bumper cars in water) and bounce against other boats until the time was up; this section was located just outside the women's bathroom. After the three of us had finished our round of minigolf and purchased our ice cream, we headed to the restrooms one last time before we drove home in our separate cars.

I caught Samantha's eye and could tell that something was not right. I asked if she was OK and she said "No," immediately followed by "I gotta go." She threw her nearly untouched ice cream in the trash, got into her car and left.

The boys who had assaulted Samantha when she was a teenager had ridden to the field that day on minibikes. The smell of the two-stroke-engine fuel from the bumper boats triggered a body memory so violent that Samantha had to pull her car into the breakdown lane of the freeway and run deep into the woods, where she was violently ill (akin to food poisoning). When we suppress or ignore traumatic memories for as long as Samantha had, implicit memories can bring intestinal distress and/or vomiting, and in this instance, Samantha's body did that with a vengeance.[2]

When she got back to her car she called me. I could hear the fear and panic in her voice as she described what happened. I stayed calm and helped her breathe. I reminded her that her body was presenting a memory to her so that she would never forget. It was misconstruing what was happening in the present moment. It falsely believed she was in danger. She arrived at her home and locked herself in her bedroom, a practice that made her feel in control and safe.

THE TERROR OF INTIMACY

As hard as it was seeing Samantha go through some of those distressing experiences on the road to recovery, it was nothing compared to the Herculean task she took on in supporting me through mine. I was living with a traumatized system (neurobiologically speaking) in a traumatizing existence of still being controlled by Mitch and watching my sixteen-year-old son self-destruct. Every implicit memory or fear-based response was triggered by being close to Samantha.

When she said something nice to me I instantly put my guard up. When she suggested she move in I felt furious, convinced she was trying to trap me. When she suggested anything that normal couples would consider as taking the next step, I became convinced I would wind up back in captivity. When I wasn't feeling angry or scared, I completely shut down. To say that our first year was fraught with confusion, turmoil and discomfort is like saying the *Titanic* had a little brush with an iceberg. It was probably the most difficult experience I've ever had to go through—and in the end, the most life-giving.

A couple of years into our relationship, Samantha's flashbacks and nightmares were abating, we were learning each other's triggers, and we'd gotten through some very difficult times that ultimately helped us recognize when the other was being hijacked by a body memory. By this point, we knew what to say—and what not to say—to help navigate these experiences.

Then when my younger son was fourteen, we decided to take him and Samantha's sixteen-year-old nephew on a ten-day vacation to Ecuador and the Galápagos Islands. Every detail of the trip was organized: the in-country transport, lodging, tours, meals, activities and guides. It was (and remains) one of the best trips we've taken together, due in no small part to our guide and encyclopedia of all things Ecuador, Miguel.

However, a week or so into the trip, I suddenly felt a shift. I couldn't see Samantha for who she was; I only saw a dangerous monster. I was inexplicably fearful for my son and had a strong urge (more like red-hot panic) to find a way to scoop him up and get both of us the hell out of there! It was awful and lasted for days.

I never mentioned anything to Samantha because I was afraid it would trigger her, and we knew from experience that when we were both experiencing body memories it created a tangle that was very difficult to extract ourselves from. I couldn't change what I was experiencing. I couldn't make myself feel different. I couldn't see anything different than what I was seeing, but because of TIMBo and all I'd learned by then, I knew it wasn't true, even though everything about it looked and felt real.

Samantha felt extremely dangerous to me, even though she wasn't. She looked dangerous, even though she wasn't. I felt as if I were in danger and that my son's safety was at risk, even though neither of us were unsafe. The only thing I knew to do was to keep reminding myself that what I was seeing and feeling wasn't the truth, even though it felt excruciatingly real.

I just kept repeating to myself, *It feels real, but it's not the truth.*

When our trauma response gets activated, we need all the tools we can grab so that we can feel the sensations associated with vulnerability. We learn to navigate through that moment in a different way and with a different end result. I reminded myself of this while I breathed, and I waited for what seemed like days. Then, it was gone.

This is something you can feel happening on the inside, yet you can't quite explain it. The experience of dissociation I had felt whenever Samantha got too close began to diminish, but in its place were all the trauma-related body sensations (sensations that dissociation protected me from feeling). Over time, with awareness of my body sensations and the use of TIMBo tools, I could sit in the feeling of fear until it shifted in my body.

The grip of fear that had been my normal for at least a quarter century would ease enough for me to notice what the absence of fear felt like, even if it was just for a moment. These new reference points helped me trust the process. I continued to engage in the journey, even though the feeling of fear was more present than absent for a while.

It wasn't until I met Samantha and engaged in the painful process of trusting (making myself vulnerable) that I understood what it meant to be truly loved by someone. The trust and vulnerability required to feel this was excruciating to me, because I too had come to believe I was fundamentally flawed. But the discomfort of vulnerability is the necessary process toward healing, freedom, real connection and love.

STOP, BREATHE AND LOOK FEAR IN THE FACE

Think of your body as the metaphorical canary in the coal mine. It will sense and respond to danger before your mind even has a chance to know what is happening. But when the (original) experience of the fight, flight or freeze response is not resolved, it is more likely to happen again in response to similar sensory triggers, whether they are outside or inside of your body. This occurs even if the danger is no longer around, like my trip to Ecuador with Samantha. When not addressed and resolved, it becomes memory.

Most long-term trauma survivors or individuals with PTSD can't access the ability to stop and be curious about what is actually happening. Without this ability, an immediate and often overblown reaction follows, usually with the intention of making the profound discomfort of the experience stop.[3]

In my case, my body had learned to dissociate, so my normal was to drift away on a cloud of body-produced opiates. But since her sobriety, Samantha would normally fight or run. We had been using the principle tools of TIMBo—paying attention to body sensations, breathing and shifting our relationship to moments of discomfort. In a sense, our relationship was the fertile ground of deep healing. But that is not to say any of it was easy or comfortable.

TIMBO TAUGHT US A NEW WAY TO HANDLE CONFLICT

Samantha and I had an argument one night, the subject of which I can't remember. What I do remember is that we both felt confused, trapped and misunderstood, and since we were both in the early stages of our recovery, we sometimes defaulted to old survival patterns. Since Samantha's tendency was to run, she would get in her car and drive away without a word—which is what she did late that evening. In response, I came face to face with the fear and panic in my body, which drove my actions—an all-out barrage of calls to Samantha, begging and pleading with her to come home.

She didn't answer my calls. It was in that moment I chose to stop and look fear in the face, recognizing that my body was telling me that I would die if I didn't get her to come back immediately. I compassionately told myself that it felt real, but it wasn't. I put the phone down and told myself that Samantha would make a choice for herself, and whether that choice was to come back home or not, I would be OK.

What I didn't know then (that I know now) is that Samantha was having this same marked moment of stopping to look fear in the face, recognizing that what she was experiencing felt real but wasn't, and responding by making a new choice. She did come back, we talked about what we learned about ourselves, and we have never had a moment like that since. Therein lies the lasting gifts of TIMBo.

NO VULNERABILITY, NO HEALING

After my marriage ended and before I met Samantha, I had descended into a five-year period of isolation and increasing fearfulness. I was also in denial of how severe my symptoms of PTSD were becoming, since I was in the throes of an addiction. Work became my superpower, but work addiction is like any other addiction in that it allowed me to circumvent any feelings of vulnerability, the feeling any trauma survivor works their whole life to avoid.

I told myself that I didn't need anyone and made friends with a few individuals in my yoga community who were single and more than ten years my junior. I told myself these were real friendships and real connections, but in reality, I was compartmentalizing my life—hanging out with my friends during the weeks that I didn't have my children. It was a way to dull the pain of having the core of my identity at the time, being a mother, ripped from me every other week. Any mother will tell you that being without their children is like having your arms chopped off—my children were like the phantom limbs described by amputees—so if I didn't have some significant distraction when they were away, I would constantly feel the pain of their absence.

I was able to operate in this world of workaholism when I did not have my children. When I did get my children back, it was like I had been starved of oxygen for a week and could suddenly breathe again. This went on for about five years. My new normal had become isolation, work and an unconscious commitment to never be vulnerable again and to live out the rest of my life (and die) alone.

I recall sitting in a TIMBo circle during a training in Port-au-Prince, Haiti, in 2012—one year before I met Samantha. As usual, a volunteer read a quote out loud, and we shared our thoughts and reactions to the quote. This particular quote by the Buddhist nun Pema Chödrön reads, "When you begin to touch your heart or let your heart be touched, you begin to discover that it's bottomless, that it doesn't have any resolution, that this heart is huge, vast and limitless.

You begin to discover how much warmth and gentleness is there, as well as how much space."[4]

I remember as clearly as if it were yesterday my reaction to this quote, or more accurately my resistance to this quote. I shared with the group that I didn't want to believe that there was any truth in this quote, because if it were true, then my entire strategy for keeping myself safe (keeping my heart tightly protected) would be challenged, and the thought of letting my heart be touched was something that felt not only impossible but also excruciatingly dangerous. I would come face to face with these feelings once I met Samantha, but back then in Haiti, I was firmly committed to my promise to never ever let myself be vulnerable again.

During that discussion I felt sure that I could extend love to others but that I would not open my heart to receive love, to which one of the dear Haitian men attending the training responded by looking softly in my eyes and saying, "But, Sue, it's the same thing. You can't love another without loving yourself." But I thought I had it all figured out and that yes, I could be outwardly loving while keeping my heart cordoned off and protected, and if this quote was true then my theory was bullshit—and that made me mad.

The next year I returned to Haiti to train a new group of facilitators, and this time Samantha came with me. In those early days we often asked individuals to raise money to support these trainings, and in exchange, they could participate in the experience. Samantha was one of those fundraisers, and at the time, I was struggling with my growing feelings for her. And once again we sat there in a TIMBo circle and read this quote.

Thankfully, Samantha was participating in a group that was meeting in a different room, and I was free to express my resistance to this quote (once again), but this time I came face to face with the pain associated with working so damn hard to keep my heart closed. By that time, Samantha was offering me pure and unconditional (and unfamiliar) love. For months prior to this trip I deluded myself into thinking that I could keep myself and my heart completely protected while allowing her to be in my world, abiding by all of my rules and conditions.

The remarkable thing is that she was willing to do that—but what I didn't count on was that my heart would eventually trust, regardless of what my head was committed to. Sitting in that circle in Haiti was the moment I realized that my head and heart were engaged in a full tug-of-war with one another—my head pulling away from the vulnerable place of love and trust and my heart pulling toward it.

Once again I spoke about the quote, and this time I mentioned that keeping my heart closed actually hurt. I began crying, and I surrendered to the grief associated with opening my heart. The fear of saying yes to vulnerability.

I cried hard while the group witnessed my grief, and through my tears I just kept repeating, "It hurts, it hurts, it hurts," and it did hurt.

Kahlil Gibran, a Lebanese-American writer, poet and visual artist, wrote (in his 1923 book *The Prophet*), "Your pain is the breaking of the shell that encloses your understanding. It is the bitter potion by which the physician within you heals your sick self. Therefore, trust the physician and drink his remedy in silence and tranquility."[5]

Silence and tranquility? More like howling and blubbering, but bitter potion it was.

This moment was instrumental in moving me into healing. It was the moment I knew that the barbed wire I had wrapped around my heart to keep people out was actually causing me pain and suffering. Until that moment I had deluded myself into thinking that it had kept me safe and that if I could maintain that for the rest of my life, I would go to my grave never having been hurt or traumatized again. I was dead wrong.

CHAPTER 15

Why Healing Hurts

If there is one piece of information I wished I had been given over nearly two decades of therapy it would be this: healing hurts. It just plain feels terrible, and walking into (and sometimes out of) this terrible-feeling process has to be done by choice. Just like no one can eat or sleep for you, no one can do your own healing work for you. It *has* to be you.

Years ago I purchased a phone book–sized text called *The Courage to Heal: A Guide for Women Survivors of Child Sexual Abuse* by Ellen Bass.[1] I really didn't give the title much thought, and I didn't read much of the book. I realize now that at that time in my life, being the mother of an infant child in an abusive marriage, the book was too triggering to read. What I didn't know then is that reading it (or any book like it) would always be triggering until I had the tools for reading through it while being triggered, which obviously takes courage.

I was under an ill-informed impression that I could just wish myself healed and one day I'd wake up changed. I tried every tool and technique I could think of to change my experience, particularly when it came to sexual intimacy, but because all of those things were either cognitive or action oriented (*Maybe buying some sexy underwear would help? How about a sexy movie?*), they never addressed the place where the trauma lived—my body. They also reinforced the trauma response, because I was making decisions to do something that my

body definitely was advising me against. My body became more traumatized and my dissociation more trigger-happy, and before you knew
it, I was so traumatized even the sound of a soft moan or the suggestive
raise of an eyebrow would trigger me.

I hated sex. I hated anyone who liked sex. I was angry when love
scenes came on TV or the movies. I hated when people took a playful
view of sex and sexuality, and by the time I met Samantha, I had made
a rock-solid decision never to engage sexually again, and I made sure
she knew it. If she wanted to be with me, that was the package she was
signing up for, like it or not. And if she didn't like it, too bad.

Yet inside myself I longed for the love that she was offering and the
love we would ultimately come to heal our way into. But as I said, at
first I didn't trust it. I didn't realize that my worldview was so warped,
and my entire worth was wrapped up in my ability to fulfill a particular sexual quota as an object for a partner's pleasure. I didn't for
one millisecond trust that anyone would ever love me or want to be
with me if that was not part of the package. And because this was so
ingrained in my belief about how the world and relationships worked, I
was committed to just waiting for the shoe to drop—because predicting that someone would leave me because I was broken was actually
easier than believing I was worth loving as is.

It wasn't until I made that SOS appointment with my long-term
therapist Joan that I had even an inkling that my worldview wasn't set
in stone. I remember fretting about being told something that I was
sure was a lie. "I'm going to believe her and get trapped, and then it will
just be the way it always has been, and I'll end up right back where I
was when I was married," I whined. In that moment Joan looked at me
and said, "Sue, relationships can look all kinds of different ways."

I was confused for a moment. "What do you mean, relationships
can look all kinds of different ways?" I wanted to know. She gave me
some examples, but that wasn't what made me believe her. It was
because I had been working with Joan for the better part of ten years.
I trusted her. She saved my life when I was on the brink of taking it.
When I was still married, she told me (more than once) that while I
may have had sexual trauma, that was not the issue in my marriage—
boy, was she right! So after nearly a decade of sitting in Joan's office

and hearing her sage advice, even if I couldn't take it in at the time, I believed her, because she had never misled me in the past. Ever.

I held on to Joan's words in the early days of my relationship with Samantha, and Samantha was true to her word. She really did love me just as I was. But after a while I had decided I wanted to heal from my sexual trauma, and nothing that Joan told me made it easier. No matter how much I told myself I wanted to heal for me and no one else (which was true) or how much Samantha tried to memorize all the big, small and in-between things she did that might trigger me—in the end, the work had to be done by me. The scary, painful work of recovering from sexual trauma hinged on my choice to do it. That is when I truly began to understand the power of what I had created.

A TRAUMA-RECOVERY MIDWIFE

For at least two years after I met Samantha, I had a front-row seat to her recovery from trauma. I witnessed her horrific flashbacks, was there when she woke from nightmares and came to learn exactly what to say to her to help her navigate those excruciatingly uncomfortable moments. She would sometimes look at me, terror in her eyes, and tell me what she was feeling. Most frequently, it was the experience of her rape: the physical feeling in her body, the smell of grass and the feeling of knees on her shoulders, holding her facedown to the ground.

Each time, I stayed with her—unafraid. Using the tools and knowledge I gained from creating TIMBo, I reminded her that her body wanted to re-create this horrible experience so that she would remember and never let it happen again. And each time, Samantha rode those memories like a series of waves, using all of her new tools to stay with the experience instead of run or fight, which had been her learned response.

Witnessing Samantha's healing using many of the skills she learned through TIMBo was inspiring. I knew that healing was possible. Samantha's hard work showed me that, but for almost a year after I proclaimed I was ready to heal, I felt stuck, frustrated and damaged. Then I finally had my pivotal moment that changed everything. After that I felt courageous enough to begin my own journey of healing from sexual trauma.

It was a typical day, and I was, once again, down on myself for not feeling like any change was occurring. I was lying in bed, wallowing in self-pity and self-judgment, when Samantha came to the doorway and flatly stated, "If you think you are going to heal by just waiting for healing to happen, nothing is going to change. If you want to heal, you have to let yourself feel all the trauma and make a choice to do something different. You can't just wait, and it's going to be uncomfortable, and I can't do it for you. It has to be your choice." I had seen her recover. I knew what she was telling me was the truth. I knew I had been waiting, hoping that I would just miraculously change. But she was right—until I chose to do the work, healing would be beyond my reach.

I had spent a lifetime engaging in sex without being vulnerable, which means I was never fully present, without really knowing it—it was my normal. But because Samantha was so in tune with me, she would often stop and say, "We can't do this—you're not with me right now." You would think I would be grateful for her ability to keep me from retraumatizing myself, but I was still fully adapted to believe that no one would love me if I didn't engage in sex. So instead of feeling grateful, I was consumed with fear that she would leave. Once I learned to recognize when I was not present (I dissociated almost instantaneously) and realized that I could say no, I was consumed with guilt. And once I began to feel different in my body and remain present during intimate moments, I was consumed with shame and so on.

Recovery from toxic stress or trauma is hard no matter how you slice it. Recovering from sexual trauma is the topic of entire books because it is so complicated. How do you learn to have a positive view and to be fully present and vulnerable in an experience once used by another in a position of power to manipulate, hurt and abuse you? Healing *does* take courage—the courage to take risks.

CHAPTER 16

It's Not a Linear Process

Healing is not a linear process. It doesn't follow a neat and tidy trajectory that we can predict. There is no instruction manual that we can follow and check off the boxes as we go. It is a continual process of noticing when you are having an abnormal response to a normal experience, using whatever tools you have in your toolbox to navigate through the moment mindfully, and then noticing the result.

In TIMBo, what I just described is known as awareness, acceptance and space. Awareness without acceptance just keeps us stuck in our old patterns of judgment. Acceptance comes from knowing why our body is overreacting—it's trying to keep us safe. Acceptance is the self-compassion we can have in those moments when we normally would judge ourselves, our body or others. In the following chapters I will be describing these seven embodied resources that are the essence of TIMBo.

The TIMBo embodied resources are already inside of you and work from the primitive parts of the brain up. This is important, because just like our brains have developed and adapted from bottom to top (primitive to more-recent sophisticated brain regions), these resources build health in your brain and body in the same direction—from bottom to top. We can't learn them all at once, and we don't need to. With time and patience, we learn, grow and change—and so much of that is moved along by our own recognition of how we are changing on the inside.

Back in 1999, when I was still married, Mitch arrived home from a trip to Chicago with a brand-new sports car as a Mother's Day gift. This is a common pattern of narcissists and abusers, almost always following some major transgression. It's like a guilt gift—an act of kindness that survivors come to distrust. After we were divorced, the car sat in the garage of a property in Maine I took ownership of, and there it stayed year after year, growing mold on the interior and rust on the exterior, eventually seeming like it was completely broken and needed to be scrapped.

But ten years after my divorce I had some encouragement to restore the car, and eventually it looked and ran good as new—but it took time. This is how healing works. Expecting ourselves to snap our fingers and be all done is no different than me expecting that car to be restored just because I willed it to be fixed or expected it to happen faster than it actually could. It takes commitment, patience, work and faith, but little by little and over time you see the original splendor emerging.

WE ARE BUILT TO HEAL

The amazing thing is that practicing the first TIMBo embodied resource will open you up to uncovering the second. It naturally happens, even without a guide telling you what to do next. The seven embodied resources remind you of what you already have inside of you. Even if you can't access one of them yet, you will in time. And when you do, you will remember reading about it in this book and say *Oh, this is what she was talking about!*

To begin, it helps to understand why we can't access them all at once, why our responses are sometimes more distressing as we heal and why both these limitations have value.

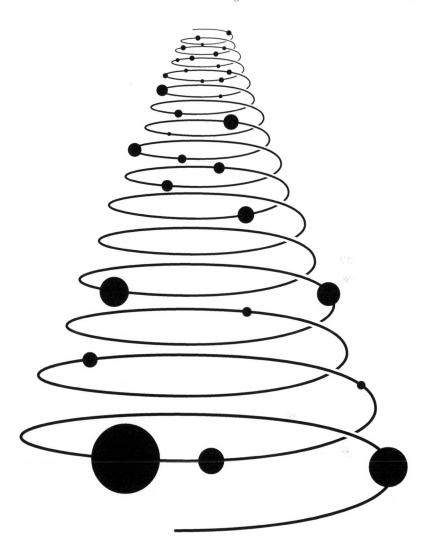

When we begin this work we likely have some degree of a constant stress feedback loop running in our bodies. The top of the spiral is where most of us are, where most of the women entering our trainings are, and where most organizations and systems are. This is the place where stress reactivity and adaptations are our normal. When we are here, we don't know what we don't know. This is why it's almost impossible to use any tool other than noticing our body sensations and choosing to breathe. We simply don't know what we're going for—we only know that we are uncomfortable.

As we use the first embodied resource (described in the following chapter), we begin to open up the space. We provide our brains with materials for learning new things. Imagine you decide to restore your house or that I restored my car using only what was already there—we'd only get so far. It is the same with your brain and body—you can't restore your health, authenticity and vitality without bringing in some new materials (neurons). Remember: the basic practice of breath and simple movement, combined with noticing the sensations in our bodies, repairs damaged neurons and creates new ones. This is quite a marvel, and the miraculous thing is that even if we only practiced that, we would notice changes in ourselves on a molecular level. This is how mindfulness contributes to neuroplasticity.[1]

Once we have more cellular learning materials and more space to consider (due to repair in the areas of our prefrontal cortex, thanks to noticing our body sensations and body in space) we can conceptualize and use more tools, which means we have the capacity to handle more distressing body responses. Why does this happen? Because our bodies can recognize when we are building resilience, and our bodies want to heal.

As Peter Levine reminds us in *Waking the Tiger: Healing Trauma*, the body is constantly looking for opportunities to renegotiate trauma. It will hand us these opportunities as it registers our capacity to navigate through them.[2] It will recognize our increased resilience and say to us, "I guess you're ready for this one now—here you go!" The problem is that we judge this process. We think we should be done by now, and in doing so we slow the process.

Let's return to the act of restoring a house or a car. If we come upon a repair that is a little more complicated or takes a little more time (like when a builder opens up a wall and realizes there are no support beams holding up the house), is it helpful to wallow in feeling like we should be done by now? No, but we do it, and that's OK. We all want a break from time to time. But it is important to recognize that there really isn't a finish line. Just like a house or a car, our bodies will always need maintenance. It's just the first part of the restoration that is likely to have us throwing our hands up in the air, saying, *Oh my God, I just wanna be done already!* Once you realize there is no "done," the job becomes a whole lot easier.

It often starts with the absence of a feeling that you have lived with your whole life. The absence of fear, anxiety, guilt, shame and so on. In mindfulness practice we are told to pay attention. We know from research and science that this changes our brains.[3] But pay attention to what? Pay attention to the sensations in our bodies as they arise and notice the absence of things you have been living with all your life.

For example, in the early stages of our relationship, it took a lot of courage and consistent use of our TIMBo tools for Samantha and me to stay in those excruciating moments and remind ourselves our lives weren't being threatened when we felt triggered. It took time. Slowly and gradually I noticed something different. We had a difficult conversation—Samantha had had enough, and out the door she went. But that time there was no trace of my usual feelings of fear, panic, guilt and responsibility. In the past I would feel crushing guilt in my chest and panic to figure out what to do and how to get her back, but this time there was no distressing sensations in response to her departure. There was an absence of everything that I had come to know as my normal. And because there were no distressing sensations, there was also no anxiety-fueled thought or actions. I had taught my body that my life was not in danger. Sweet relief!

I was also puzzled, mildly amused and at a bit of a loss for what to do. So in the space that was created by the absence of my adaptive *This is your fault, you have to fix it now!* response, I chose to have faith that Samantha would also be using her tools to notice whatever experience she was in, and I would remember this new experience.

We call this a new reference point. When you pay attention to even the most challenging moments without judgment and use a simple tool to help you just be in the moment without reacting, you have tiny new experiences that you collect over time. All of these new reference points, big and small, are creating a reference library for you—a reference library of new memories. What's more, as you are doing this you are replacing your out-of-date library of trauma- or stress-informed memories.

At first, accessing this new response takes work, and because we're up at the top of the spiral, it's not uncommon that the only thing we can access is deciding to breathe. But over time, and with more tools in your toolbox, it becomes easier to make different choices in response to internal or external stress triggers. Then finally, like my example above when I had a different response to Samantha walking out the door, it becomes an implicit memory.

Implicit memories happen when neural connections have been repeated enough that they no longer take work.[4] Like learning to walk or talk or eat with a fork when we're children. Our responses to the people and things in our lives are learned and remembered, and we can relearn and re-remember new responses. There is nothing to fix in ourselves, but there is something to teach our bodies, and all it takes is awareness, nonjudgment and a few simple tools in our toolkit.

HOW THE HEALING SPIRAL WORKS

That's the good news. Take a look at that spiral figure again. You'll notice that the spiral becomes more and more open as it moves down, but the dots vary in size. Allow the line of the spiral to represent time and the dots to signify those difficult moments in our lives—stress, reactivity, trauma activation, panic attacks, anxiety, etc. As you go through the journey of restoring your body back to a place of calm, freedom and non-reactivity, you're moving from the top of the spiral downward.

The top of the spiral signifies when you don't know what you don't know. Your normal is fueled by your old reference library of stress-reactive or trauma-activated memories. You can access breath, and that may be it for a while. But as you continue, you are teaching your body new responses to old triggers and replacing old body memories with new ones, and the time between moments of distress becomes longer.

This means that things like anxiety, depression and PTSD are no longer our normal, so we become increasingly aware of the distress when it visits us again (which it will). Sometimes it feels even worse. This is because it simply is no longer our normal, now that we have something to compare it to, or because our body is presenting us with a more significant piece of trauma to work through, because we have built the capacity to do so. This is the good news–bad news part of healing.

Healing is often described as peeling an onion. We usually begin with the outer layer, going through the process of distress, awareness, nonjudgment, space, grief, compassion and an eventual clearing with newer events, such as relationships, recent traumas or life events that cause distress. But as we continue to use the tools, do the work and replenish our reference library, our bodies hand us traumas, moving backward through our lifeline. So, like peeling that onion, the longer you are doing it, the more tears involved! As we peel away adaptive responses and gain tools and strength for the healing process, we are working our way back to the earliest moments of our lives. These are often deeper wounds. The process of recovery is not about any destination; it is about the journey—a journey of awareness.

IT TAKES TIME TO GROW YOUR GARDEN

In the next seven chapters you will learn each of the seven embodied resources to help you find your way back to a place of balance and freedom. It is not unlikely that you may find some of them hard to access at first and a little confusing to conceptualize. This is perfectly normal and 100 percent OK.

I have spoken with many, many women who have been through our trainings who reach out to me months or years later. They tell me that they didn't understand everything in the training until they experienced it themselves. And they couldn't experience it themselves by willing it to happen. It doesn't happen like that. These resources aren't things that you learn cognitively and then use like behaviors. They are levels of awareness that grow from inside of you over time, because you are cultivating the space inside of you to allow that growth.

Like a garden that has only one little plant, with care and fortification of the soil, new growth springs forth, and before you know it you have an abundant garden from which to choose tools for awareness and nonjudgmental presence in the midst of any event or person in your life.

Presence is a state of being, not doing. Our true authentic state of human *being* is a state of compassion, curiosity and trust—even in the midst of some of our darkest moments. That is freedom.

CHAPTER 17

Perspective: Changing Your Response to the Things You Feel

The remainder of this book focuses on the seven embodied resources you can cultivate from within yourself and use in any difficult moment to change your neurological response to sensory triggers (somatic markers). You have to commit only to this first one to begin to feel change in your life.

As your body begins to learn new responses to old triggers, the subsequent embodied resources are likely to naturally develop in you, because they are actually already there. This book can serve as a reference point when you feel like you aren't making any progress (you are!), and a way to put words to an experience that is difficult to describe.

The process of recovery, restoration or unraveling our stress response is not a thinking journey—we feel this process inside of us. As we create space in our bodies and minds by using this first embodied resource (which we sometimes call a *TIMBo tool*), our body will work for us, not against us. The key is in changing our perspective on things we feel in our bodies, enough to become aware of what we are feeling and create space.

In nearly all of our programs and trainings (trainings are like program intensives) we see a similar discussion around fear and perspective. Group members take a moment to write about some of the things they fear (just like you were invited to do in chapter 6). After a breathing exercise they then have an opportunity to write a new perspective on those fears. More often than not, the ensuing discussion comes around to the fact that most people's fears revolve around things, people or events that we cannot control.

This presents us with an opportunity to notice the sensations in our bodies when put up against something that we can't control. Most of the time these things are not life-threatening in the moment (the moment being in a room with a dozen other women at a retreat center).

For example, let's say you are sitting in your living room reading this book, and you write something that, were it to happen, would be life-threatening, like *I am afraid of getting kidnapped and murdered.* In doing so, you feel tightness in your chest, perhaps a racing heart, constriction in your throat or other feelings of unease. You can look around at your surroundings (your living room) and cognitively understand that you are not actually in that life-threatening situation in the present moment, but your body is responding with fear. The perspective you can cultivate is simply to recognize this. When we can put the sensations in our bodies up against the reality that our life is not actually in danger, we can then use a breath or a simple movement to calm our bodies down.

Healing is not about the specific fear or circumstance—it is 100 percent about noticing the messages your body is giving you and cross-referencing it with the present moment. The body gives you one of two messages: fear or trust. Everything else is a construct of your mind, including how we perceive any given thing. We may not be able to choose how our body responds, but we can choose how we perceive those responses and the corresponding sensations. We must use our minds to focus on the sensations in our bodies, ask ourselves if our lives are literally in danger, and use a new tool to calm our body down. If we continue to go through life without the ability to do this, our thoughts begin to create a false reality.

Renee

Renee was in her late forties when I first met her. By all appearances, she was intelligent, resourceful and confident. She had a career in academia, completed a yoga teacher training, started her own business and, with her husband, built a life and family for herself.

About twenty years earlier, Renee struggled with an eating disorder, and while she didn't show it on the outside, she was consumed with a constant hum of fear and anxiety. Every thought in her head defaulted to the potential catastrophe that could be looming. Every piece of good news in someone else's life provided fodder for Renee to feel angry and resentful about her own life. She constantly strove to find happiness, always looking for an answer that seemed just out of reach. If and when she attained what she thought would bring her happiness, she was still anxious, dissatisfied and unsettled.

In her early adult years, she was involved in an unhealthy relationship. During that time she had an unplanned pregnancy and a secret abortion. But she eventually extracted herself from that life and found a healthy relationship. When she got married and started a family, the constant buzz of anxiety and unease was a daily undercurrent in Renee's life. As she approached middle age, she couldn't understand why she constantly felt so unsettled when her life was in a good place.

It took Renee time to recognize the fear- and stress-associated sensations in her body. Renee considered herself a spiritual person and had practiced yoga for years, but she still couldn't reconcile why she continued to have this constant anxiety coursing through her life. Prior to TIMBo she just felt abnormal or broken.

During TIMBo trainings we often discuss the current research about the effects of inherited trauma and how this can cause strong physical symptoms in the body with no specific story or trauma memory attached to them. This was when Renee began to wonder whether her constant anxiety could be an inherited survival response run amok.

After her mother shared with Renee that her pregnancy (meaning Renee) was the result of an affair and that she had made a failed attempt at aborting the pregnancy, things began to make sense. Renee took a leading role in her own healing, starting to accept her body sensations for what they were, using simple tools to change her relationship to them and sitting with them without judgment.

The key for Renee was to recognize that her head, meaning her intellect, was getting in the way of her healing. By straining to find a good reason that we are feeling what we are feeling, we rob ourselves of the experience of connecting directly with the reality of our bodies. The anxiety Renee had lived with daily was a constant current of fear with which she had been born. It was her normal state. It was not conscious. The first step in her healing was to accept the anxious feelings, create space around them and see them from a neurobiological perspective.

In order for Renee to truly allow her body to heal, she learned to breathe and create space whenever she noticed the sensations of anxiety coursing through her. She compassionately reminded herself that the discomfort she felt was her body's survival response, not a real threat. Time and again she told herself the TIMBo mantra, "It feels real, but it's not the truth." From there, she replaced this litany of anxious fear-based thoughts with new ones.

Over time Renee grew increasingly skilled at identifying when she was getting hijacked and creating space so she could shift her perspective. The undercurrent of anxiety no longer rules her thoughts and behaviors. Now Renee is teaching others to do this same kind of healing work on themselves. And when Renee slips back into old ways of thinking and behaving, as we all do while learning new skills, she gently reminds herself that she doesn't have to react that way anymore and starts again.

EMBODIED RESOURCE #1: AWARENESS, ACCEPTANCE AND SPACE

I can't stress this enough—any hope for change hinges upon changing your perspective of your body's stress reactions. The best way to begin this process is to bring awareness to your body sensations, accept them for what they are (your survival response), and instead of resisting them, create space for something truer to emerge.

This new perspective I am talking about is not a giant leap. It is simply moving from *This feeling sucks, and I want to do something about it* to *This is my body's survival response, and I can create space with breath.*

That's it. Simple, but not easy. Here's why.

Take a look at the illustration below. This represents us at the top of the spiral. The lines on the body of this woman represent the body sensations, and the circle around her represents the closed system. The closed system is what we often feel in times of difficulty when we can't gain perspective on the truth of the situation—our body is telling us we are in danger. The words in the circle represent aspects of our experience—they list just a few of the things we may be experiencing.

There is no way to get any outside perspective when all of this is going on inside of us and our minds are buying into this as truth. Our most embodied resource is being aware when we are in moments like this—to compassionately understand what is happening in our bodies (nonjudgment) and create space with a simple breath tool.

Nonjudgment is critical. As you can see in this illustration, judgment is a part of the false reality. Our ability to change our perspective requires us to change our relationship via nonjudgment. If you continue to create any judgment of your body sensations, you will not be successful in accessing the tools to create space.

So it comes full circle—perspective is required to change your experience, and nonjudgment is required to access that perspective. Our minds want to complicate it—we must keep it simple. Take a look at the illustration below.

In my example of becoming paralyzed with guilt and responsibility in various instances with Samantha, I had to start with nonjudgmental awareness and breathing to create space, because my mind was screaming at me, *Do something to fix this!* My habitual reaction would be to chase, to beg, to take responsibility for something that I didn't do (which always led to resentment) or to engage in something I didn't want to. All of those habitual actions serve to strengthen the system that was causing me distress in the first place.

The idea of this tool is simple, yet I know from firsthand experience that it is not easy because of all of the space the mind takes up. But it won't take very long for you to recognize how powerful this resource is. Remarkably, you have had it with you your whole life—it is your breath!

TIMBO IN A WOMEN'S CORRECTIONAL FACILITY

I remember the pilot TIMBo program we ran in the maximum-security correctional facility for women here in Massachusetts. At that time I had little to no knowledge of the impact of the program, and we were essentially taking it for a test run. The version of the program we were piloting is the one we use today, with some changes using all the learnings from our pilot with the pregnant and new moms in substance-abuse recovery. We knew from that pilot that focusing on body sensations and using breath was essential, particularly in the early stages of the program. Other than that, we were still learning.

A few sessions in, one of the inmates spoke into the discussion circle. The session was about grief and resentment, and she had an experience to tell us about. The majority of female inmates have a history of trauma. And as I mentioned, the majority of this trauma happened in relationships or social situations. So you can imagine the hotbed of stress and trauma activation that might occur in a facility where humans are caged like animals, forced into the same space with one another and given little to no resources for physical or mental health.

This particular inmate shared an experience she had in the dining area just a day or two prior. She said she was sitting within earshot of a fellow inmate whom she found very irritating. She could hear this inmate talking, and she could feel herself becoming more and more irritated at the sound of her voice. Very quickly she became enraged. "I felt like my blood was boiling," she told us. She said she wanted to leap across the table and wrap her hands around this woman's neck—an action that would most certainly have landed her in solitary confinement. She explained how she remembered our program and the things we practiced in the group.

Thanks to a shift in her perspective, she knew what the sensations in her body were (the survival response), and she decided to breathe. She calmed down enough to return to her cell and breathe some more.

She looked at me with tears in her eyes and said, "I can't believe I've had the ability to do this all my life, and I never knew it. I'm so grateful for this program. If I had had this a long time ago, I probably wouldn't be here."

FEAR OVERWHELM: TOOLS FOR MANAGING A PANIC ATTACK

I believe it's safe to say that any incarcerated individual is living at the top of the spiral, meaning their stress/survival response is on a continuous feedback loop. This existence is their normal, but it is not how it needs to be. Having the capacity to identify that there are sensations happening in your body, regardless of your capacity to identify what they are, is step one. Choosing to breathe is step two. Between step one and two is changing your relationship to those sensations from one of resistance to one of acceptance. The piece of information that helps nearly all the women I see, from those in prison to court-mandated rehab to Haiti, is the fact that these sensations are the neurobiological manifestation of fear.

Take a look at the Emotional Anatomy Pyramid again. Fear is at the foundation of this pyramid, with every emotional-anatomy disruption building on top of it. Fear is a primitive, noncognitive sensation in the body fueled by the biological drive to survive. It is this first tool of awareness, acceptance and space that works directly with the primal fear response. This is the place we must start, because without this action, we remain in a state of fear, and we can't cultivate any new perspectives or behaviors from within.

There are instances when the survival response is so powerful in our bodies that we become completely hijacked.[1] Sometimes this looks like an anxiety attack or a panic attack. Panic attacks are aptly named, because the system is in a state of such profound fear that all systems (respiratory, motor, gastrointestinal, etc.) flip into intense overdrive, and the experience feels frightening and out of control. I recall several instances of this happening to a woman who experienced this in trainings, and I also recall the power of breathing to bring the panic down and return her to balance.

There is no predicting if and when this will happen to you or anyone else, but if and when it does, it is a function of right-brain-hemisphere activity. The right hemisphere is the earliest to develop, right along with the survival response. So in the case of a panic attack, it is extremely useful to visualize a number in your head (think *Sesame Street*–style numbers) while counting down from ten to one on every inhale and exhale.

Visualizing the numbers re-tasks the right hemisphere, which is very busy creating traumatic sensory memories and causing the panic. When we give it something else to do (visualizing numbers), we guide it away from its current functioning (creating vivid traumatic memories). When we count, we bring the left-hemisphere activity into the experience in a way that can quickly balance or integrate brain function and calm the panic attack down.[2]

The left-brain hemisphere is linear, thinks in numbers and conceptualizes past and future. Where the right hemisphere is bringing the past into the present moment, the left hemisphere can keep it in the past without the distress of feeling it in the present.[3]

I have guided many women very quickly out of their panic attacks using the breath and number visualization/counting method in just about a minute or two. If you have anxiety or panic attacks you can do this for yourself. It will take some courage and work at first, but it will quickly become one of your most-relied-upon tools.

YOU'VE CREATED SPACE WITH BREATH—WHAT COMES NEXT?

The embodied resources described in the remainder of this book are all choices of what to do in the space you create with breath. The areas of the brain that help us stop and consider are hard to access when we are in fear. Keep in mind that a state of dissociation or numbness happens when our bodies are in collapse or immobilization mode, which is also fear. Over time our neuronal bodies become damaged, and we stop producing more of them, which makes considering our options very difficult.[4] So we end up reacting and fueling the stress feedback loop further.

When we stop and create space with breath, we increase our neuronal bodies, we repair damaged ones, we bring health back to our prefrontal cortex (the place that allows us to stop, consider and make better choices), and we set ourselves up to access the remainder of the embodied resources. These inner choices are the building blocks to cultivating resilience, which is conversely associated with being faced with too many external choices and all the stressful effort we put into trying to predict a desired outcome that we believe will give us a feeling of control, satisfaction, freedom and happiness. Just watch the TED Talks of Harvard psychologist Dan Gilbert or psychologist Barry Schwartz for some fascinating scientific evidence of how and why overabundant choice makes us paralyzed and unhappy.

The good news is that the choice to stop, feel and breathe is with us every minute of every day. It's an instant one-choice package. We just have to make it.

Things to Notice

Healing is 100 percent dependent on your ability to notice. And your ability to notice hinges on your ability to be curious, suspend judgment and use your newly learned tools to get you through the moment. All aspects of these uncomfortable moments—from before, to during, to after—are of equal importance. I am providing reminders and suggestions in each chapter of things you can consider noticing. In time, noticing will be as automatic for you as breathing—and just as crucial.

As you go through your day, notice times when you feel an uncomfortable sensation in your body. These are likely to be felt anywhere from the head down through the throat, chest, solar plexus, belly or pelvic area. Place your hand on that area, and use one of the breathing techniques learned in this book.

Notice how you feel after the breath.

When you have some time to reflect, write about the following in the space provided or in your journal:

Who or what were these sensations responding to? Describe the sensation you felt in your body. Describe how the situation may have reflected one of the three triggers of stress (lack of control, uncertainty, lack of information).

_____

_____

_____

_____

_____

_____

_____

_____

_____

_____

_____

_____

_____

_____

Once you become able to respond to stressful situations in your life by stopping and noticing your body and breathing, you are ready to move on to the next chapter.

CHAPTER 18

Creativity: Reimagining Your Inner Critic

You could put the book down right now, use embodied resource #1 and experience many powerful changes in your life. The tools of awareness, acceptance and space begin to change your perspective on the sensations you feel in your body—enough so that each time, you can access the tool more quickly and easily. It's like learning to ride a bike; it's a little hard and scary at first, but once you practice it enough, you can't believe you've never done it before.

But we are human beings with a conscious mind and the gift of language and thought. Our thoughts, judgments and stories we tell ourselves are the source of our suffering. But the effort to exile these things only causes more suffering. One of the most crucial yet most challenging steps on the path to healing is changing our perspective of the self-critical thoughts that often flood our inner world.

Remember the second dart in chapter 7, when we were exploring guilt? Any self-recrimination or guilt-ridden thinking that arises from visceral body sensations is a second and unnecessary dart. The issue is that your body and lifelong process of adaptation believe this kind of self-critical thinking is necessary.

Herein lies the difficulty with just thinking positively. If you have learned to judge or criticize yourself in order to make sure you're good enough, your body will protest letting this adaptation go, because it believes it is protecting you.

Remember: when we are young, connection means survival, and any perceived threat of losing that connection is going to become a part of that second-dart wiring. But there is a way to creatively interact with that second dart that has sustainable healing potential. Again, this requires a little perspective shift and some willingness to think outside of the box.

YOUR HELPFUL INNER CRITIC VOICES

Feeling guilt and responsibility can show up in the form of self-determined expectations about anything. Performing well on exams, for example. Not ever making a mistake. Staying quiet. Being funny, etc. These are all things that in and of themselves are not bad—and at times they are even appropriate. But when they carry with them a biological survival alarm when we do the opposite (failing a test, being loud, not cracking jokes, etc.), we know they are adaptations.

Remember: these feelings of responsibility, causation or expectation develop as early as our ability to conceptualize cause and effect. Labeled on the Emotional Anatomy Pyramid as guilt and responsibility, it is the second stage of development after the primal development of fear.

Anything that can be perceived by your young developing self as judgment, rejection, abandonment or betrayal will be understood as being caused by something we did. It is completely adaptive in that the rationale behind it is *If I did this thing to cause this rejection, I can make sure I don't do it next time.* Or the converse, *If Mommy and/or Daddy likes this thing that I do (or way that I am), I must do it always to make sure I'm loved.* When it comes to early childhood trauma, this is a very ineffective survival mechanism, because nothing any child can do or change about themselves will control the trauma or traumatic experience.

Over time the second-dart feelings of guilt or responsibility turn to shame, when our critical voices take on another tone altogether. Critical voices are an ineffective survival adaptation in the long term. When we feel we are not good enough or that we have failed in some way, our critical voices are trying to help us be the right way in order to be worthy. Our critical voices will helpfully point out that we are not smart enough, thin enough, pretty enough, brave enough and so on. We set expectations that, when not met, unleash a barrage of self-criticisms that fuel the suffering we seek to end. When everything we try fails, we then resign ourselves to the belief that we were just born wrong. We are just a mistake, and no one could possibly love us.

As you've now learned, feeling responsible when we are children manifests into pervasive inner critic voices. These critical voices are a protective mechanism, because they put control over rejection in our hands. But like the perspective shift to body sensations in the previous chapter, there is a way to change your relationship to your critical voices that, while difficult at first, will change your experience of them. It starts with noticing the body sensations that are informing those voices, then bringing a little creativity to how you see and hear your critical voices and how you communicate to them.

Creativity is not accessible unless you first create space with breath. Everything really does hinge on the space you create first. This next embodied resource taps into your ability to externalize and creatively speak to your inner critic.

EMBODIED RESOURCE #2: CREATING A NEW RELATIONSHIP WITH YOUR INNER CRITIC

There are thousands of ways we internalize messages from the adults (and later peers) around us when we are children. It does not have to be a traumatic situation for us to decide something about how we are going to think and behave from that moment forward in response to perceived rejection.

During trainings Erin often offers a story from her personal life to illustrate this point. When Erin was young she remembers hanging around with her sister and her mother. She was a vivacious and exuberant girl who loved to dance and sing, and on this particular day, just when she was losing herself in what she felt was her lovely song, her sister blurted out, "Please stop! Can't you hear that you are so out of tune?" Erin remembers that moment like it was yesterday, and she remembers making the decision right then and there to never sing again.

We have hundreds of these moments in our developing years that all work together to create our adapted self. The caretaker, the pleaser, the smart one, the beautiful one, the funny one, etc. Mixed in with all of that is also the unworthy one, the unlovable one, the stupid one, the ugly one, etc. These are all versions of a survival adaptation that is designed to keep us away from a place of vulnerability, which creates a false sense of control and predictability.

By the time we are adults we resist and judge these voices, which are mechanisms of guilt and shame, which (you guessed it) are fueled by the biological survival response. So, the path to healing and freedom is not to judge or resist these things. Take a look at the diagram below to understand why.

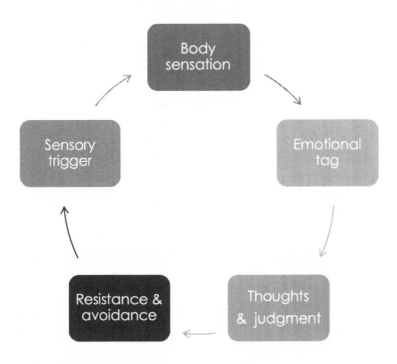

Our fear-based body sensations are triggered by any number of external or internal sensory markers. Our minds conceptualize this as an emotion, and this cocktail fuels an onslaught of thoughts and judgments, either toward and about ourselves or directed at others.

This recipe feels so uncomfortable because the basis of it is the physiological alarm mechanism of our body telling us that our life is in danger—because at the time it originated, it was more or less true. Remember: this is a primitive system. If we were rejected by our caregivers back in the days when we lived in caves, we would be eaten by saber-toothed tigers. So when we judge or resist these things, our bodies will only fight harder—because they are trying to keep us alive. This fuels more sensory triggers, but now it's all emanating from inside of us by way of all the stress-related hormones, neurotransmitters and biochemicals coursing through us—and the implicit memory gets strengthened as a result. It's like a Chinese finger trap: the more you struggle to free yourself of it, the stronger the hold it has on you.

Once we get stuck in the trap of negativity, judgment and resistance, it is difficult to step out of, which is why breathing is the first action we must take. Breathing loosens the grip (neurologically speaking) of that trap so we can utilize tools that, over time, replace the implicit memory with a new, updated one. The opposite of negativity is not positivity—it's nonjudgment.

ROLL OUT THE WELCOME MAT FOR THE INNER CRITIC

I recall years ago, sitting in a small circle with some of the earliest trained TIMBo facilitators. Samantha was in that group, and we were doing the exercises you just completed in this book. Samantha chose to share the drawing of her inner critic with the group. She was an angry little girl locked in a cage. Samantha described this girl with anger and disdain. She felt triumphant that she had finally locked her away—for good this time!

It was in that moment that I suggested she imagine opening the door of the cage, taking the girl by the hand and leading her into a place of safety. I told her to imagine sitting the girl down in front of a fireplace and wrapping her in a warm blanket.

Because of what Samantha had shared with us, I knew that her inner critic was young. She was repeating many of the hurtful things her mother had said to her when she was just a child. She was reminding Samantha of all the things she needed to fix to be lovable.

I suggested to Samantha that she tell this little one that she didn't have to work so hard anymore. Samantha was an adult and was able to care for her now. Samantha could care for little Samantha in the way that she wasn't cared for by her mother. This perspective shift was something Samantha had never considered, but it was the moment when everything changed for her. She began to bring this creative perspective into her experience of traumatic stress and flashbacks, using breath to create the space that allowed her to do so.

Samantha has since reminded me of this moment and the power of this creative practice when she remained by my side as I traveled through some excruciating moments of healing. She is able to do that for me, because she has been through it herself.

REMEMBERING WHO THIS INNER CRITIC REALLY IS

The most useful concept I've come to understand as a crucial practice in healing is creatively externalizing the inner critic. This is not synonymous with rejecting our inner critic or banishing it, but instead loving and appreciating it. Because it is *you* at an age when this adaptation formed.

As counterintuitive as it sounds, we must imagine these inner beings as children and feel appreciative of the voices that are telling us negative things about ourselves, because that is how they believe they are keeping us from experiencing the traumatic or negative event again.

Imagine if you were sitting in the living room of your home and in bursts a child of four screaming, "We're all gonna die! There's a fire! There's a fire!" while it's very clear that there is absolutely no fire. Then imagine you don't move from your couch, and they start yelling insults at you like "You idiot! Get out of here! What the hell is wrong with you?" And when that doesn't work, they go into a full-blown tantrum. Would you tell this little child that you hated them and kick them out of the living room? Would you ignore them and just let them scream and shout and work their way into an absolute unstoppable tantrum? Probably not. More often than not you would soothe this little child. You would perhaps scoop them up and let them know that it's OK, there is no fire. You might let them know that you can see that they are scared and that they are trying to save you, but it's not necessary right now. You might even hold them close and show them around so they can see that there is no fire. They can rest, and you might just let them sleep in your arms after all that expenditure of energy. *This* is the action of externalizing the inner critic.

Ruthie

When Ruthie, whom we met in the denial chapter, first began with TIMBo, her most pervasive critical voice said that she was unlovable, disgusting and dirty. This is not an uncommon adaptation in those who survive barbaric sexual assaults like the one Ruthie experienced when she was raped by the teenage boys in the car.

Ruthie is an absolutely lovely and physically stunning adult woman, but because of that attack, she has an internal protector (albeit misguided) that tells her that she is not fit for anyone to get close to. Compassionately externalizing the inner critic has been challenging for Ruthie, because this particular adaptive response has a strong hold on her. It won't let anyone close to her. It initiates panic, judgment and physical feelings of illness at just the thought of intimacy—especially with men.

Ruthie has reached out to me many times over the years when this adaptation is running the show. I only have to remind her that this is a little girl who was brutally attacked and is just trying to protect Ruthie by reminding her that she is dirty and disgusting—therefore she won't allow anyone to get close. This protects her against any chance of getting hurt again. But grown-up Ruthie suffers because, like all human beings, she needs closeness and connection for her own health, happiness and well-being.

Even when we convince ourselves we don't need loving connection, biologically we do. Remember: I had sworn to go to the grave alone, but when Samantha offered me real authentic connection, my body and my head went to war with one another. This is what happens with Ruthie. When she steps into the vulnerability of a possible connection (romantic or not), her protector starts to pitch a little fit. It makes absolute sense, because the implicit memory is born from the moment Ruthie trusted those boys and got into the car. In her fierce protective inner landscape, the thirteen-year-old Ruthie sees trust and vulnerability as the most dangerous place imaginable.

Ruthie has worked hard on externalizing her inner critic, and it has paid off. She has an eight-by-ten photo of herself at about age six that she looks at when she gets swept away in self-judgment and shame. When you have an opportunity to connect a visual image of yourself at a young age and recognize that this is the young person criticizing you to make sure you stay alive, it's easier to feel compassion.

Take a look at the girl below. This is me at about age three or four.

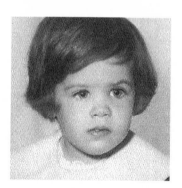

Whenever I judge myself for not being enough (good enough, smart enough, productive enough, pretty enough), I imagine her. Whenever I feel like I am broken because my healing from sexual trauma is not going fast enough, I imagine her. Whenever I feel resentful that someone might be getting more attention than me, I imagine her. If I were to criticize her, resist her or banish her, she will try all that much harder to get me to listen to her.

Instead, it's important to recognize what these old adaptations are trying to do, to thank them for working all of our lives and to let them know that we (the adult, grown-up person) will drive the bus from now on. She can take a seat anywhere she likes and enjoy the ride.

REPLACING MEMORY MARBLES

Each time you use the embodied resource of externalizing your inner critic and seeing it as a young protective voice, you create a new memory for your reference library. Think of this file of implicit memories as a jar of blue marbles. The blue marbles are all of the memories created by way of your early life experiences and reinforced by your adaptive responses and behaviors. In any given circumstance we pick a blue marble (memory/reaction) that drives our habitual response.

But when we practice embodied resources (two of which we now have in our toolbox) we have a *new* outcome—even if that outcome is that we chose to breathe or to compassionately talk to our inner critic instead of any number of things that we would habitually do. Each new experience becomes a new memory, and let's say new memories are green marbles. This new green marble replaces an existing blue marble. The jar is still primarily full of blue marbles, with just one or two green ones, which makes using an embodied resource involve some work.

This is often the reason I get calls and texts from women like Ruthie or why women in our community reach out to our Facebook group for support. They simply need to be reminded of their new tools. Over time more green marbles replace blue ones, and eventually our jar has more green marbles than blue. This allows us to make new choices in response to old triggers much more easily. The effort to remember using a new tool simply dissolves, and what we have left is a new way of being in relationship with ourselves and the world around us.

It's important to recognize that this takes time, and it requires that we simply *be with* all of the body sensations and noise that customarily accompany stress triggers. But if we can breathe to create space, talk kindly to our inner critic and notice the impact of making those choices, you will be amazed at how quickly you begin to feel different.

Using the embodied resource of externalizing the inner critic is a creative way to respond in the moment to your own adaptive voices. It can take some time to become curious about the things your thoughts are telling you about yourself or others around you. I recently had dinner with the once soft-spoken and skittish Alexa to catch up on how things were going in her life. We talked about her journey through TIMBo and our shared experiences spending years with a dangerous narcissist, and we marveled at how much we have both healed in just a few short years.

Alexa had a sense of wonder in her voice as she shared her realization that before TIMBo, her adaptations were completely running the show, and she felt convinced that everyone hated her, no matter what they actually said or did. She looked at me with a wide smile on her face and said, "I had no idea that everything was happening inside of me. I just thought that everyone out there was the problem!" She looked about ten years younger. Her face was lighter, her eyes were brighter, and she wore a smile that was rarely there when she first found her way to TIMBo. Like all of us, difficult feelings still visit her, but her reference library is slowly being updated, and because of this, Alexa will likely never go back to the days when her adaptations ran the show.

Things to Notice

As you go through your day, notice times when you are judging yourself or judging others. Stop to notice the sensations you feel in your body at that moment. Take some deep breaths, and visualize your inner critic as a young version of you (or any young child or being that is accessible to you). Tell that little being you know that what they think is happening is actually not happening. Remind your little protector that it feels real, but it is not the truth.

Remember: the adaptations think your life is literally in danger. Perhaps place your hand on your heart, and assure this being that you will sit with them until they calm down—for as long as that takes. Remember to use your breath to keep you grounded and calm.

Eventually the grip of your inner critic will soften. Notice how you feel when this happens.

When you have some time to reflect, write about the following in the space provided or in your journal:

Describe how the situation may have reflected one of the three triggers of stress (lack of control, uncertainty, lack of information). Describe what your adaptive inner critic looked like in your mind. Describe what it felt like to talk kindly to them. Describe what it felt like to take this child under your arm in the midst of this moment.

_____

_____

_____

_____

_____

_____

_____

_____

_____

_____

Once you learn to respond to situations in your life by stopping, noticing your body, breathing, and speaking kindly and compassionately to
your inner critic, you are ready to move on to the next chapter.

CHAPTER 19

Confidence: Rebuilding Self-Worth

The first two TIMBo embodied resources (or tools) are critical because they empower you to change your relationship to things you have likely been judging and resisting your whole life. It is not easy, but it's crucial to remember that these sensations and thoughts were created at a time when your system had made a solemn vow to keep you away from vulnerability. When we shift our response to these things from one of resistance to one of awareness, acceptance and space, opportunities begin to present themselves.

In my recent conversation with Alexa, she told me that once she started practicing yoga and TIMBo, she started walking through every open door that presented itself to her. This does not mean that she no longer had difficult days, but her capacity to walk into a place of uncertainty (which is in itself a vulnerable place) increased, because she had effective tools to use in the moment she felt uncomfortable.

What she may or may not have realized was her brain was changing. Whereas once the neural circuit in her neurology automatically responded to uncertainty with fear and a literal running away from (like the hand that automatically pulls away from the fire), now things had changed in such a way that Alexa could walk into those spaces with some curiosity and faith.

To the survival adaptation this feels excruciatingly risky—simply because the belief is we will die. But the more we use the embodied resources to help us stay in the moment, the more confidence we have in them to navigate us through those moments with a new awareness.

Another way to see this is the more confidence we have in the tools, the more confidence we have in ourselves and the more risks we are willing to take. And the more risks we take (realizing that we won't, in fact, die), the more green marbles—or new memories—we have to choose from in the future.

Naomi

Naomi signed up for the online TIMBo facilitator training in 2016. She had been suffering from chronic pain and migraines, had a PTSD and borderline personality diagnosis and had attempted suicide a year prior to joining the training. Naomi was raised by a single mother who was a narcissist.

As a child Naomi was kept away from friends and the outside world. She came under constant criticism, belittling and blame. Naomi developed a rock-solid adaptation that everything was her fault, and it was her job to take care of everybody—particularly her mother and her younger stepbrother. Naomi's escape from her childhood home was joining the military, and after the events of September 11, she found herself in basic training, preparing for active duty. The screaming verbal abuse and blame associated with basic training felt familiar to her, and she breezed through it with no problem.

During her time in the military she was involved in a serious car accident that left her with a debilitating back injury and in chronic pain. At nineteen years old she felt her life of freedom from her mother was just beginning, but the injury left her feeling broken and hopeless. She met a male service member who was several years her senior, and while she had a gut feeling that it was the wrong move, she married him, and together they moved to Colorado.

Very quickly after they married, Naomi told her husband she wanted to leave, and in response, he raped her. Though she pressed charges, she felt it was her fault, so she simultaneously was seeking justice for her assault while unconsciously seeking attention and forgiveness from him. She remained in close physical proximity to him, which led to an evening when he came home intoxicated, spiked her drink with a drug and sexually assaulted her a second time. She finally moved out. She continued to have sexual partners but consciously chose to engage without any emotional attachment. This felt like she had some control, but ultimately it left her feeling empty and dissatisfied.

A few years later she met a second military man, but this time she felt a false sense of safety in knowing he would be deployed at some point. Because of the dozens of boyfriends her mother had that came in and out of her childhood home, she had come to believe that people leave, which was a way of providing predictability for herself around something that left her feeling crushed and unworthy.

When he was finally deployed, she felt relieved and turned her focus and her caretaking tendencies toward animals in need by fostering a litter of kittens. After he returned from his deployment, he began to come home intoxicated and belligerent, and Naomi's PTSD symptoms worsened. One night he threatened to harm the kittens, and feeling fiercely protective of them, she lost control and shoved him. A physical fight ensued, culminating in him getting thirty days of jail time and mandatory alcohol and anger management counseling.

Still, Naomi felt like the entire thing was her fault, so when he was released, he came back to live with her for ten months before she finally got him to leave. She immediately allowed her narcissistic grandmother and dysfunctional brother to live with her, at which time her chronic pain, migraines and PTSD symptoms felt completely debilitating and paralyzing. Finally, she swallowed a few bottles of pills and looked forward to just going to sleep. It was only her grandmother's unexpected return home that foiled the attempt.

After her suicide attempt, Naomi sought psychiatric help. She found a widely used mindfulness-based behavioral therapeutic treatment. It was offered at a local hospital. She felt that the mindfulness component of the treatment was helpful, but she eventually felt triggered by the clinical atmosphere of the hospital, as well as the emphasis on a diagnosis of borderline personality disorder. She ended the treatment and began searching elsewhere.

When Naomi was told about trauma-sensitive yoga, she began searching online, which is how she found TIMBo. Right away Naomi was relieved to hear that TIMBo was something that could be used in conjunction with other methods of treatment, and in fact it could *enhance* the effectiveness of other treatments. Freed from the constraints of having to choose just one program to pledge allegiance to, she knew she could follow this through.

Immediately she began to feel shifts happening inside of her. The connection and trust she began developing with the women in her TIMBo training helped her consider that maybe not all people are shitty, which had become a deeply ingrained adaptive thought. Most powerfully she felt seen, heard and unconditionally accepted, and she was able to express her anger enough to recognize that it was a stockpile of grief going all the way back to her childhood. She grieved for the childhood she never had, the mother she never had and for having to be an adult from as far back as she could remember. It was the unconditional acceptance of the group that allowed her to continue through to the end of the training.

Using TIMBo's embodied resources, Naomi discovered she could cultivate healing from within. Practicing TIMBo changed her relationship to herself and the world around her. These tools gave Naomi increased day-to-day confidence, and she began to feel worthy and useful. She helped people (as is her inclination) by sharing the tools. This gave Naomi even more confidence and a sense of freedom, because she could help people help themselves.

The drive to help others is in our DNA as human beings. When we lack confidence (trust) in ourselves, we feel we have nothing to offer. But confidence in her newly learned tools naturally inspired Naomi to share them with others. This feeling of worth has tremendous life-changing impact—like when I realized having an emotional breakdown on stage during my teacher training actually helped people. What could have easily been an experience that catapulted me into a shame spiral was instead a significant turning point in my life. Helping others made me recognize my worth. The value of this resource can't be understated.

The crushing blame and responsibility Naomi carried all of her life dissolved, because she knew from her own experience of TIMBo that just learning how to breathe or learning to visualize and speak compassionately to your critical voices can change a life. Here is an excerpt from a message Naomi recently posted on the TIMBo facilitator Facebook group:

Today, I was able to see my littlest self for the powerhouse that she is and see that instead of being protected, she was abused. A life of shame that I never understood before made sense. I was able to connect all the dots, and most importantly I was able to sit with myself, TIMBo facilitator and abuse-neglected child. I was able to breathe through the sensations. I was able to be present and aware. I was able to protect myself and reassure my younger self that no one would ever use or exploit my strengths again. And I believed myself.

Naomi's use of her embodied resources allowed her to emerge from the other side of discomfort with gratitude, compassion and incredible confidence in her ability to guide her own healing.

EMBODIED RESOURCE #3: USING AND SHARING THE TIMBO TOOLS TO BUILD CONFIDENCE

There is a quote in the TIMBo program that pisses a lot of people off. It reads, "If you think you can, you can, if you think you can't, you're right," often attributed to Henry Ford.[1]

By this time in the program, participants are aware that any response or reaction they have to a quote is 100 percent fine. There is no right or wrong response—there is only noticing without judgment, and this quote presents a lot for us to notice. I believe some of the strong reactions to this quote are coming from a feeling of being judged, and this can stir up adaptive responses that are useful to observe.

Some people feel angry and start defending themselves, some start to criticize the quote, and others have different reactions. How is it that just a few words on a piece of paper can incite such visceral responses in our bodies? Isn't that just a little bit curious?

If just a few words on a page can stir some of us up so much, imagine what can happen when we are in relationships with real human beings! Just like Alexa came to realize in herself, the responses that stir up inside of us have very little to do with what is outside of us and more to do with our adaptive survival wiring. After all, what is the value in arguing with words on a page?

The work then becomes taking the risk to suspend the habitual response, which makes us feel vulnerable. And as I've said before, vulnerability (unpredictability, uncertainty, etc.) is where our traumas happened, but it's also the birthplace of change and growth. The defining factor is simply how we choose to see it.

What makes this challenging is that every individual has different survival wiring that developed according to their own life experiences. Therefore, it must be something each person comes to recognize in their own bodies.

For women like Erin and Alexa, vulnerability is the place of allowing themselves to be seen and heard. To take up space and be noticed.

Their survival wiring connected speaking or being seen with being judged, criticized or rejected.

For others like Naomi and me, vulnerability is in stepping back. The survival wiring has come to connect being quiet or not taking center stage with a risk of being invisible or forgotten.

I recall one particularly memorable training when Erin and I had made the decision to switch roles. She would step up to be more of a lead trainer, and I would step back to let her shine. We both had to be acutely and compassionately aware of our adaptive responses (vulnerability) and silently use our TIMBo tools (remember: we call that TIMBo-ing ourselves) while holding space for all the women in the training. This is why we refer to them as embodied resources—they are inside of you, and they can be accessed without it being obvious.

During that training my body felt incredibly uneasy. My adaptations were screaming at me, Erin felt like a judgmental shaming mother—all of it completely constructed inside of me, and all of it false. I had to breathe, talk to my inner critic, the girl who was actually the shaming voice telling me I completely messed up every time I spoke. By this time in my career I was a seasoned trainer, and I had guided many, many women through these trainings with Erin by my side. But she had always taken a supporting role, and I was always in the driver's seat. During this same training I was able to compassionately understand that my survival adaptation was screaming at me that if I wasn't the captain of the boat, the whole ship would go down. It was a feeling of intense responsibility for others that was creating uncomfortable feelings of fear and vulnerability in me.

If I hadn't given myself the opportunity to navigate through that experience feeling excruciating discomfort, I would have continued believing this was my unchangeable personality (which wasn't in itself a bad thing) and never allowed myself to build confidence by risking vulnerability. Nor would I have allowed Erin to risk vulnerability and step into a place of leadership. Of course, she had her own TIMBo-ing of herself to do during that training, but today Erin is an incredible trainer with an embodied confidence that is powerfully seen and felt.

USING CONFIDENCE TO HELP OTHERS

Embodying confidence by using new tools in challenging times helps us and gives us the gift of helping someone else. It is true, authentic help—not just advice from the sidelines.

Just as a woman who has given birth can support another through childbirth from a place of experiential knowing, we all can help others from a place of knowing what sitting in that vulnerability feels like and feeling the freedom of being on the other side. This sharing of TIMBo tools and embodied resources makes us feel a sense of purpose and meaning in the world.

As humans we are wired to connect and support others—but when our survival adaptations connect helping others with feeling responsible for the experiences and outcomes of others, we know we have some preliminary work to do. Ultimately, we don't always know that we are potentially changing people's lives with what we share, but Erin recently received the following message from a woman participating in a training with her:

Erin, as a senior facilitator, you guided this training in a powerful way that was life-changing for me. You have a gift for using the embodied resources and all of your training and experiences to train in a highly educational, compassionate and meaningful way.

These tools have a distinct pay-it-forward capacity that benefits everyone involved. Because they are simple to use and immediately impactful, they are simple to teach and pass on. Our bodies will recognize a new experience if we allow it to have one and are aware of what it feels like.

Remember: each new experience is like a green marble replacing a blue one until the green outnumber the blue. What is additionally valuable in this memory-update process is that sharing the tools creating new experiences in you with others is *also* a new marble and puts another green-marble memory in your library. Over time the result is a growing compassionate knowledge of yourself, predictability in the outcome of using these simple tools, and confidence in navigating through moments of vulnerability.

The miraculous thing is that in time, this recipe changes the nature of vulnerable moments, because instead of experiencing them as reasons to be stressed and afraid, we experience them as opportunities and possibilities. All that change is happening inside of us, yet our entire life ends up feeling different.

Things to Notice

As you go through your day, notice times when you are using one or both of the embodied resources that you have learned so far. Remembering to always use your breath to keep you grounded and calm—counting down from ten while visualizing—helps keep your brain in the present. Simple movements like sun breath help when things seem especially difficult.

When you're confident these resources are helping you, take any opportunities to help someone you care about by teaching them to breathe and move. Let them know how this has helped you, and demonstrate it for them. Notice their reaction to learning this embodied resource.

When you have some time to reflect, write about the following in the space provided or in your journal:

Describe the confidence and empowerment you might be feeling as you come to rely on these tools throughout your day. Notice any experiences that feel new or different. Describe how it feels to share these simple things with the people you care about. Notice how it feels to help another person empower themselves with the embodied resources you have taught them.

_____

_____

_____

_____

_____

_____

_____

_____

_____

_____

_____

_____

_____

Once you feel confident in the use of these initial embodied resources and have started to feel helpful to others in your willingness to share them, you are likely to be feeling the impact of new experiences. When you are aware of this, you are ready to move on to the next chapter.

CHAPTER 20

Compassion: The Cornerstone of Resilience

It can't be stressed enough that compassion is critical for creating an environment of healing. Oftentimes compassion (to feel *with*) is confused with sympathy (to feel sorry *for*). This often leads women to believe they can show compassion for others while struggling with practicing self-compassion.

Boiled down, the ability to be with others in their suffering—while not being attached to any outcome—requires being with oneself. If we were to reverse engineer this idea, imagine that you are with a beloved friend or family member who is suffering. To truly be with this person while not being attached to any outcome, you would also have to be with (but not react to) the feelings in you that want to fix it or make it better.

Those feelings are often rooted in unconscious survival adaptations of feeling responsible—meaning that the discomfort in someone else not being OK triggers your body's survival response and creates anxiety, worry, stress, etc. Some people take action and do everything they can to help—which is not a bad thing at all. Some people are so uncomfortable that they run or disconnect themselves physically from the pain they might feel in the presence of someone else's suffering.

These are all mechanisms of survival adaptations. But when self-judgment becomes a part of that picture, a lack of self-compassion inhibits our ability to be compassionately present. Why? Because we become consumed with feelings of *I should be doing more, I should have done something different, I should have been there* and so on. These judgmental feelings and thoughts remove us from the present, take us into past rumination of what we should have said or done, or into future projection, focusing on fixing ourselves. This sabotages our ability to be present and feel *with*. When we practice being present and compassionate with ourselves first, being compassionate with others in this way becomes more accessible.

Amanda

Amanda is a forty-five-year-old mother of three girls who came to one of our first TIMBo trainings in 2012. At the time her children were small, and she was just a few years past the devastating loss of her younger sister to drug overdose. Amanda found the first of three training modules powerful, but I didn't see her for the next training until five years later.

When Amanda was young, she was a constant witness to physical and sexual violence toward her mother by her father. Amanda's mother, who was afraid and unsupported, was unable to provide a safe environment for Amanda and her sister. At a young age Amanda assumed responsibility for the safety of her mother and her sister and felt guilty when she was unable to control the abuse.

When she was a teenager, she experienced a series of traumas that would alter her life forever. Her mother was admitted to the hospital for a routine surgery and never returned home. She died tragically as a result of complications from the surgery, leaving Amanda grief-stricken and catapulted into the full-time role of protector for her sister.

She sought connection in her peer group and became involved with a boyfriend who eventually became physically abusive. Still, she stayed in the relationship, confused about her rights and her sense of worth and desperately wanting to feel loved, which she felt on occasion with this boy—at least enough to keep her with him.

One night at a party, she was sexually assaulted by a classmate, but when she ran to her boyfriend for support, he became enraged and broke her nose. Eventually she left the relationship, and she focused her energy on trying to save her younger sister, who had gotten involved with the wrong crowd and began using drugs. When her sister was just twenty-three years old, she became pregnant. Amanda stuck by her side and supported her sister's decision to carry the baby to term and give him up for adoption.

The day came when her sister went into labor, and Amanda was there at the hospital. But when the baby was born, Amanda's compounded lifelong survival adaptations of avoiding or controlling the pain of loss were screaming at her to run like hell. She left the hospital without saying a word. Shortly after, her sister died of a drug overdose.

Amanda judged herself bitterly for her actions on the day of her sister's labor and delivery. During that first TIMBo module she felt the discomfort of her life experiences and the grief associated with all of her life's decisions and wanted nothing to do with it. But something brought her back five years later, and Amanda finally spoke of this incident through a tidal wave of grief and tears. This moment of self-compassion was critical for Amanda. It allowed her to *be with* her own feelings of suffering around that particular event, with the new perspective that her life traumas leading up to it had created survival adaptations that drove her to run.

Prior to TIMBo, Amanda was constantly consumed with fear over caring for her three young girls. Her feelings of responsibility were causing her disproportionate suffering, because they were connected with the traumas of her own life and the fear of those events happening again.

Once she was able to compassionately sit with her survival adaptations, she learned to peel apart which responses to her girls were appropriate parenting responsibilities and which were being driven by fear in her body. She could see that her own fear was trying to engineer an outcome of everyone and everything turning out the way she wanted. But we simply cannot engineer a guaranteed outcome, and true compassion is the ability to sit in that knowing, feeling whatever there is to feel from one moment to the next, knowing that our presence is in itself a gift.

COURAGEOUS COMPASSION: THE ABILITY TO *BE WITH* SUFFERING

There is a lesser-known TED Talk by Joan Halifax, a Buddhist roshi. Ms. Halifax works with people at the last stage of life (in hospice and on death row) and is intimately familiar with the strength it takes to feel with another in their suffering. In her TED Talk she asserts that to sit in true compassion we must first be fully aware that we are not separate from this suffering. She goes on to say, "but compassion has another component, and that component is really essential. That component is that we cannot be attached to outcome." [1]

Attachment to outcome is the need for predictability, certainty and control. It is driven by the survival response in our bodies and has fear as its emotional root. Fear, along with pity and moral outrage, is the enemy of compassion.

Ms. Halifax goes on to say that the seeds for compassion grow via the waters of suffering. We cannot avoid suffering and cultivate compassion. It is like trying to learn without failing or grow without eating. Our own suffering is 100 percent necessary for us to have the capacity to feel with another in theirs. [2]

But when we have unconsciously adapted to avoid the painful feelings of loss, rejection and vulnerability of our early developmental years, it becomes a tall order to open the door to our feelings of pain and loss so we can *be with* others. So we continue to interact with those who are suffering in our adaptive ways, trying to fix, take away or run from the suffering of others, all the while reinforcing our stress responses each time we do.

Ms. Halifax also presents a compelling case for accessing courageous compassion. According to neuroscience, people who experience true compassion feel suffering more deeply, but they return to baseline much more quickly. Compassion is directly related to resilience. [3]

Compassion can be defined in myriad ways by many people, but regardless of what definition you prefer, the impact it has on the body is the same. Compassion enhances neural integration, hooking up all parts of our brain, which allows us to feel *with*, free from past and future or outcome-focused thoughts. Compassion also enhances the immune system, which makes sense, since true compassion is to suffer *with*, devoid of fear or stress in the body.[4]

Almost all our confusion about compassion and barriers to being in true compassion go back to our early life experiences, when we developed survival adaptations that created a feedback loop of stress and fear in our bodies that has become our normal. So overcoming this resistance and making more green marbles relies on our ability to sit in compassion with and for ourselves. And the only way to do that is to nonjudgmentally recognize how our survival adaptations have kept us from living a life we didn't know we could live.

EMBODIED RESOURCE #4: SELF-COMPASSION—GRIEVING THE ADAPTED SELF

This particular embodied resource is a turning point in our healing, but it is inaccessible without the foundational work of the first three practices. Without paying attention to body sensations nonjudgmentally and creating space, compassionately externalizing our inner critic, and growing our confidence and sense of worth by using and sharing the tools, we prohibit ourselves from having a new experience.

These experiences are feelings we feel in our bodies. When we have these new experiences, we have a sudden *aha* moment, which is usually a combination of the realization that we didn't know what we didn't know and grief over how we have lived our lives and what we've lost out on. This grief cannot and does not need to be forced—rather, it is a natural by-product of healing.

Often we think we have to feel grief over what happened to us, and I'm not suggesting that feeling this sadness is bad. It can, however, involve pity, which can keep us in that place of feeling stuck. It can also cultivate feelings of moral outrage, much like the anger and resentment Molly brought into her trainings with her. No one is saying that these feelings are inappropriate in response to the things that happened to us when we were young (or older) and vulnerable. But pity and outrage combined with fear are the barriers to compassion, so the question becomes how can we move beyond what happened to us and understand why they might have happened for us. If surviving abuse and trauma brought me to the point of helping others, then it was not a curse, but a gift. It brought me to create TIMBo. Which brought me to Samantha, which led me to writing this book and hopefully helping many more others. This trajectory occurred not in spite of what I've been through but because of it. Seeing our life experiences this way frees us from the cage that we have kept ourselves locked inside of for most of our lives.

It sounds simple, but arriving at this place happens through practice of our embodied resources, noticing when we have a new experience (like the absence of fear or unconditional love) and grieving the fact that our own survival adaptations kept us away from true peace, love and connection, even though their origins were intended to ensure the opposite outcome—that we would feel safe and worthy of love and connection.

THE HEALING POWER OF COMPASSIONATE TOUCH

We see these moments repeatedly when we offer compassionate touch during the movement and meditation part of the program. Women experience what many refer to as an unconditionally loving touch. For many, it is an experience that they've never had. Many women had abusive or love-starved childhoods, grew up with violent or mentally ill parents, or came to understand touch as something that came with conditions. In experiencing the unconditionally loving touch we offer in TIMBo, they often grieve, because this experience is the birthright of every human, and there is then a recognition that you didn't know that this experience existed.

Our deep need for connection coupled with our body's fear of unpredictability led us to neurologically develop an aversion to vulnerability. In doing so, we trained our body to be afraid of the very thing that is actually necessary for true connection. Touch that can provide a truly healing moment of compassion, grief and presence is perceived as dangerous vulnerability until we have an experience that can teach us otherwise.

A Stanford University study on touch has given me a deeper understanding as to why this work takes such strength and courage. For this experiment, researchers selected ninety-five women and split them into two groups. The first group was women who had high social anxiety, and the second was a group of women that did not have any social anxiety. On the day of the experiment, they were greeted by one of two male researchers. One by one they were led into a room with a table and told to place their dominant hand on the table. They were told that they would be touched on the wrist for two minutes, then given several minutes after the touch to recover.[5]

During the touch, researchers also collected physiological measures especially relevant to emotional responding, such as heart rate and respiration. Participants completed self-reported surveys on touch attitude before and after the experiment. Not surprisingly, the women with social anxiety reported the touch as uncomfortable, embarrassing and constricting, while the low social anxiety group reported the touch experience as supportive and nurturing.

However, regardless of an initial spike in sympathetic activity during the anticipation of touch, both groups experienced a deceleration in heart rate and an increase in parasympathetic activity. These physiological responses are largely caused by increased vagal nervous outflow to the heart, which suggests that touch has a direct and beneficial impact on heart health, even if the mind is averse (at first) to the experience. All this suggests that the mind can create an aversion to touch due to protective and adaptive developments, while the body may experience the touch as calming and neurologically beneficial.[6]

It takes a lot of courage to sit through something that our minds are telling us feels bad. It cannot be done by anyone but us, and it has to be our choice. Engaging in something when we feel obligated or pressured can be retraumatizing. Engaging in that same activity by choice can be healing—as long as you have a robust toolbox at your disposal. I am intimately familiar with this very experience and the life-changing implications of choosing to *be with* discomfort in order to heal.

A few years ago, Samantha took a course on massage therapy, and she asked if she could practice on me. Massage has traditionally been difficult for me, due to a lack of nurturing touch in my family of origin, an abundance of unwanted touch by various men throughout my life, and the cumulative abuse of my marriage. Touch ended up being something that I just didn't want, need or like. I avoided massage, was an awkward hugger and almost always responded with confusion and embarrassment when someone reached out to connect with me via touch.

Once I discovered yoga, I experienced what are commonly known as assists, where the instructor or an assistant places their hands on you to correct your alignment in the pose. I began to feel an increase in my tolerance to be touched, but only in the yoga class. When Samantha asked if she could massage me, I agreed to help her, but only because I trusted her.

Several times the same thing happened. She set up her table and had me lie facedown. She massaged my back, my shoulders and the back of my legs, which all went fine. But when she had me turn over, I immediately felt exposed and vulnerable. She was able to massage my arms fine, but when she got to my legs, I began to feel extremely uncomfortable and jumpy and had a strong urge to kick my legs. I told her what was going on, and she let me move my legs the way they were wanting to mobilize, then moved on to my feet and finished the massage.

Over time I decided to be more curious about what was going on with my legs, so when she massaged them, I told her I didn't want her to stop this time. She cautiously continued to massage my legs while I kept my mind curious, even though my whole entire body was screaming, *Get the hell out of here!* Consciously I knew I was safe. I was in my house with someone who I knew loved and respected me and would never ever hurt me. Yet my body was reacting as if my very life were at risk and I needed to run (which explains why my legs wanted to kick). I chose to breathe and feel what was happening, while directing her in her touch so I had a feeling of control and predictability.

What I experienced was fascinating and life-changing. There came a moment on that massage table when I recognized that my entire body was responding with a feeling of aversion, constriction and fear to having my legs touched. But when I willingly sat with the feelings in my body and brought a sense of curiosity to them, they transformed from fear to what I can only describe as an opening or a letting go.

What I recognized further was that the level of vulnerability in the moment of being touched did not change at all—it was an excruciatingly vulnerable feeling. But something about how my body was registering the touch changed—it was still difficult to sit with, but I became curious.

When it comes to touch, especially intimate touch, the vulnerability required to accept and embrace it can feel terrifying. When we are survivors of sexual or physical abuse, our bodies become like sea anemones, pulling inward as a matter of protection. When we spend the majority of our lives engaging in intimacy out of obligation or retraumatizing ourselves through unhealthy sexual practices, we delude ourselves into thinking sexual intimacy is about power and control. We lose the capacity to soften the body, to reach out instead of pull in and experience the true vulnerability and beauty of intimacy without aversion or fear, which is even more difficult to sit in when you have become neurologically wired to avoid touch. Our protective wiring is perceived to be a lifesaving necessity, so when it begins to change it is confusing, uncomfortable and scary, and it takes time.

In this particular case I had only the feeling to help me track any progress—there was no conscious memory as to why having my legs touched would trigger such strong responses in my body. But noticing the sensations in my body (with curiosity instead of judgment) from one moment to the next was enough to bring me to this pivotal moment. It was a moment when I knew something was different. As I allowed myself to be curious, I noticed that the vulnerability felt both terrifying (about 90 percent) and exciting (the other 10 percent), and in response I dissolved into tears—a natural occurrence when this kind of change is being noticed in the body. Even with just a tiny new feeling, I recognized that there has always been an experience that I was unaware of. Grieving provided a natural discharge of the bottled-up trauma-associated biochemicals that I have lived with my whole life. It is the moment that healing begins.

The experience of renegotiating touch doesn't have to start with a leap into an experience that feels as vulnerable or scary as the one I described above. From the start of our work with women, we invite them to place their own hand on their own heart. Kristin Neff, PhD, is one of the world's leading experts on self-compassion. I was introduced to Dr. Neff's work the same way I am often introduced to the work of others—women who have been through my training emailing me something they found that is very TIMBo.

This is how I came to know of Dr. Neff's work, and that so much of it resonates with me both personally and professionally. Dr. Neff's work confirmed the value of placing your hand on your own heart as one of the most powerful acts of self-compassion.[7] After all, how can we expect ourselves to connect with others from a place of pure compassion and presence if we cannot first connect with ourselves that way?

Things to Notice

As you continue using your first three embodied resources or tools (creating space with breath, compassionately communicating with your inner critic and building confidence through using and sharing your TIMBo tools), notice if you have moments when you experience something new. A new feeling in your body might be the absence of a fear-associated feeling you've always had or the absence of a guilt or shame response that is habitual for you. Remember: these feelings will be recognized in your body, not your mind. Allow yourself to feel compassion for the adapted self you have become and let the sadness and grief over what you missed out on wash through you.

When you have some time to reflect, write about the following in the space provided or in your journal:

Describe the feeling of the new experience or the feeling of an absence of a difficult sensation. Bring a sense of curiosity and intrigue to what you are noticing. Try to use words like *interesting, fascinating* and *curious*. Describe the sadness you feel around all the adaptations you needed when you were young that kept you from your authentic self and true connection as you grew older. Notice how grieving might pave the way for feeling more alive and free—even if it's just for a moment.

Self-compassion that allows for grief is the turning point of healing, but we resist it because our minds create judgments around it. We might feel that it's weak or that we are over it. We might resist being sad due to internalized messages of *Don't cry,* or we might feel like our grief is uncomfortable for others. Until we can grieve the loss of experiences we missed out on due to our own survival adaptations sticking around too long, we will stay in the feedback loop of stress. Like a record album with a scratch, no matter how we might will it to move forward, without the wash of grief, our bodies will just continue to skip back to the place it started—fear.

_____

_____

_____

_____

_____

_____

_____

_____

_____

_____

Once you feel you have had even a small experience of this kind of grief and self-compassion, you are on your way. When you are aware of this, you are ready to move on to the next chapter.

CHAPTER 21

Communication: A New Way of Seeing, Hearing and Speaking

We often think of communication as language-based and unidirectional. In other words, we think of communication as spoken or written words coming from one place and received in another. But using communication to aid healing requires that we understand the many directions that we can and should pay attention to in our communication.

As you've learned in the first four embodied-resources chapters, critical communication happens between you, your body and your mind. We can use our minds to communicate messages of safety and assurance to our bodies. But we can also use our minds to communicate the same messages of safety to our thoughts. Using communication this way puts us in charge of every step of our healing process. I call this embodied communication.

A NEW WAY OF ATTUNING TO AND SPEAKING WITH YOUR BODY

Embodied communication means becoming acutely aware of what you are feeling in your body. To be aware of body sensations is only one (and difficult enough at that) part of the restorative process—it is what we *do* with that awareness that is equally important.

It's only after we create space with breath and fortify our learning and memory materials that we can recognize the choices we have in how to respond to the sensations we feel in our bodies. Part and parcel with those sensations are often self-critical thoughts, blame and judgment toward others.

We judge ourselves for our actions and behaviors that are knee-jerk and immediate, and this self-judgment continues to intensify after we react in ways that we wish we hadn't. But once we notice what we feel inside and breathe to create space, we begin to change the inner circuitry that has developed in our body.

From here the next critical practice is to communicate with our body sensations. This gives our thinking minds something to do other than criticize and blame. We are redirecting our stress-fueled, judgmental, resistant or blame-filled thoughts toward the new communication we're offering. We then say to our bodies that we understand they feel our life is in danger, but that is not, in fact, the case.

The neurological benefit of this is astounding, because as you might remember, the practice of paying attention to our sensations strengthens and grows areas of our brain that give us the capacity to consider what additional options for responses we have. The embodied resources listed here will become your menu from which to choose.

Dropping old communication habits of flooding our bodies with stressful, judgment-filled thoughts takes work, because as we know, they are a (cognitive) survival adaptation. But as we increase strength and capacity in the regions of the brain needed to pay attention (insular cortex and cingulate cortex), accessing new, more self-compassionate responses becomes easier. Areas of the brain that have gone quiet simply because their function is deemed nonessential during the stress response begin to find a valuable use as we continue to notice our bodies, breathe, move mindfully and listen to guided visualizations (something we do at the end of each TIMBo session).

As this process unfolds, we feel more empathetic, compassionate, grounded, curious and resilient—because we are increasing the functionality of where (in our brains) these things are governed. Over time, the simple practices of stopping, noticing, breathing and talking to our body create an amazing ability to curiously observe all aspects of the self.

I feel beyond grateful that I was a firsthand witness to Samantha's trauma recovery process. Because we were in a relationship, it took significant personal resilience, faith, curiosity and even a sense of intrigue to help us both navigate through it. But each time one or both of us were triggered and reacted with our habitual survival adaptations (which, honestly, was very tough in the moment), we would use our foundational tools as best we could and come back together to share what we observed and learned.

One particularly memorable time we had an argument, the details of which I can't remember. I was triggered and panicked (froze), and she was triggered, and as was her habitual reaction, she got in the car and drove away (ran). It was late at night, I couldn't reach her, and I realized I had some opportunities in front of me. I made my choice to be aware of my body sensations, communicate with them, breathe and navigate through the moment, trusting that whatever happened I would be OK.

I felt my whole survival system firing, complete with fear-injected and catastrophizing thoughts. At the same time I held compassionate awareness for what was happening in my brain and body, and I communicated to the entire system as if I had an army of protectors at the ready. I told them to stand down—that we weren't heading into battle, that I could remain calm and that I would be all right no matter what happened. I had no idea what Samantha was doing at the time—it could have been anything.

I finally did reach her on the phone, and she rattled off a tirade of things she felt like doing—things that normally would have sent me into a spiral of fear, panic and worry. This time I just created space for myself while I created space for her to say what she was saying. I didn't try to talk her out of anything. In that moment I knew that it was how

I communicated with *myself* that was more important than anything I was saying to Samantha. Once again, I felt my body sensations, noticed my fear-based thoughts and noticed how I wanted to react (begging her to come back). Then I had another little private chat with the whole survival system of mine. I reminded it (me) that I wouldn't be able to stop Samantha from doing something if she really wanted to do it. All I had control of was how I chose to respond to everything that was out of my control. I hung up the phone and again reminded myself that my life wasn't in danger and that I would be OK. I continued breathing like my life depended on it.

To my great relief Samantha returned home unharmed. We let the dust settle that night and reconnected in the morning. Samantha shared something with me that has helped me personally and professionally with conceptualizing this stage of recovery. As she shared her experience with me (an experience I have now heard many other women share and have experienced myself), I recognized what a gift I was being given in that moment.

Samantha described to me exactly how the program I created was working inside of her. She described how she was reacting in all of her habitual ways, but she had a place in her that was aware of that fact. This place, which we now refer to as the emergent observer, was watching herself with curiosity and even a little fascination.

That night she drove to the parking lot of a hotel, and there she felt all of the familiar and powerful desires to take away her pain through drugs, alcohol and sex. She described her ability to observe all of this while making the choice not to do any of it. The prior night on the phone she was telling me that she wanted to do all of those things, but the next day she shared with me that she was also observing herself saying she wanted to do all those things, while simultaneously communicating with her entire survival system that she didn't have to act on any of her thoughts and desired actions.

She didn't yet have the capacity to stop herself from saying these things, but it was like there was a new part of her that was hovering above every aspect of this experience, watching and observing it all. At the same time, this emergent observer was gently offering reminders that this system is old and unhelpful. That she didn't need to act on anything she was thinking and feeling, and that she could just curiously observe for a while. This phenomenon occurs naturally by way of our newly strengthened prefrontal cortex. Our survival response inhibits our ability to be aware of anything but the life-threatening present moment and prioritizes all measures to save ourselves.

Our new capacity is that of a different communication style: we are able to create space and change our habitual brain reactivity so we can see more than the threat that is in front of us and choose new ways to communicate with ourselves. This is not unlike driving: if we were to focus only on the road just ahead of us and think that this hyperfocus will allow us to travel down the road without harm, we are not seeing the full picture of our driving experience. Instead, our newly fortified brain allows us to see all around us while we are driving. We see what's in front, what's behind, what's on either side. We listen to music or the news, allow our kids to play games in the back and enjoy the experience, knowing that we are aware of all aspects of our surroundings.

In this way we can observe all the moments that make up our lives—physiologically, physically, cognitively and emotionally—without an immediate and reactive response.

EMBODIED RESOURCE #5: THE EMERGENT OBSERVER—A NEW WAY OF SEEING YOURSELF

As we practice our new communication skills, we access and strengthen a new way of simultaneously being with and observing ourselves. You begin to observe all aspects of yourself while an inner voice communicates, *This is your old way.* Sometimes you continue to act out old reactions and habits, but sometimes this new way of observing yourself gives you access to a new way of being. And even a new feeling of confidence.

American neuroanatomist Jill Bolte Taylor, MD, gave a fascinating and inspiring TED Talk that we show in every TIMBo foundations training. It is one of my favorites and moves me to tears every time. In this talk, Dr. Bolte Taylor describes with sparkling clarity the day that she suffered a massive hemorrhage on the left side of her brain. What she describes is an extreme example of the emergent observer.[1]

Because the left hemisphere of her brain was compromised, she was disconnected from the areas of her brain that formed her identity. Our identity is the thing that distinguishes and separates us from others.[2] It is the *I am* statements that we are conditioned to make about ourselves and ask about others. "What do you do for a living?" is often one of the first questions we ask and are asked by people. We might tell people where we are going to school or how many kids we have. Our identity is formed by the things we do and the life roles we play, and they are disproportionately important to us—sometimes to our own detriment.

When I was married to Mitch, I lost my individuality and came to see my identity, and eventually my worth, as his wife. I recall one of the first experiences after I had separated from him that allowed me to realize this fact. I had traveled to Taos, New Mexico, to participate in a Habitat for Humanity build. Habitat for Humanity is an organization strongly supported by President Jimmy Carter and his wife, Rosalynn. The organization uses paid and volunteer workers to build and improve homes for poor and under-resourced families around the world.

The trip would last two weeks, and I would be working on a fourteen-person team comprising people from all around the country. I brought a close friend who was a lifeline for me at the time, and during the two weeks, she and I lived, worked and closely bonded with the rest of the group.

Two of my strongest memories of this two-week period were antithetical to one another—yet held together, they provided me with a realization that changed the course of my life, because they shifted my concept of my identity. One memory is of Mitch calling me during that trip and berating me for abandoning my children (his words). He took great lengths to remind me that I was selfish, a bad wife and an even worse mother and that I was damaging my children (ages three and eight) by being away for two weeks. Each time I hung up the phone, I went back to this group of people and felt a growing connection with them. The juxtaposition of these two things brought me to a recognition that I had not considered in years—*these people seem to take an interest in me, even like me, and they don't even know my husband.*

This may sound ridiculously obvious, but because my sense of worth was so attached to being the wife of someone who I thought was a superior person to me, it was a watershed moment. *Maybe I'm not just someone's wife or mother. Maybe I've got value just because I'm here with these people, having a shared experience.* This would stick with me for years to come, and the same sort of realization is likely to be the impetus for the bonding experience created during every TIMBo program and training.

In Dr. Bolte Taylor's TED Talk, she explains that the *I am* identity is a construct of the left hemisphere. The left hemisphere is logical—it thinks in language and processes linearly. It takes everything from the past, categorizes it and projects it toward future possibilities. It works together with our right hemisphere to form responses and thoughts associated with sensory reminders of the past (the basis of survival adaptations). What we end up with is an identity that is not our authentic self—it is a self-construct that can often give us a false sense of worth or a false sense of worthlessness. As a reminder, this false sense is correlated with the denial stage of emotional anatomy.

But when Dr. Bolte Taylor lost the function of her left hemisphere, she was left with brain function free (as she says) of the decades of emotional and cognitive baggage that influence right-brain processing. She was able to float above herself and watch herself having this stroke with a fascination for all that she was observing. The right hemisphere is devoid of the *I am* identity—it is concerned only with right here and right now. It thinks in pictures and learns kinesthetically through the movement of our body. Information streams in through all sensory systems of the body and becomes aware of what that moment looks, feels, smells, tastes and sounds like.[3]

Dr. Bolte Taylor describes the consciousness of our right hemisphere as being responsible for connecting us as one human family. "And in this moment of connection we are perfect, we are whole, and we are beautiful," she says. She describes the beautiful feeling of being expansive and connected and loving. She describes the peace and tranquility that this expansiveness brings with it. And she describes the pain of the sensory input, such as lights and sounds feeling unbearable.

The right hemisphere is our place of expansion and connection, but our left hemisphere works in cahoots with it. This can become a problem, because the cataloging of past memories by our left hemisphere and the right hemisphere's ability to bring sensory experiences into the present moment can create what we know as traumatic flashbacks.[4]

But wishing for a hemorrhage in our left hemisphere is not the way to an expansive, peaceful life. Instead, our simple TIMBo practices bring left- and right-brain functioning into balance and strengthen the brain areas that allow us to suspend our identities (which encompass our thoughts, judgments, and preconceived and catastrophizing thoughts) and come into a place of curious observer.

Even if we are participating in a habitual activity, to be aware that we are doing something that has an alternative is part of the process. We have the teacher and the student within us simultaneously, and making mistakes or doing something that we know can be done differently is a part of healing and change.

WHEN WILL I EVER GET THERE?

I once had a training participant articulate this process in a way that I appreciated and use to this day. "It's like building a bridge," she said. The way she explained it was that you have to travel over the old bridge for a while first, but you are aware that a new bridge is being built, because you see it. Then when the new bridge is built, you travel over that, but you see the old bridge still, and sometimes you still take the old bridge because it's a habit. But you don't berate yourself, because you know that next time, you'll remember to take the new bridge. Eventually you stop taking the old bridge, and over time, you forgot that you ever did.

I have been asked more than once, "When will I ever get there?" This level of awareness is the *there*. The observer of the self, or emergent observer, brings with it a compassionate understanding, curiosity and fascination for all it is observing. Even judgmental, resentful and blame-filled thoughts are observed with a curious fascination.

With the emergent observer available to us, we can learn, change and grow with every experience we have. Especially the difficult ones that until now have been the source of our suffering and disconnection. Imagine if every substance abuser was able to stop, create space, recognize the grief and survival adaptations at the source of their urge to use, and choose another action. It's possible, and we see it in the TIMBo groups we run at substance-abuse treatment centers.

The tie that binds these groups is the shared experience. A shared language and practice in a space where we are permitted to simply be. We are valued and respected just because we are human beings on earth, and this gives us the chance to consider that maybe we are worthy of love and connection regardless of our past or future and just because we exist.

Things to Notice

If you have been using the embodied resources in this book so far, you will naturally become a compassionate and curious observer to your experiences. Remember: this is not possible until you practice noticing the sensations in your body and creating space with breath. This is the foundational practice that can clear the way for every other resource that you have within you. Allow yourself to be curious about every aspect of your experience—even your own thoughts and judgments about yourself or others.

When you have some time to reflect, write about the following in the space provided or in your journal:

Describe the experience of observing yourself and your experiences from this new place of the objective self. Describe the feeling of curiosity or fascination you had when observing your sensations, thoughts, actions, reactions and responses. Describe how you might communicate with any aspect of yourself (your protector, your body sensations, your thoughts and reactions, your resentments and blame, etc.).

You may not have responded in the way you wished you had, but observing yourself with a nonjudgmental curiosity and communicating with pieces of yourself lovingly will create fertile soil for you to grow new circuitry and change your responses and behavior to yourself and the world around you.

Once you feel you have had an experience with the emergent observer, you are ready to move on to the next chapter.

CHAPTER 22

Awareness: The Key to Empowerment

Awareness is the *there* that everyone wants to get to. Most of the women I work with have a different notion of what it means to be done. They often have an idea in their mind of everlasting peace and happiness that will never be threatened, sullied or punctured.

But life is unpredictable. Life is a constant ebb and flow of uncertainty woven together with times of little to no control and little to no information. We can never stop our bodies from feeling uncomfortable, but when we use our embodied resources to recognize that our bodies are responding to something, we understand that this response likely has more to do with a past memory than the current circumstance. However, we can use simple tools to help us navigate through the moment. This continues to build our confidence, our self-knowledge and our resilience.

With practice you will find yourself acutely aware of your own body sensations in the midst of a difficult conversation or moment with others. You will notice the thoughts in your mind, the things you would habitually say and the actions you'd habitually take, all from a place of a higher observer. You'll be able to simply hold space for all of those things without acting on them, and this will allow you to feel extremely empowered—especially if others around you are clearly lacking these skills and reacting from a place of stress reactivity.

I was recently asked to speak to a group of clinicians about TIMBo. In the past, not being a clinician myself, this speaking engagement would have had me feeling intimidated and unsure of myself. I have no higher degrees or impressive letters after my name, and because of that I've needed to work even harder to prove my credibility. But TIMBo has been around long enough for me to know that it works. Regardless of the preliminary quantitative data we have showing statistically significant reductions in PTSD-related symptoms, the mountains of qualitative data have given me the evidence I need to speak about the effectiveness of TIMBo with full confidence. Still, having been an apathetic student in high school, I internalized messages of not being smart or not good enough, so that little niggling voice is always there to remind me of that.

I showed up to a group of about fifteen social workers and psychologists. I gave an informal talk about TIMBo, showed them some of our materials and let them ask some questions. They were all very kind and respectful and showed interest in the information. However, one of the clinicians began to challenge me. I immediately felt it in my body but had enough awareness to remain grounded and calm. The others came to my defense, but I quickly assured them that her questions were reasonable ones, and I did not feel disrespected at all. I could feel inside of me a confidence, a feeling of being like the eye in a hurricane—calm and peaceful. Watching while things started to swirl around me. The energetic flare-up was soon over and so was the meeting.

After everyone left, the woman who had invited me to speak was astounded. "How did you remain so calm?" she asked. "That was absolutely amazing to watch!" she added. And finally, "I could never have stayed that together, and I wasn't the only one who was upset that she challenged you."

The fact of the matter was, it was very easy for me. I have had years of practice using my TIMBo tools of awareness, acceptance and space. I have called upon my embodied resources time and time again. Having to coparent with a person who I would prefer not to be in relationship with has given me plenty of opportunity to practice. And trust me, there have been times when it felt like a lot of work. But the work has paid off, because in the moment, sitting around with all of those clinicians, I did not feel the familiar gut punch of *You're a fraud* when I was asked some challenging questions. I could be compassionate, because my knowledge of myself and of emotional anatomy told me she was likely operating from a place of doubt. In fact, I actually felt excited about using all of my inner awareness and practices so that the woman who was challenging me could feel seen and heard.

BRINGING COMPASSIONATE AWARENESS INTO RELATIONSHIPS

When it comes down to it, knowing it is our bodies that react first, with our thoughts, behavior and actions following, helps us to determine when a moment has gone from peaceful to stress-reactive. It's like a dance where our own self-awareness helps to influence the flow of the choreography for others. The term *self-regulation* is an accurate description of the action and outcome of using our embodied resources and TIMBo tools. With this ability we can participate in the coregulation of those around us.

The idea of coregulation began when educating parents how to interact with their infants. But there is now awareness that our own capacity to regulate our bodies can have a direct and beneficial impact on anyone with whom we are in relation.[1] Coregulation can happen naturally when we use all of our skills to self-regulate.

When we practice TIMBo while in relationship with others or the world around us in general, we are actively aware of our reactive wiring. We are monitoring, evaluating and mindfully choosing our responses. The process of learning to do this takes practice and the capacity to recognize when we have gone over the old bridge and make a correction for next time.

Every time we use the embodied resources in this book, we are repairing the social emotional networks of our brain. This has incredible implications for driving social change, because life is a series of relational experiences strung together from one moment to the next.

We can have an influence on the systems of those around us just by regulating ourselves from moment to moment. This is why the use of these tools is so valuable to leaders in organizations or communities. When teachers, parents or leaders are aware of their inner felt sense, and use tools and practices to remain grounded, calm and empathetic, the individuals they are leading will feel it, and change can and does occur in the brains and bodies of those individuals.

This is good news, because when we focus on regulating ourselves, the relationships around us change. Eventually this becomes easy to do, because we are no longer seeing the world around us through our adaptive lens. We are taking each moment at a time for what it is—an opportunity to compassionately understand and heal ourselves.

EMBODIED RESOURCE #6: COMPASSIONATE AWARENESS OF SELF AND OTHERS

There is nothing that feels more empowering than keeping your cool when someone around you is losing theirs. But after a lifetime of survival adaptations, we sometimes lose our ability to be embodied.

Being embodied means that it is not just your mind taking in information, making decisions and running the show. It is a beautiful interplay of both your mind and your body, communicating back and forth with one another from one moment to the next. In this communication you can make decisions from an awareness of how you are experiencing each moment viscerally.

Without being embodied we walk through life with little to no awareness of our bodies or how our bodies are influenced by our survival wiring. What we end up with is being reactive to people and things that we can actually be compassionately responsive to—because the truth is every person on the planet has survival adaptations. It's just that most people are unaware of them and are reacting from them. It almost always has nothing to do with you.

This is why awareness is so important. It has a ripple effect. Not only does it have the capacity to heal you, it has the capacity to heal others. In other words, to heal humankind.

When women go through our training, they must take an exam to become a licensed TIMBo facilitator. The last question asks participants to give some examples of how TIMBo is being used in their lives.

We truly believe that the most impactful way to teach or help people with TIMBo is if you practice it yourself and believe in the power of it.

Here is an example of one answer:

"I find myself using TIMBo tools with my daughters' dad a lot. Trying to coparent with him is very difficult because he is emotionally and verbally abusive when he is faced with a universal trigger of stress. What I have been able to do is exercise self-compassion, take breaths and hold space for myself while he's throwing a fit. So when I respond it's not from a place of stress or fear. Using TIMBo tools in these moments changes the way he responds to me."

This is a beautiful example of how using TIMBo tools and embodied resources changes our experience in a moment that could be difficult and stressful. But what's more powerful is that in doing so, we impact and influence the manner in which others relate to us. Here is another response:

"Working on the inpatient psychiatric unit I use [TIMBo tools] daily, especially with my boss. I am able to notice my sensations, create acceptance for them and tap into my breathing to help calm them down. I have also been able to create a new compassionate view of family members that used to really push my buttons, but now I can notice where they are in the emotional pyramid and have a new perspective of why they do what they do."

The embodied resource of compassionate awareness of ourselves and others is a natural by-product of practicing the first five resources. Take a look at the diagram below. The descending line indicates the process of survival adaptations in the developing years becoming maladaptive as we get older.

As you can see, embodied resource #1, awareness, acceptance and space, is closest to disconnection/death. This is because at the time of this reading (or training or program) you are at the furthest point along your life timeline. It's at this point that you start to use the tools of TIMBo and begin cultivating your embodied resources. Embodied resource #1 is at this point in the timeline because this is the resource we start with. Using these simple tools and embodied resource #1 fortifies our brains with new learning materials that help us access additional embodied resources.

Thankfully, as we learn and use the subsequent embodied resources, we take a healing journey backward through many of our life traumas. We must be willing to feel the sensory memories associated with these experiences in order to track back through fear, guilt and shame (using creativity and confidence) to arrive at a place of compassionate understanding and grief over how and why we needed to adapt.

The capacity to truly grieve the fact that our adaptations were well-founded at first but ultimately kept us from living a full and loving life is the key to our recovery and restoration. As we become more and more able to access the first four embodied resources, which are always preceded by our ability to notice the sensations in our bodies, we nudge our healing forward naturally.

Grief is like a hairpin turn on our developmental timeline. Our recovery turns upward toward connection and freedom, because we see ourselves and the whole world around us through a more compassionate lens. We embrace the vulnerability necessary to feel self-compassion simultaneously with compassion for the people around us, and we facilitate a connection that has been unwittingly sabotaged by our own survival adaptations for much of our life.

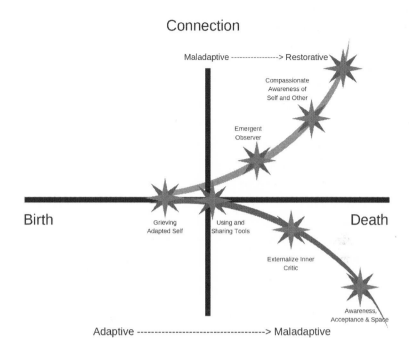

When asked how TIMBo is being used in her life, another woman told us:

"Not reacting has allowed me to hear out the other person's side to more length instead of cutting it off in a brawl or other interruption. With this, I am also noticing that I am seeing the other person's side more [compassionately]. For instance, I see that my sister may be saying certain things because of her adaptations and her attempt to keep herself alive. This has been especially useful when I strongly disagree with someone but still love and support them to their core. Since TIMBo, I find that I am way more comfortable being openly emotional with people. This even includes being emotional (vulnerable) at work. For example, my colleague expressed that she was leaving the company for another job, and I started to cry and share how genuinely I would miss her. Before TIMBo, I had more walls up, which stopped me from expressing myself genuinely—especially at work."

As these participants are showing us, the capacity to be aware, compassionate and vulnerable in life opens the space for true human connection. But even if we don't genuinely love another person, we can use this awareness to clear away any suffering that would be created via our adaptive wiring. We don't even need to like a person to have a compassionate awareness of what is behind their behavior.

Most of us have been in traffic with the impatient person beeping and hollering at us. I know I recognize an immediate surge of body sensations in response to being scolded by some nameless person in a car that I don't even know. But when I can take a second to practice compassionate awareness by first recognizing my own body sensations and breathing for a moment, it gives me the ability to bring compassionate awareness to the other person. I can see they are simply reacting from their survival wiring that is activated by one of the three universal triggers of stress (uncertainty, lack of information, lack of control). From there, I can at least feel empowered—because I actually know more about what is happening in their body than they (likely) do. I can only know this because I know myself in that way.

Things to Notice

Your ability to have an emergent observer will naturally lead you to a compassionate awareness of those around you. The capacity to stay aware, calm and grounded has a direct reciprocal influence on the experience of the other person. The capacity to change the nature of a relational experience simply by being compassionately aware of your own inner sensations has the ability to positively impact families, communities and larger societal systems. Notice how having full awareness and effective tools for mindful responses impacts your confidence, your sense of self and your sense of worth.

When you have some time to reflect, write about the following in the space provided or in your journal:

Describe the experience of observing yourself compassionately and making different choices while in relationship with others. Notice how it feels in your body to have bidirectional compassion and the ability to create space for yourself and for those with whom you are in relationship. Notice if this makes you feel confident, empowered and influential. Describe how that feels in your body, and recognize it as a new reference point to go back to when you lose your way.

_____

_____

_____

_____

_____

_____

_____

_____

_____

_____

_____

_____

_____

_____

Once you feel you have had an experience of the compassionate awareness for yourself and others, you are ready to move on to the next chapter.

CHAPTER 23

Faith: Feeling Comfortable in Uncertainty

Life is constantly changing, and we are constantly placed in situations where we are unsure of the outcome or unsure of the pathway through. We are usually not conscious that our survival response is running the show and that it is doing so because of some long-ago experience when we were too young to have a full conscious understanding of self and others. We may not be conscious that we took it upon ourselves to feel responsible for all of the difficult things that befell us, but this is very often the case.

The more life and all of its uncertainties happens, the more this whole fear-fueled system in our bodies strengthens—*especially* when it comes to relationships. In the end, the fear fuels our desire to predict or control an outcome when we are in the midst of uncertainty or change. But difficult things happen—it is a part of life. We can't control outcomes no matter how hard we try. In fact, it may usher us into a place of more suffering, even if our minds are telling us that it is what we want. At times all of us unconsciously choose familiarity over the unknown, even if what we are familiar with is unhealthy for us or for others.

Faith is not trusting that everything will turn out all right. That's an impossible expectation, and things very often don't turn out the way we anticipate. Faith isn't even thinking everything happens for a reason, because sometimes things don't. In the context of TIMBo, faith is trusting that *you* have the tools to navigate through life's ups and downs. That doesn't mean that it's not difficult or challenging—it means you have the resilience to navigate even the roughest waters of life and come out the other side a stronger person.

The six embodied resources you have learned and practiced so far will naturally give you this faith. Having the capacity to stop and check in with your own body as a first order of business is the first step in changing your relationship to things that had previously sent your life into upheaval. Very rarely are life's unpredictabilities a life-or-death situation, but because of early traumas, implicit memory and survival adaptations, we perceive and respond to them that way. On the other hand, we want our survival response to stay sharp, just in case we really are in a life-threatening situation.

I happened to be driving home from a state hospital recently and caught an interview on National Public Radio. The fellow they were interviewing was named Jia Jiang, and he had given a TED Talk about a life challenge he took on and the learning that came out of it. It started when he was six years old and his teacher thought it would be a good idea to teach the value of appreciating one another and accepting compliments and gifts. She bought forty gifts, one for every student in the class, then had them all stand up and instructed, "Say something nice about someone, and they can go get their gift and sit back down."[1]

The compliments started flowing, and quickly forty standing students became twenty standing students, then ten then five then three. Jia was one of the remaining three students, and there was an excruciating silence in the classroom while they waited for someone to say something, anything nice about them. It never happened, even when the teacher encouraged the class to say something nice about those remaining three. Finally, she instructed them to collect their gifts and behave better the next year so maybe someone would say something nice about them then. Six years old![2]

Jia makes it clear in the TED Talk that this was a moment of adaptation for him. He doesn't use those words, but he says from that moment on he would rather die than be rejected in public like that again. He goes on to talk about the next twenty-four years of his life. He was inspired by meeting Bill Gates at his school in China and had big dreams for himself. But every time he wanted to do something that ran the risk of possible rejection, he froze and became stuck. Finally, he felt completely stagnant in his life.

Somewhere around that time he heard about a thing called *rejection therapy*, which could be best understood as exposure therapy (slowly exposing yourself to the things you fear) for rejection. He decided he would manufacture one hundred days of rejection, asking strangers for things he was pretty confident they would reject. Things like borrowing $100 from a stranger or asking for a burger refill at a fast-food joint. He planned on blogging and filming all of his experiences, and here's what happened.

The first day he planned on asking a stranger in his work building if he could borrow $100. As he approached the stranger, he began to feel all of the physiological symptoms of fear in the body. He began sweating, and the hair on the back of his neck stood up and his heart began racing. He approached the stranger and asked if he could borrow $100. The man said, "No," and then, "Why?" Jia turned on his heels and ran. Literally.

Later that evening he watched the video he had made of himself getting rejected. He was able to see clearly that he was petrified, as if this were a life-and-death situation. He recognized this as a microcosm of his whole entire life—every time he wanted to do something, his fear of rejection would send him running, and he never got anywhere.

In fact, he had a dream of becoming an entrepreneur, but ask any successful entrepreneur, and they'll tell you the ladder you climb to the top is built in part with rungs of rejection! So he made a commitment to walk toward rejection the next day, asking a clerk at his favorite burger joint if he could have a burger refill. As expected, the clerk said no. But this time, instead of running, he engaged with the clerk behind the counter. He told them he loved their place and would love them even more if they gave burger refills. He walked away feeling like he learned something about himself. His commitment to not letting the six-year-old protector make decisions for him seemed like a possibility.

In the following days he had many experiences, some that involved rejection and some that didn't, but all of them involved authentic engagement and connection. He began to feel a confidence inside of himself, not because he was able to predict whether he would be rejected or not, but because his body wasn't perceiving rejection as a matter of life and death. This changed his belief system about himself and about the world around him, and he even started to see the value in taking risks.

He asked if he could teach a college-level course in Austin, Texas, despite the fact that he didn't have a PhD, and to his surprise it happened. This is a true example of faith: taking a risk with no attachment to any particular outcome. In the end he turned his greatest fear (rejection) into his greatest gift. He began teaching people how to use rejection as opportunities and has published a book. Jia had to teach his body to respond differently to rejection, and in doing so he developed a resilient responsiveness—seeing obstacles as opportunities and failures as gifts.[3]

FAITH IS NOT RELIANT ON SUCCESS

Faith builds resilience through the process of failure as much as any success. Faith develops when risks are taken with the confidence that whatever happens, you will be OK. Winston Churchill said, "Success is going from failure to failure without losing enthusiasm."[4] But when our survival adaptations are running the show—like Jia's six-year-old had been doing his whole life—it's a tall order to simply change our view of a situation. With the tools to communicate with our body and even to our sabotaging thoughts, we begin to dip our toes into situations that involve emotional risk, we notice that we did, in fact, survive, we see the opportunities that have come from taking those risks, and over time we heal and change.

The end point is not that good things happen in our life from here on out and we'll never have to face obstacles, failure or loss. The end point is we have developed the ability to take risks—particularly emotional risks. This builds emotional resilience and a healthy responsiveness. It is how we respond to each moment of our lives that allows them to be an opportunity for us. This can be as simple as the opportunity to be curious and notice something about ourselves.

When fear is replaced with curiosity, intrigue or possibility, our bodies learn a new way of responding to the world, and faith strengthens. When faith strengthens us, we build resilience. When resilience builds, our suffering eases, and this brings the peace we have been searching for all of our lives.

EMBODIED RESOURCE #7: RESILIENT RESPONSIVENESS

It's not realistic to expect we will always feel great. Sometimes life hands us challenges that are difficult to navigate and feel bad. And sometimes our bodies remember something that our minds don't, and we just feel off.

When we are aware that our bodies very often respond to current situations or old implicit memories by preparing us to fight, flee or freeze, we can communicate directly to our bodies to help them recognize that our life is not in danger. Each of us will have varying tools that we find more helpful than others. For some it will be the simple choice to breathe, and for others it will be talking compassionately to the inner critic. And for some it might be seeking out a friend or colleague who practices TIMBo and asking to be led through some breaths. When we have an effective toolbox and can access our embodied resources, we can navigate through the unpredictable waters of life with resilience and the ability to accept what is, for however long it decides to stick around.

CREATE YOUR HEALING COMMUNITY

Throughout these pages I have shared my own story and journey of recovery—a journey that I am still on. I have shared the stories of just a handful of the courageous and inspiring women throughout this book. Women who have helped me just as much as I have helped them. Healing and the ensuing restoration is a process, and it is one that can constantly teach us about ourselves if we use these tools of awareness and self-compassion.

But we don't heal in a vacuum. The power of TIMBo is in sitting in a circle and hearing the awareness and insights of the other women in the group. As human beings, and women in particular, we listen to the wisdom and recognition of other women, and we reflect inward and uncover things in ourselves.[5] We make choices to *be with* discomfort and share what we notice with others, and they develop a little more courage to give it a try.

Mindfulness is described as "a mental state achieved by focusing one's awareness on the present moment, while calmly acknowledging and accepting one's feelings, thoughts, and bodily sensations, used as a therapeutic technique."[6] The theories presented in this book allow us to recognize that the present moment may be infiltrated by past implicit memories and felt through every cell in our body. Then what?

Very recently I have been visited by a body memory. I call these things *visitors* because I recognize they are not the present-day adult me, but some me of the past protecting me from a danger that doesn't exist. She sometimes sticks around for a while, and sometimes I fall into an old habit of just hoping she'll go away. I can spend days, even weeks sitting in awareness of her, watching her squeeze me tighter and tighter, and still I will wait in silence for her to leave.

But silence is a part of my trauma story, so after a period of time spent observing, being aware and curious, and noticing the full cocktail of adaptations that come along with this memory, I gather up courage and take the risk to speak how I am feeling out loud. It sometimes takes me awhile to get there, and I often notice self-judgmental tapes running in my head. I listen to them, knowing that they are all a part of this past memory and my adaptive development trying to keep me safe. Now they are like a soft din in the background instead of drill sergeants screaming insults at me to get me to act.

We must take risks to heal, and those risks are different for each of us. When I've spent days or weeks in the grip of an old fear-based memory, I know I must take the risk to come out of silence. Each time I do, I gather more new experiences for my memory bank (more green marbles), and I build more resilience.

Resilience doesn't mean that we never feel uncomfortable again. Resilience is how we view ourselves and everything around us. Resilience is feeling comfortable in feeling uncomfortable. We can feel crappy and at the same time see opportunities. We can have losses or feel fear, guilt, shame and resentment and still be curious. Times might be so challenging that the only opportunity we can see is to breathe.

We might be struggling so deeply that the opportunity is to simply notice without judgment. To be curious even though we feel bad.

Eventually we will take the risk that we *know* we must take, no matter how big or small. No matter if anyone else besides us recognizes the feeling of fear inherent in what feels vulnerable or risky for us. But when we do it just one time, we discover that we won't die. The spiral of trauma continues to unravel, and we can never really go back to our old normal. Once we are aware, it's difficult to become unaware.

Having a community is a beautiful thing, and the TIMBo experience, whether it is a program or training, gives us that. Sitting in a circle with women can and does feel like a risk for so many, because many of our hurts and traumas are relational. It feels safer to hide away and pretend everything is fine, and that *is* an option. Some women listen to their adaptive voices and leave the group, but most don't, and most experience a shift in their lives that positively impacts their husbands, partners, children and other relationships.

These practices are not to be held close to the vest. People will notice the change in you, and they will ask you what you have been doing! Share this stuff with the people you care about, and your life will continue to move toward authentic and courageous connection. You will begin to feel what living really is all about.

Reaching out to Renee, Erin, Molly, Amanda or any of the other women of my community that speak TIMBo has always been a helpful place to turn, because I know that all of these women get it. But it is Samantha who is my rock. Samantha landed on my couch several years ago and told me that *God told her she needed to be there.* She told me she didn't know what it meant exactly or what it was supposed to look like but that it was a message she was receiving from somewhere that she couldn't ignore.

The faith that Samantha had at that time changed her life, and it changed my life. Neither one of us could have known the path that we would walk together, but because of her faith to be in the place of the unknown, I was able to cultivate trace amounts of it myself. Watching Samantha navigate the treacherous waters of trauma recovery gave me the courage to step into my own. Listening to Samantha's continual and developing awareness of what the program I designed was helping her do gave me a way to put words to what I had developed. But it has been Samantha's unwavering and unconditional love and support that has helped me continue to use my own life traumas and recovery as real-time experience in using my own program to heal. I never could have written this book without that experience.

CHAPTER 24

Connection: The Elixir of Life

As you have learned through this book, our early developmental years and life experiences inform an adaptive process. But over time we become disconnected to our authentic selves. When we are not willing to be our true, unfiltered and unadapted (vulnerable) selves we lose authentic and intimate connection with others. But it's not too late. We can change our lives, journey back to our true nature and allow for authentic loving connections. I have done it. I have seen hundreds of others do it. You can do it too.

Bronnie Ware is a hospice nurse who spent many years caring for patients who had gone home to die. Through those years she asked her patients if they had any regrets, and she noticed a few recurring answers, so she decided to keep track of them. What resulted was a published article and a subsequent book on the top five regrets of the dying.

Not surprisingly, each of these regrets had something to do with missed or lost connection, either with oneself or with family, friends and communities. The irony is that when we are born, all of our adaptive changes occur for the express purpose of maintaining connection. Tragically, those adaptations create the exact opposite of what they were originally intended to do, and we end up on our deathbeds feeling regret over not feeling connected and wondering how we ended up there.

The first and most-expressed regret is *I wish I'd had the courage to live a life true to myself, not the life others expected of me.* Through the pages of this book you have come to understand that when we are young, our desire to be loved, accepted and worthy is often connected with what we do or how we act.

When we make fear-based choices in favor of connection (as young people, this doesn't actually feel like a choice), we begin to journey away from our authenticity—our true selves. We'll turn away from things that feel like our true nature and prioritize what we think others will value us for. Wires get crossed along the way, traumatic experiences happen to many of us, and before we are aware of it, we are far from our true selves and looking for connection based on who we think we need to be, not who we really are. Without compassionate awareness that this is happening, we end up regretting our disconnection with our true selves and blaming ourselves for the traumatic experiences in our lives. Bronnie Ware's research is proof that this is a fundamental human experience.

The rest of the regrets follow in the same vein: *I wish I hadn't worked so hard.* This came with regret over not being connected with children, family and close friends.

I wish I'd had the courage to express my feelings. This was often an expression of regret over repressing true feelings, settling for a mediocre existence and never becoming who they were truly capable of becoming. Many individuals with this regret developed illnesses relating to the bitterness and resentment they carried as a result, just like Dr. Maté describes in his book.

I wish I had stayed in touch with my friends was another one, and Ms. Ware states here that "It all comes down to love and relationships in the end."[1]

I wish I'd let myself be happier is the fifth. Ms. Ware says, "Fear of change had them pretending to others, and to their selves, that they were content. When deep within, they longed to laugh properly and have silliness in their life again."[2]

We can feel the entire kaleidoscope of emotions when we recognize that journeying away from these vital human experiences *was* a matter of survival. We are unconscious that this is happening as we grow from embryos to toddlers to adolescents and through adulthood. When we can look back in awe and recognize that the ingenious organism we call our body has made calculations in the name of connection through every experience we have had, we can appreciate how we have adapted.

We can appreciate the voices in our heads that tell us we must be better, do better and feel better so that people will like us. We can marvel at the voices in our heads that whisper (or sometimes shout) to us that we will never be loved—that we are broken, flawed and unfixable. How clever that our adaptations came up with a way to be completely in control of our rejection! We can take refuge in the miracle of our breath and the life-changing possibilities of moving our body—even if it's just holding a power pose for two minutes. Healing is hard because our body has learned to keep us safe, but through the years, its partnership with our minds has facilitated disconnection from ourselves and the world around us. We no longer need such fierce protection.

The beautiful thing is that through the knowledge of the human experience we all share, we can connect. We don't have to wait until we're all done. We need only to pluck up enough courage to recognize that true authentic connection requires vulnerability, and vulnerability is messy but beautiful. It allows us to see how our imperfections, fears, guilt, shame, heartbreak and grief connect us with our fellow humans. In recognition, we can help others just by saying "Me too."

My hope is that this book has helped you. But nothing can compare to sitting in a safe and contained circle with a group of women who, over the course of just a few short days, feel bonded to you for life. Not because of what they do in the world or any other label that would contribute to their identity. But because they dared to put their guard down, to feel and to be present for the other human beings in that space.

I have laughed, cried and felt love in the deepest part of me with and for the women (and men) with whom I have crossed paths. Yes, my work is fulfilling to me, because I have seen it help people, but it is just as fulfilling to me because I get to feel my heart and my true humanity each time I authentically connect with every precious human being that I'm fortunate enough to share the sacred space of TIMBo with. Each time is as powerful as the last, whether I am in the U.S., Haiti, Kenya, a homeless shelter, a yoga studio or a state hospital. It wouldn't matter if I was in a circle with a group of inmates or Oprah—the experience would be one of raw, healing, compassionate, unconditional and exhilarating human connection. The kind of connection that we have been seeking our entire life.

We all deserve to live fully. We yearn to be seen and accepted by others, to love ourselves unconditionally and to feel a sense of belonging without expectations or conditions. I offer these chapters to you not because I ran a bunch of experiments and collected data to support a theory. I offer them because I have witnessed the life-giving miracle of this process in each woman whose story is told in this book and hundreds more whose story is not.

Finally, I offer you these chapters because I have witnessed this miracle myself. At midlife, I am finally understanding what unconditional love truly is, and I do not blame anyone for any of the adaptations I developed that clouded that truth. I want you to experience this, too, and together we can live the rest of our days not with regrets of inauthentic living—but rather as fully feeling, fully loving and unconditionally loved human beings.

ACKNOWLEDGMENTS

Writing this book was one of the most fulfilling experiences of my life. But it would not have been possible if it weren't for the love, encouragement and steadfast support of my wife and best friend, Samantha. She made this book possible in myriad ways, not the least of which was showing me that what I had created really did have the capacity to heal. My love, you gave me a story of hope, healing and love to share in the pages of this book. This is as much your story as it is mine. You are my rock, my confidant and the best thing that has ever happened to me. I love you.

This book would not be what it is without my incredible editor, Gail Hudson. Gail encouraged me to write my story, she listened to me through the fear of writing about the worst time in my life, and she patiently held space for me as I cried through the process. But most of all Gail took what I can only call a "lump of clay" and helped me sculpt it into this beautiful book. Gail, I truly feel that this book is as much yours as it is mine. I know our paths will cross again!

I'm eternally grateful to Dr. Rick Hanson, who after just one conversation told me "you have a book" and encouraged me to write it. His faith in the value of my work, willingness to make connections for me and continuous positivity helped me keep the faith in myself—even when it was hard.

Sometimes you need people you hold in the highest regard to remind you to keep going. Dr. Nan Herron has been one of my biggest cheerleaders and a true friend from the moment we met! Nan's constant reassurance that I have something to offer has kept me believing that I have worth, regardless of any higher educational degrees or special letters by my name. Nan has vouched for me in a community that values her professional opinion and therefore has been willing to listen to my work. Her constant insistence that I am "brilliant" is deeply appreciated. Nan, thank you for saying it even when I couldn't take it in.

I owe a deep dept of gratitude to Jacqui Bonwell, Marika Michelangelo and Katherine Bicer, all of whom never gave up on TIMBo even when everyone else walked away. All three women stayed by my side to help finish the design of the TIMBo curriculum so that we could pilot it at a women's correctional facility. Jacqui Bonwell, a wealth of knowledge, shared all of her expertise on chakra and chakra development in a way that I could translate into the simple language that has become TIMBo. Katherine Bicer provided insight and guidance as we put our first program draft together chapter by chapter. Marika Michelangelo is my angel. She was the one person who stayed with me through *years* of ups and downs. She helped calm me when my self-doubt and fear got the best of me, always reminding me to "look back at where we were a year ago," and easing my anxiety about the uncertainty of the future. Marika, I would not have persevered were it not for your belief in and dedication to me.

Love and gratitude for Dan Banks, my dear friend and college roommate. Dan's generous offer and beautiful design turned mere words on a page into a beautiful workbook. Through the years Dan has been there to offer his talents to bring ideas to life in ways that have helped thousands of women. I'm deeply indebted to you, my dear friend.

TIMBo would not exist without the vision and generosity of a few incredible individuals. Jennifer Walsh, Susan Zankel and Lynn and David Eikenberry. This book also would not exist without your incredible faith in me and support for this work. I'm forever indebted to you all.

To Danielle Rousseau, who saw something in TIMBo and was instrumental in coordinating our very first pilot program at MCI Framingham Women's Correctional Institution. Danielle, TIMBo wouldn't be where it is today without your faith and belief in me and the program. Your dedication to sharing the research findings on TIMBo has given this method the credibility that would not be possible without you and your partners, Elizabeth Jackson and Catherine

Cook-Cottone. This book would not exist without you and your faith in me.

Thank you to Zoe MacLaren for encouraging me to "just write." Zoe, thank you for editing all my blogs and for reminding me that if I write enough blogs, a book will appear. You were right!

This book wouldn't be what it is without all of the courageous women who allowed me to tell their stories. I am deeply grateful for your courage and willingness to have the story of your trauma and your triumph told in these pages. Whether your story made it into the final text or not, I am forever honored by your willingness to share so that those out there who still feel voiceless can feel seen, heard and understood. This is *your* book.

To my incredibly dedicated marketing team, Lynn Eikenberry, Jenny Silverberg, Today Baker and Hannah Colbert. I can't thank you ladies enough for all your support, hard work, enthusiasm and dedication in helping this book become visible (not to mention funded!). And to Aviv Marotz, for spending an afternoon recording beautiful videos and taking photos for our successful (and nerve-racking) Kickstarter campaign!

Writing a book about TIMBo and all that I have experienced as a result would not be possible without Lola Remy, who was my very first partner in training. Lola, you stepped in at a crucial moment to help spread TIMBo both in the U.S. and in Haiti. Your tireless work as both trainer and translator for all of our projects in Haiti will never be forgotten—your commitment to TIMBo changed my work and my life immeasurably.

And to Emily Peterson, my partner in training for the last five years. Emily's dedication to getting TIMBo to her community and her continued commitment to stick with me through thick and thin has directly impacted my life and the lives of so many women. Emily, you are a powerful living and breathing testament to the power a woman has to create change in the world—healed people heal people!

Thank you to all of the "Timbettes" for believing and spreading the word about TIMBo. You have been the boots on the ground and have made a difference in the lives of so many women. You have helped me stay the course when things felt hard by reminding me what TIMBo has done for you. We're all in this together.

I'm so thankful for everyone who was willing to read early copies of this book, provide feedback, proofread, find research interns, share the excitement and continue to encourage me. Writing this book was not a solitary venture; it has literally taken a village, and I'm so grateful for all of you.

To my unbelievable production team at Girl Friday Productions. Bethany and Georgie, from the start of our work together the synergy between GFP and this book has been so evident. I never could have gotten this project from a Word document to what it is today without all of your expert help and guidance. From finding the right editors and cover designers, to marketing strategy, interior design, formatting, proofreading and navigating through all the ins and outs of what it means to self-publish, you have been there every step of the way. I never, ever could have done this on my own, and I'm so very grateful for you and the entire GFP team.

To my sister, Jessica Austin, and to David Bamford, Elizabeth Palmer and Joan Leibovich. You were there when I needed you. I am here because of that.

To my entire family.

Especially to my mom, for always inspiring me to be the best that I can be. Mom, your example of what it means to take risks and live life with confidence has shaped the woman I have become: mother, leader, innovator and now author. But most of all you have always been there me for whenever I have felt alone and scared. Thank you for always being there to catch me when I slip and fall.

And finally, to my father, who is the best man I know. Dad, your love, humility and generosity have been a true gift in my life. Your willingness to allow me to share a memory in this book—even though you don't recall it—is incredible enough. But your words to me, "Put down the burden of worrying about me," confirmed to me what a truly incredible human being you are. I love you more now than I ever have. You are an extraordinary human being, a true gift to me as my dad, and an outstanding grandfather to my children. I love you with all my heart and soul.

NOTES

Introduction

1   Nadine Burke Harris, MD, *The Deepest Well: Healing the Long-Term Effects of Childhood Adversity* (New York: Mariner Books, 2019).
2   Mark Epstein, *The Trauma of Everyday Life* (New York: Penguin Books, 2014).

Chapter Two

1   I learned years later that she did talk to me the next day, but I have no memory of it.
2   Gabor Maté, MD, *When the Body Says No: Exploring the Stress-Disease Connection* (Hoboken: Wiley, 2003).
3   Peter A. Levine and Ann Frederick, *Waking the Tiger: Healing Trauma* (Berkeley: North Atlantic Books, 1997).
4   Barbara E. Bloom, Barbara Owen and Stephanie S. Covington, *Gender-Responsive Strategies: Research, Practice, and Guiding Principles for Women Offenders* (National Institute of Corrections, 2003), https://nicic.gov/gender-responsive-strategies-research-practice-and-guiding-principles-women-offenders; Barbara E. Bloom and Stephanie S. Covington, "Addressing the Mental Health Needs of Women Offenders," in *Women's Mental Health Issues across the Criminal Justice System*, ed. R. Gido and L. Dalley (Upper Saddle River, NJ: Pearson Prentice Hall, 2008); Stephanie S. Covington and Barbara E. Bloom, "Gender-Responsive Treatment Services in Correctional Settings," *Women & Therapy* 29, no. 3/4 (April 10, 2006): 9–33; Vanessa Alleyne, "Locked Up Means Locked Out," *Women & Therapy* 29, no. 3/4 (April 10, 2006): 181–94, https://doi.org/10.1300/J015v29n03_10; Preeta Saxena, Nena P. Messina and Christine E. Grella, "Who Benefits from Gender-Responsive Treatment?: Accounting for Abuse History on Longitudinal Outcomes for Women in Prison," *Criminal Justice and Behavior* 41, no. 4 (April 1, 2014): 417–32, https://doi.org/10.1177/0093854813514405.
5   Babette Rothschild, *The Body Remembers: The Psychophysiology of Trauma and Trauma Treatment* (New York: W.W. Norton & Company, 2000); Belleruth Naparstek, *Invisible Heroes: Survivors of Trauma and How They Heal* (New York: Bantam, 2005).

6   Caroline Myss, *Anatomy of the Spirit: The Seven Stages of Power and Healing* (New York: Harmony, 1996).

7   Myss, *Anatomy of the Spirit.*

Chapter Three

1   Erica A. Wehrwein, Hakan S. Orer and Susan M. Barman, "Overview of the Anatomy, Physiology, and Pharmacology of the Autonomic Nervous System," *Comprehensive Physiology* 3, no. 6 (July 2016), https://onlinelibrary.wiley.com /doi/abs/10.1002/cphy.c150037.

2   Gabor Maté, MD, *When the Body Says No: Exploring the Stress-Disease Connection* (Hoboken: Wiley, 2003).

3   Hugo D. Critchley and Neil A. Harrison, "Visceral Influences on Brain and Behavior," *Neuron*, no. 77 (February 20, 2013): 624–38; Stephen W. Porges, PhD, "The Polyvagal Theory: New Insights into Adaptive Reactions of the Autonomic Nervous System," *Cleveland Clinical Journal of Medicine* 76, no. 2 (April 2009): 1–8.

4   Markus Heinrichs, Bernadette von Dawans and Gregor Domes, "Oxytocin, Vasopressin, and Human Social Behavior," *Hormones & Social Behavior* 30, no. 4 (October 2009): 548–57, https://doi.org/10.1016/j.yfrne.2009.05.005; Michael Kosfeld, Markus Heinrichs, Paul J. Zak, Urs Fischbacher and Ernst Fehr, "Oxytocin Increases Trust in Humans," *Nature* 435, no. 2 (June 2005): 673–76; Andreas Meyer-Lindenberg, "Impact of Prosocial Neuropeptides on Human Brain Function," *Progress in Brain Research* 170 (2008): 463–70, http:// www.sciencedirect.com/science/article/pii/S0079612308004366.

5   Matthew D. Taves, Celso Gomez-Sanchez and Kiran K. Soma, "Extra-Adrenal Glucocorticoids and Mineralocorticoids: Evidence for Local Synthesis, Regulation, and Function," *American Journal of Physiology, Endocrinology, and Metabolism* 301, no. 1 (2011): E11–E24, https://doi .org/10.1152/ajpendo.00100.2011.

6   Kendra Cherry, "How the Fight or Flight Response Works," Verywell Mind (website), accessed August 8, 2019, https://www.verywellmind.com/what -is-the-fight-or-flight-response-2795194.

7   Louis Cozolino, *The Neuroscience of Human Relationships: Attachment and the Developing Social Brain* (New York: W. W. Norton & Company, 2006).

8   Peter A. Levine and Ann Frederick, *Waking the Tiger: Healing Trauma* (Berkeley: North Atlantic Books, 1997); Danny Brom et al., "Somatic Experiencing for Posttraumatic Stress Disorder: A Randomized Controlled Outcome Study," *Journal of Traumatic Stress* 30, no. 3 (June 2017): 304–12.

9   Rick Hanson, *Buddha's Brain: The Practical Neuroscience of Happiness, Love, and Wisdom* (Oakland: New Harbinger Publications, 2009).

10   Belleruth Naparstek, *Invisible Heroes: Survivors of Trauma and How They Heal* (New York: Bantam, 2005).

11   Michelle Bosquet Enlow et al., "Mother–Infant Attachment and the Intergenerational Transmission of Posttraumatic Stress Disorder," *Development and Psychopathology* (2013); Amy F. T. Arnsten, "Stress Signalling Pathways That Impair Prefrontal Cortex Structure and Function," *Nature Reviews Neuroscience* 10 (June 1, 2009): 410–22.

12   Vincent J. Felitti et al., "Relationship of Childhood Abuse and Household
      Dysfunction to Many of the Leading Causes of Death in Adults," *American
      Journal of Preventive Medicine* 14, no. 4 (1998): 245–58.

13   Peter A. Levine, *In an Unspoken Voice: How the Body Releases Trauma and
      Restores Goodness* (Berkeley: North Atlantic Books, 2010).

14   Louis Cozolino, *The Neuroscience of Human Relationships: Attachment and the
      Developing Social Brain* (New York: W. W. Norton & Company, 2006); Daniel
      Schacter, "Implicit Memory: History and Current Status," *Journal of
      Experimental Psychology: Learning, Memory, and Cognition* 13, no. 3 (1987):
      501–18.

15   Stephen W. Porges, PhD, "The Polyvagal Theory: New Insights into Adaptive
      Reactions of the Autonomic Nervous System," *Cleveland Clinical Journal of
      Medicine* 76, no. 2 (April 2009): 1–8; Seth D. Pollak, "Experience-Dependent
      Affective Learning and Risk for Psychopathology in Children," *Annals of
      the New York Academy of Sciences*, no. 1008 (2003): 102–11; Daniel J. Siegel,
      Mindsight: The New Science of Personal Transformation, reprint ed. (New York:
      Bantam, 2010).

Chapter Four

1   Matthew D. Lieberman, *Social: Why Our Brains Are Wired to Connect* (New
      York: Crown, 2013); Louis Cozolino, *The Neuroscience of Human Relationships:
      Attachment and the Developing Social Brain* (New York: W. W. Norton &
      Company, 2006); Mark Epstein, *The Trauma of Everyday Life* (New York:
      Penguin Books, 2014).

2   Norbert Skokauskas et al., "Shaping the Future of Child and Adolescent
      Psychiatry," *Child and Adolescent Psychiatry and Mental Health* 13 (April 11,
      2019), https://doi.org/10.1186/s13034-019-0279-y.

3   Cozolino, *The Neuroscience of Human Relationships*; Lieberman, *Social*;
      Michelle Bosquet Enlow et al., "Mother–Infant Attachment and the
      Intergenerational Transmission of Posttraumatic Stress Disorder," *Development
      and Psychopathology* (2013); Allan N. Schore, "Dysregulation of the Right
      Brain: A Fundamental Mechanism of Traumatic Attachment and the Psycho-
      pathogenesis of Posttraumatic Stress Disorder," *Australian and New Zealand
      Journal of Psychiatry* 36, no. 9 (2002); Antonia Bifulco et al., "Adult Attachment
      Style as a Mediator between Childhood Neglect/Abuse and Adult Depression
      and Anxiety," *Social Psychiatry and Psychiatric Epidemiology* 41, no. 10 (2006):
      796–805.

4   Marcela Matos, Jose Pinto-Gouveia and Vania Costa, "Understanding the
      Importance of Attachment in Shame Traumatic Memory Relation to Depression:
      The Impact of Emotion Regulation Processes," *Clinical Psychology &
      Psychotherapy* 20, no. 2 (2013): 149–65.

5   Lieberman, *Social*.

6   Cozolino, *The Neuroscience of Human Relationships*.

7   "Maternity Leave in the United States," Wikipedia, accessed August 16, 2019,
      https://en.wikipedia.org/w/index.php?title=Maternity_leave_in_the_United
      _States&oldid=911021767.

8   E. E. Nelson and J. Panksepp, "Brain Substrates of Infant-Mother Attachment: Contributions of Opioids, Oxytocin, and Norepinephrine," *Neuroscience and Biobehavioral Reviews* 22, no. 3 (May 1998): 437–52.

9   "Orphans' Lonely Beginnings Reveal How Parents Shape a Child's Brain," NPR. org, accessed August 8, 2019, https://www.npr.org/sections/health -shots/2014/02/20/280237833/orphans-lonely-beginnings-reveal-how -parents-shape-a-childs-brain; Cristina Merrill, "Cortisol Kids," *Harvard Magazine*, 1997, https://harvardmagazine.com/1997/05/right.kids.html.

10   Mary Carlson and Felton Earls, "Psychological and Neuroendocrinological Consequences of Early Social Deprivation in Institutionalized Children in Romania," *Annals of the New York Academy of Sciences* 807 (1997): 419–28.

11   Janet McConnaughey, "Study of Romanian Orphans Show Importance of Touch," Associated Press, October 28, 1997, https://www.apnews.com /a6cec231a453aa20429cef7f8694beb6.

12   Robert Melillo and Gerry Leisman, *Neurobehavioral Disorders of Childhood: An Evolutionary Perspective*, 2010 ed. (New York: Springer, 2009).

13   Hugo D. Critchley and Neil A. Harrison, "Visceral Influences on Brain and Behavior," *Neuron*, no. 77 (February 20, 2013): 624–38; Stephen W. Porges and Senta A. Furman, "The Early Development of the Autonomic Nervous System Provides a Neural Platform for Social Behavior: A Polyvagal Perspective," *Infant and Child Development* 20, no. 1 (February 2011): 106–18, https://doi .org/10.1002/icd.688; Peter A. Levine, *In an Unspoken Voice: How the Body Releases Trauma and Restores Goodness* (Berkeley: North Atlantic Books, 2010); Rebekah Levine Coley and Caitlin McPherran Lombardi, "Does Maternal Employment Following Childbirth Support or Inhibit Low-Income Children's Long-Term Development?," *Child Development* 84, no. 1 (January 2013): 178–97, https://doi.org/10.1111/j.1467-8624.2012.01840.x.

14   S. Terbeck, J. Savulescu, L.P. Chesterman and P.J. Cowen, "Noradrenaline Effects on Social Behaviour, Intergroup Relations, and Moral Decisions," *Neuroscience & Biobehavioral Reviews* 66 (April 2016): 54–60; Stephen W. Porges, PhD, "The Polyvagal Theory: New Insights into Adaptive Reactions of the Autonomic Nervous System," *Cleveland Clinical Journal of Medicine* 76, no. 2 (April 2009): 1–8; Gabor Maté, MD, *When the Body Says No: Exploring the Stress-Disease Connection* (Hoboken: Wiley, 2003).

15   Jane Bybee, *Guilt and Children* (San Diego: Academic Press, 1997); Tamara J. Ferguson, Heddy Stegge, Erin R. Miller and Michael E. Olsen, "Guilt, Shame, and Symptoms in Children," *Developmental Psychology* 35, no. 2 (1999): 347–57, https://doi.org/10.1037/0012-1649.35.2.347; Peter Muris and Cor Meesters, "Small or Big in the Eyes of the Other: On the Developmental Psychopathology of Self-Conscious Emotions as Shame, Guilt, and Pride," *Clinical Child and Family Psychology Review* (May 28, 2013), https://doi.org/10.1007/s10567-013 -0137-z.

16   David Kealy, Simon M. Rice, John S. Ogrodniczuk and Alicia Spidel, "Childhood Trauma and Somatic Symptoms among Psychiatric Outpatients: Investigating the Role of Shame and Guilt," *Psychiatry Research* 268 (2018): 169–74.

17   Maté, *When the Body Says No*.

18   Kenneth M. Adams and Donald W. Robinson, "Shame Reduction, Affect Regulation, and Sexual Boundary Development: Essential Building Blocks of

Sexual Addiction Treatment," *Sexual Addiction & Compulsivity* 8 (October 13, 2011): 23–44; Jesse R. Cougle, Heidi Resnick and Dean G. Kilpatrick, "A Prospective Examination of PTSD Symptoms as Risk Factors for Subsequent Exposure to Potentially Traumatic Events among Women," *Journal of Abnormal Psychology* 118, no. 2 (2009): 405–11, https://doi.org/10.1037 /a0015370; Matthias Majer et al., "Association of Childhood Trauma with Cognitive Function in Healthy Adults: A Pilot Study," *BMC Neurology* 10 (July 14, 2010), https://www.doi.org/10.1186/1471-2377-10-61; David W. Brown et al., "Adverse Childhood Experiences and the Risk of Premature Mortality," *American Journal of Preventive Medicine* 37, no. 5 (November 1, 2009): 389–96, https://doi.org/10.1016/j.amepre.2009.06.021.

19   Lieberman, *Social.*

20   Lieberman, *Social.*

21   Itismita Mohanty, Martin Edvardsson, Annie Abello, and Deanna Eldridge., "Child Social Exclusion Risk and Child Health Outcomes in Australia," *PLoS ONE*, (May 6, 2016): 1–16.

22   Dana Reid and Paul Weigle, "Social Media Use among Adolescents: Benefits and Risks," *Adolescent Psychology* 4, no. 2 (2014): 73–80, https://www .ingentaconnect.com/content/ben/aps/2014/00000004/00000002/art00003.

23   Roger Kobak and Joanna Herres, "Social Networks and Attachment Bonds during Adolescence: Implications for Early Pair Bonding and Risky Behaviors," in *Interdisciplinary Research on Close Relationships: The Case for Integration,* ed. Lorne Campbell and Timothy J. Loving (American Psychological Association, 2012), 135–52, https://psycnet.apa.org/record/2011-12631-006; Stephen Cope, *Yoga and the Quest for the True Self* (New York: Bantam, 2000).

24   Aurora Szentagotai-Tatar and Andrei C. Miu, "Individual Differences in Emotion Regulation, Childhood Trauma and Proneness to Shame and Guilt in Adolescence," *PLoS ONE* (November 29, 2016): 2–10; Muris, "Small or Big"; Kathleen O. Nader and Lynn A. Fairbanks, "The Suppression of Reexperiencing: Impulse Control and Somatic Symptoms in Children Following Traumatic Exposure," *Anxiety, Stress & Coping* 7, no. 3 (1994): 229–239, https://doi.org /10.1080/10615809408249348.

Chapter Five

1   Allan N. Schore, "Dysregulation of the Right Brain: A Fundamental Mechanism of Traumatic Attachment and the Psychopathogenesis of Posttraumatic Stress Disorder," *Australian and New Zealand Journal of Psychiatry* 36, no. 9 (2002).

2   Belleruth Naparstek, *Invisible Heroes: Survivors of Trauma and How They Heal* (New York: Bantam, 2005).

3   Naparstek, *Invisible Heroes*; M. A. Fullana et al., "Neural Signatures of Human Fear Conditioning: An Updated and Extended Meta-Analysis of FMRI Studies," *Molecular Psychiatry* 21 (2016): 500–508, https://www.nature.com/articles /mp201588.

4   "Laozi," Wikipedia, accessed August 8, 2019, https://en.wikipedia.org/w/index .php?title=Laozi&oldid=909960145.

5   Peter A. Levine and Ann Frederick, *Waking the Tiger: Healing Trauma* (Berkeley: North Atlantic Books, 1997).

6   A.D. Craig, "The Significance of the Insula for the Evolution of Human Awareness of Feelings from the Body," *Annals of the New York Academy of Sciences* 1225, no. 1 (2011): 72–82.

7   Xiaosi Gu, Patrick R. Hof, Karl J. Friston and Jin Fan, "Anterior Insular Cortex and Emotional Awareness," *The Journal of Comparative Neurology* 521 (2013): 3371–88.

8   Amy F. T. Arnsten, "Stress Weakens Prefrontal Networks: Molecular Insults to Higher Cognition," *Nature Neuroscience* 18 (September 25, 2015): 1376–85; Amy F. T. Arnsten, "Stress Signalling Pathways That Impair Prefrontal Cortex Structure and Function," *Nature Reviews Neuroscience* 10 (June 1, 2009): 410–22.

9   Nick Medford and Hugo D. Critchley, "Conjoint Activity of Anterior Insular and Anterior Cingulate Cortex: Awareness and Response," *Brain Structure and Function*, no. 214 (2010): 535–49.

10   Micah Allen et al., "Cognitive-Affective Neural Plasticity Following Active-Controlled Mindfulness Intervention," *The Journal of Neuroscience* 32, no. 44 (October 31, 2012): 15601–10, https://doi.org/10.1523/JNEUROSCI.2957-12.2012; Norman A. S. Farb, Adam K. Anderson and Zindel V. Segal, "The Mindful Brain and Emotion Regulation in Mood Disorders," *Canadian Journal of Psychiatry* 57, no. 2 (February 2012): 70–77.

11   George B. Richerson and John M. Bekkers, "Learning to Take a Deep Breath—with BDNF," *Nature Medicine* 10, no. 1 (January 1, 2004): 25–26, https://doi.org/10.1038/nm0104-25; Ryan W. Bavis and Peter M. MacFarlane, "Developmental Plasticity in the Neural Control of Breathing," *Experimental Neurology*, no. 287 (January 1, 2017): 176–91, https://doi.org/10.1016/j.expneurol.2016.05.032.

12   John J. Ratey, *Spark: The Revolutionary New Science of Exercise and the Brain* (New York: Little, Brown and Company, 2008); Havan Furmaga, Flavia Regina Carreno and Alan Frazer, "Vagal Nerve Stimulation Rapidly Activates Brain-Derived Neurotrophic Factor Receptor TrkB in Rat Brain," *PloS One* 7, no. 5 (2012): e34844, https://doi.org/10.1371/journal.pone.0034844.

13   Rick Hanson, *Buddha's Brain: The Practical Neuroscience of Happiness, Love, and Wisdom* (Oakland: New Harbinger Publications, 2009).

14   Shoshanna Vaynman, Zhe Ying and Fernando Gomez-Pinilla, "Hippocampal BDNF Mediates the Efficacy of Exercise on Synaptic Plasticity and Cognition," *The European Journal of Neuroscience* 20, no. 10 (November 2004): 2580–90, https://doi.org/10.1111/j.1460-9568.2004.03720.x.

Chapter Six

1   "Eleanor Roosevelt," Wikipedia, accessed August 10, 2019, https://en.wikipedia.org/w/index.php?title=Eleanor_Roosevelt&oldid=910180547.

2   Anodea Judith, *Eastern Body, Western Mind: Psychology and the Chakra System As a Path to the Self* (New York: Celestial Arts, 2004).

3   Judith, *Eastern Body, Western Mind.*

4   Judith, *Eastern Body, Western Mind.*

5   Bruce S. McEwen, "Stress, Sex and Neural Adaptation to a Changing Environment: Mechanisms of Neuronal Remodeling," *Annals of the New York Academy of Sciences* 1204 (September 2010); Simeng Gu et al., "An Integrative

Way for Studying Neural Basis of Basic Emotions With FMRI," *Frontiers in Neuroscience* 13 (2019): 628, https://doi.org/10.3389/fnins.2019.00628.

6   A.D. Craig, "How Do You Feel—Now? The Anterior Insula and Human Awareness," *Nature Reviews Neuroscience* 10, no. 1 (January 2009): 59–70.

7   Bruce D. Perry, MD, PhD, *Stress, Trauma and Post-Traumatic Stress Disorders in Children* (The ChildTrauma Academy, 2007); Elizabeth I. Martin, PhD, et al., "The Neurobiology of Anxiety Disorders: Brain Imaging, Genetics, and Psychoneuroendocrinology," *Psychiatric Clinics of North America* 32, no. 3 (2009): 549–757.

8   Lauri Nummenmaa et al., "Bodily Maps of Emotions," *Proceedings of the National Academy of Sciences of the United States of America* (2013): 1–6.

9   Peter A. Levine, *In an Unspoken Voice: How the Body Releases Trauma and Restores Goodness* (Berkeley: North Atlantic Books, 2010).

10   Gabor Maté, MD, *When the Body Says No: Exploring the Stress-Disease Connection* (Hoboken: Wiley, 2003); David W. Brown et al., "Adverse Childhood Experiences and the Risk of Premature Mortality," *American Journal of Preventive Medicine* 37, no. 5 (November 1, 2009): 389–96, https://doi.org/10.1016/j.amepre.2009.06.021.

11   Judith, *Eastern Body, Western Mind*; Caroline Myss, *Anatomy of the Spirit: The Seven Stages of Power and Healing* (New York: Harmony, 1996).

12   Judith, *Eastern Body, Western Mind*; Myss, *Anatomy of the Spirit*.

Chapter Seven

1   Tamara J. Ferguson, Heddy Stegge, Erin R. Miller and Michael E. Olsen, "Guilt, Shame, and Symptoms in Children," *Developmental Psychology* 35, no. 2 (1999): 347–57, https://doi.org/10.1037/0012-1649.35.2.347; Peter Muris and Cor Meesters, "Small or Big in the Eyes of the Other: On the Developmental Psychopathology of Self-Conscious Emotions as Shame, Guilt, and Pride," *Clinical Child and Family Psychology Review* (May 28, 2013), https://doi .org/10.1007/s10567-013-0137-z.

2   Susan L. Morrow and Mary Lee Smith, "Constructions of Survival and Coping by Women Who Have Survived Childhood Sexual Abuse," *Journal of Counseling Psychology* 42, no. 1 (1995): 24–33, https://doi.org/10.1037/0022 -0167.42.1.24.

3   Anodea Judith, *Eastern Body, Western Mind: Psychology and the Chakra System As a Path to the Self* (New York: Celestial Arts, 2004).

4   Judith, *Eastern Body, Western Mind*.

5   Judith, *Eastern Body, Western Mind*; Caroline Myss, *Anatomy of the Spirit: The Seven Stages of Power and Healing* (New York: Harmony, 1996).

6   Judith, *Eastern Body, Western Mind*; Myss, *Anatomy of the Spirit*.

7   Rick Hanson, *Buddha's Brain: The Practical Neuroscience of Happiness, Love, and Wisdom* (Oakland: New Harbinger Publications, 2009).

Chapter Eight

1   K. A. Arditte et al., "Interpersonal Risk for Suicide in Social Anxiety: The Roles of Shame and Depression," *Psychiatry Research* 239 (May 2016): 139–44.

2   Frans Schalkwijk, "A New Conceptualization of the Conscience," *Frontiers in Psychology* 9 (October 8, 2018), https://doi.org/10.3389/fpsyg.2018.01863.

3   "Diana: In Her Own Words," Netflix, accessed August 10, 2019, https://www.netflix.com/title/80221317.

4   "Diana: In Her Own Words."

5   Brené Brown, "The Power of Vulnerability," TED video, accessed August 10, 2019, https://www.ted.com/talks/brene_brown_on_vulnerability.

6   Brown, "The Power of Vulnerability."

7   Brené Brown, "Listening to Shame," TED video, accessed August 10, 2019, https://www.ted.com/talks/brene_brown_listening_to_shame.

8   Donald L. Nathanson, MD, *Shame and Pride: Affect, Sex, and the Birth of the Self,* 3rd ed. (New York: W. W. Norton & Company, 1994); Schalkwijk, "A New Conceptualization."

9   Melissa Healy, "Suicide Rates for U.S. Teens and Young Adults Are the Highest on Record," *Los Angeles Times,* June 18, 2019, https://www.latimes.com/science/la-sci-suicide-rates-rising-teens-young-adults-20190618-story.html.

10   Brown, "Listening to Shame."

11   Anodea Judith, *Eastern Body, Western Mind: Psychology and the Chakra System As a Path to the Self* (New York: Celestial Arts, 2004).

12   Judith, *Eastern Body, Western Mind.*

13   Judith, *Eastern Body, Western Mind*; Caroline Myss, *Anatomy of the Spirit: The Seven Stages of Power and Healing* (New York: Harmony, 1996).

14   Judith, *Eastern Body, Western Mind*; Myss, *Anatomy of the Spirit.*

15   D. R. Carney, A. J. Cuddy and A. J. Yap, "Power Posing: Brief Nonverbal Displays Affect Neuroendocrine Levels and Risk Tolerance," *Psychological Science* (September 20, 2010): 1363–68.

Chapter Nine

1   Peter A. Levine and Ann Frederick, *Waking the Tiger: Healing Trauma* (Berkeley: North Atlantic Books, 1997); Robert Scaer, *The Body Bears the Burden: Trauma, Dissociation, and Disease,* 3rd edition (New York: Routledge, 2014).

2   David V. Baldwin, "Primitive Mechanisms of Trauma Response: An Evolutionary Perspective on Trauma-Related Disorders," *Neuroscience and Biobehavioral Reviews* 37, no. 8 (September 2013): 1549–66, https://doi.org/10.1016/j.neubiorev.2013.06.004.

3   Peter A. Levine, *In an Unspoken Voice: How the Body Releases Trauma and Restores Goodness* (Berkeley: North Atlantic Books, 2010).

4   Babette Rothschild, *The Body Remembers: The Psychophysiology of Trauma and Trauma Treatment* (New York: W. W. Norton & Company, 2000).

5   Levine, *Waking the Tiger.*

6   Levine, *Waking the Tiger.*

7   "RESENTMENT: How It Destroys Your Mind and Body, and How to Fix It," Don'tjudgeyourlife.com, accessed October 7, 2016, https://dontjudgeyourlife

.com/2016/10/07/resentment-how-it-destroys-your-mind-and-body-and-how
-to-fix-it/.

8   Brené Brown, "The Power of Vulnerability," TED video, accessed August 10,
     2019, https://www.ted.com/talks/brene_brown_on_vulnerability.

9   David W. Brown et al., "Adverse Childhood Experiences and the Risk of
     Premature Mortality," *American Journal of Preventive Medicine* 37, no. 5
     (November 1, 2009): 389–96, https://doi.org/10.1016/j.amepre.2009.06.021;
     Vincent J. Felitti et al., "Relationship of Childhood Abuse and Household
     Dysfunction to Many of the Leading Causes of Death in Adults," *American
     Journal of Preventive Medicine* 14, no. 4 (1998): 245–58.

10   Gabor Maté, MD, *When the Body Says No: Exploring the Stress-Disease
     Connection* (Hoboken: Wiley, 2003); Mercy Manyema, Shane A. Norris and
     Linda M. Richter, "Stress Begets Stress: The Association of Adverse Childhood
     Experiences with Psychological Distress in the Presence of Adult Life Stress,"
     BMC Public Health 18, no. 835 (2018): 1–12.

11   Matthias Majer et al., "Association of Childhood Trauma with Cognitive
     Function in Healthy Adults: A Pilot Study," *BMC Neurology* 10 (July 14, 2010),
     https://www.doi.org/10.1186/1471-2377-10-61.

12   Maté, *When the Body Says No.*

13   Brown, "The Power of Vulnerability."

14   Benjamin P. Chapman et al., "Emotion Suppression and Mortality Risk over a
     12-Year Follow-Up," *Journal of Psychosomatic Research* 75, no. 4 (October 1,
     2013): 381–85, https://doi.org/10.1016/j.jpsychores.2013.07.014.

15   Anodea Judith, *Eastern Body, Western Mind: Psychology and the Chakra System
     As a Path to the Self* (New York: Celestial Arts, 2004).

16   Judith, *Eastern Body, Western Mind.*

17   Judith, *Eastern Body, Western Mind*; Caroline Myss, *Anatomy of the Spirit: The
     Seven Stages of Power and Healing* (New York: Harmony, 1996).

18   Judith, *Eastern Body, Western Mind*; Myss, *Anatomy of the Spirit.*

19   Daniel J. Siegel, *Mindsight: The New Science of Personal Transformation*, reprint
     ed. (New York: Bantam, 2010).

20   Tânia Brandão et al., "Measuring Emotion Regulation and Emotional Expression
     in Breast Cancer Patients: A Systematic Review," *Clinical Psychology Review* 43
     (February 1, 2016): 114–27, https://doi.org/10.1016/j.cpr.2015.10.002.

21   D. M. Kissen and H. J. Eysenck, "Personality in Male Lung Cancer Patients,"
     Journal of Psychosomatic Research 6 (June 1962): 123–27; Tom Cox and Colin
     Mackay, "Psychosocial Factors and Psychophysiological Mechanisms in the
     Aetiology and Development of Cancers," *Social Science & Medicine* 16, no. 4
     (January 1, 1982): 381–96, https://doi.org/10.1016/0277-9536(82)90048-X.

Chapter Ten

1   "Understanding the Impact of Trauma," chap. 3 in *Trauma-Informed Care
     in Behavioral Health Services* (Maryland: Substance Abuse and Mental
     Health Services Administration, 2014), https://www.ncbi.nlm.nih.gov/books
     /NBK207191/; Anodea Judith, *Eastern Body, Western Mind: Psychology and the
     Chakra System As a Path to the Self* (New York: Celestial Arts, 2004).

2   Arielle Schwartz, Barb Maiberger and Robin Shapiro, *EMDR Therapy and Somatic
     Psychology: Interventions to Enhance Embodiment in Trauma Treatment* (New

York: W. W. Norton & Company, 2018); Belleruth Naparstek, *Invisible Heroes: Survivors of Trauma and How They Heal* (New York: Bantam, 2005).

3   Judith, *Eastern Body, Western Mind*.

4   Judith, *Eastern Body, Western Mind*.

5   Peter A. Levine, PhD, *Trauma and Memory: Brain and Body in a Search for the Living Past: A Practical Guide for Understanding and Working with Traumatic Memory* (Berkeley: North Atlantic Books, 2015).

6   Judith, *Eastern Body, Western Mind*.

7   Bessel van der Kolk, MD, *The Body Keeps the Score: Brain, Mind, and Body in the Healing of Trauma*, reprint ed. (New York: Penguin Books, 2015).

8   R. G. Phillips and J. E. LeDoux, "Differential Contribution of Amygdala and Hippocampus to Cued and Contextual Fear Conditioning," *Behavioral Neuroscience* 106, no. 2 (1992): 274–85, https://doi.org/10.1037/0735-7044 .106.2.274; Ruth A. Lanius et al., "Fear Conditioning and Early Life Vulnerabilities: Two Distinct Pathways of Emotional Dysregulation and Brain Dysfunction in PTSD," *European Journal of Psychotraumatology* 1 (December 10, 2010), https://doi.org/10.3402/ejpt.v1i0.5467.

9   Christopher Peterson, Steven F. Maier and Martin E. P. Seligman, *Learned Helplessness: A Theory for the Age of Personal Control*, reprint ed. (New York: Oxford University Press, 1995); van der Kolk, *The Body Keeps the Score*.

10   Judith, *Eastern Body, Western Mind*; Caroline Myss, *Anatomy of the Spirit: The Seven Stages of Power and Healing* (New York: Harmony, 1996).

11   Judith, *Eastern Body, Western Mind*; Myss, *Anatomy of the Spirit*.

Chapter Eleven

1   "14th Dalai Lama," Wikipedia, accessed July 23, 2019, https://en.wikipedia .org/w/index.php?title=14th_Dalai_Lama&oldid=907563470.

2   Dustin Albert, Jason Chein and Laurence Steinberg, "The Teenage Brain: Peer Influences on Adolescent Decision Making," *Current Directions in Psychological Science* 22, no. 2 (April 1, 2013): 114–20, https://doi .org/10.1177/0963721412471347.

3   Vito Zepinic, "Disintegration of the Self-Structure Caused by Severe Trauma," *Psychology and Behavioral Sciences* 5, no. 4 (June 21, 2016): 83, https://doi .org/10.11648/j.pbs.20160504.12.

4   Fereshteh Bakhshi Bojed and Zahra Nikmanesh, "Role of Early Maladaptive Schemas on Addiction Potential in Youth," *International Journal of High Risk Behaviors & Addiction* 2, no. 2 (September 2013): 72–76, https://doi .org/10.5812/ijhrba.10148; David W. Brown et al., "Adverse Childhood Experiences and the Risk of Premature Mortality," *American Journal of Preventive Medicine* 37, no. 5 (November 1, 2009): 389–96, https://doi .org/10.1016/j.amepre.2009.06.021.

5   Jeong Won Jahng, "An Animal Model of Eating Disorders Associated with Stressful Experience in Early Life," *Hormones and Behavior* 59, no. 2 (February 1, 2011): 213–20, https://doi.org/10.1016/j.yhbeh.2010.11.010; J. F. Kinzl et al., "Family Background and Sexual Abuse Associated with Eating Disorders," *The American Journal of Psychiatry* 151, no. 8 (August 1994): 1127–31, https://doi .org/10.1176/ajp.151.8.1127.

6   Christine Hammond, MS, LMHC, "7 Tactics Narcissists Use to Escape
     Responsibility," *The Exhausted Woman* (blog), *PsychCentral*, May 31, 2016,
     https://pro.psychcentral.com/exhausted-woman/2016/05/7-tactics-narcissists
     -use-to-escape-responsibility/.

7   Matthew G. Whalley et al., "An FMRI Investigation of Posttraumatic Flashbacks,"
     Brain and Cognition 81, no. 1 (February 2013): 151–59, https://doi.org/10.1016
     /j.bandc.2012.10.002; Bessel van der Kolk, MD, *The Body Keeps the Score: Brain,
     Mind, and Body in the Healing of Trauma*, reprint ed. (New York: Penguin
     Books, 2015).

8   Anodea Judith, *Eastern Body, Western Mind: Psychology and the Chakra System
     As a Path to the Self* (New York: Celestial Arts, 2004).

9   Judith, *Eastern Body, Western Mind.*

10   Judith, *Eastern Body, Western Mind*; Caroline Myss, *Anatomy of the Spirit: The
     Seven Stages of Power and Healing* (New York: Harmony, 1996).

11   Judith, *Eastern Body, Western Mind*; Myss, *Anatomy of the Spirit.*

12   Judith Lewis Herman, *Trauma and Recovery* (New York: BasicBooks, 1997).

Chapter Twelve

1   Gabor Maté, MD, *When the Body Says No: Exploring the Stress-Disease
     Connection* (Hoboken: Wiley, 2003).

2   Stephanie S. Covington and Barbara E. Bloom, "Gender-Responsive Treatment
     Services in Correctional Settings," *Women & Therapy* 29, no. 3/4 (2006): 9–33;
     Stephanie S. Covington, "Curricula to Support Trauma-Informed Practice with
     Women," in *Moving the Addiction and Mental Health System Towards Being
     More Trauma-Informed* (Toronto: Centre for Addiction and Mental Health,
     2012), http://stephaniecovington.com/assets/files/2013/Curricula-to-Support
     -Trauma-Informed-Practice-with-Women-_2012_-CAMH-article-.pdf.

3   Anodea Judith, *Eastern Body, Western Mind: Psychology and the Chakra System
     As a Path to the Self* (New York: Celestial Arts, 2004).

4   Judith, *Eastern Body, Western Mind.*

5   Judith, *Eastern Body, Western Mind*; Caroline Myss, *Anatomy of the Spirit: The
     Seven Stages of Power and Healing* (New York: Harmony, 1996).

6   Judith, *Eastern Body, Western Mind*; Myss, *Anatomy of the Spirit.*

7   "Sexual Abuse by Yoga Gurus," in Wikipedia, accessed August 7, 2019, https://
     en.wikipedia.org/w/index.php?title=Sexual_abuse_by_yoga_gurus&oldid
     =909759512.

Chapter Fourteen

1   Judith I. Langmuir, Shari G. Kirsh and Catherine C. Classen, "A Pilot Study of
     Body-Oriented Group Psychotherapy: Adapting Sensorimotor Psychotherapy
     for the Group Treatment of Trauma," *Psychological Trauma: Theory, Research,
     Practice, and Policy* 4, no. 2 (March 2012): 214–20.

2   Sally E. Tarbell et al., "Anxiety and Physiological Responses to the Trier Social
     Stress Test for Children in Adolescents with Cyclic Vomiting Syndrome,"
     Autonomic Neuroscience: Basic & Clinical 202 (January 2017): 79–85, https://
     doi.org/10.1016/j.autneu.2016.08.010; Urmila Parlikar, *The Sensitive Gut: A*

Harvard Medical School Special Health Report (Harvard Medical School, 2008); "Anxiety Nausea: Why It Happens and What You Can Do to Stop It," Healthline (website), accessed August 18, 2019, https://www.healthline.com /health/anxiety/anxiety-nausea.

3   Bruce D. Perry, MD, PhD, *Stress, Trauma and Post-Traumatic Stress Disorders in Children* (The ChildTrauma Academy, 2007).

4   Pema Chödrön, *Start Where You Are: A Guide to Compassionate Living* (Boulder: Shambhala, 2018).

5   "Khalil Gibran," Wikipedia, accessed August 15, 2019, https://en.wikipedia .org/w/index.php?title=Khalil_Gibran&oldid=910996404.

Chapter Fifteen

1   Ellen Bass and Laura Davis, *The Courage to Heal: A Guide for Women Survivors of Child Sexual Abuse, 20th Anniversary Edition.* New York: William Morrow Paperbacks, 2008.

Chapter Sixteen

1   John J. Ratey, *Spark: The Revolutionary New Science of Exercise and the Brain* (New York: Little, Brown and Company, 2008).

2   Peter A. Levine and Ann Frederick, *Waking the Tiger: Healing Trauma* (Berkeley: North Atlantic Books, 1997).

3   Norman A. S. Farb, Adam K. Anderson and Zindel V. Segal, "The Mindful Brain and Emotion Regulation in Mood Disorders," *Canadian Journal of Psychiatry* 57, no. 2 (February 2012): 70–77.

4   Louis Cozolino, *The Neuroscience of Human Relationships: Attachment and the Developing Social Brain* (New York: W. W. Norton & Company, 2006).

Chapter Seventeen

1   Elizabeth I. Martin, PhD, et al., "The Neurobiology of Anxiety Disorders: Brain Imaging, Genetics, and Psychoneuroendocrinology," *Psychiatric Clinics of North America* 32, no. 3 (2009): 549–757.

2   Joan Borysenko, *Minding the Body, Mending the Mind,* revised ed. (New York: Da Capo Press, 2007).

3   Jill Bolte Taylor, *My Stroke of Insight: A Brain Scientist's Personal Journey* (Penguin, 2009).

4   John J. Ratey, *Spark: The Revolutionary New Science of Exercise and the Brain* (New York: Little, Brown and Company, 2008).

Chapter Nineteen

1   "Henry Ford," Wikipedia, accessed August 12, 2019, https://en.wikipedia.org/w /index.php?title=Henry_Ford&oldid=910472821.

Chapter Twenty

1   Joan Halifax, "Compassion and the True Meaning of Empathy," TED video,
    accessed August 15, 2019, https://www.ted.com/talks/joan_halifax.
2   Halifax, "Compassion and the True Meaning of Empathy."
3   Halifax, "Compassion and the True Meaning of Empathy."
4   Halifax, "Compassion and the True Meaning of Empathy."
5   Frank H. Wilhelm et al., "Social Anxiety and Response to Touch: Incongruence
    between Self-Evaluative and Physiological Reactions," *Biological Psychiatry* 58
    (n.d.): 181–202.
6   Wilhelm et al., "Social Anxiety and Response to Touch."
7   Kristin Neff, "Self-Compassion: An Alternative Conceptualization of a Healthy
    Attitude Toward Oneself," *Self and Identity* 2, no. 2 (April 1, 2003): 85–101,
    https://doi.org/10.1080/15298860309032.

Chapter Twenty-One

1   Jill Bolte Taylor, *My Stroke of Insight: A Brain Scientist's Personal Journey*
    (Penguin, 2009).
2   Taylor, *My Stroke of Insight.*
3   Taylor, *My Stroke of Insight.*
4   Bruce D. Perry, "Examining Child Maltreatment Through a Neurodevelopmental
    Lens: Clinical Applications of the Neurosequential Model of Therapeutics,"
    Journal of Loss and Trauma 14 (April 28, 2009): 240–55; Allan N. Schore,
    "Dysregulation of the Right Brain: A Fundamental Mechanism of Traumatic
    Attachment and the Psychopathogenesis of Posttraumatic Stress Disorder,"
    Australian and New Zealand Journal of Psychiatry 36, no. 9 (2002); Belleruth
    Naparstek, *Invisible Heroes: Survivors of Trauma and How They Heal* (New
    York: Bantam, 2005).

Chapter Twenty-Two

1   K.D. Rosanbalm and D.W. Murray, *Caregiver Co-Regulation Across Development:
    A Practice Brief* (OPRE Brief #2017-80, 2017).

Chapter Twenty-Three

1   Jia Jiang, "What I Learned from 100 Days of Rejection," TED video, accessed
    August 18, 2019, https://www.ted.com/talks/jia_jiang_what_i_learned_from
    _100_days_of_rejection.
2   Jiang, "What I Learned from 100 Days of Rejection."
3   Jiang, "What I Learned from 100 Days of Rejection."
4   "Winston Churchill," Wikipedia, accessed August 14, 2019, https://en.wikipedia
    .org/w/index.php?title=Winston_Churchill&oldid=910731115.

5   Stephanie S. Covington, PhD, LCSW, and Janet L. Surrey, PhD, "The Relational
     Model of Women's Psychological Development: Implications for Substance
     Abuse," *Gender and Alcohol: Individual and Social Perspectives* (1997): 335–51.
6   Lexico Dictionaries, s.v. "mindfulness," accessed August 18, 2019, https://www
     .lexico.com/en/definition/mindfulness.

Chapter Twenty-Four

1   Bronnie Ware, *Top Five Regrets of the Dying: A Life Transformed by the Dearly
     Departing* (Hay House Inc, 2019), Kindle.
2   Ware, *Top Five Regrets of the Dying.*

ABOUT THE AUTHOR

Author Photo © Aviv Marotz

Suzanne Jones is an expert in the field of trauma recovery through somatic methods. She has presented workshops and talks at Omega Institute, Kripalu, mental and behavioral health facilities in the greater Boston area, and national conferences. She has been profiled on CNN and in *Yoga Journal*, the *New York Times*, *Shape*, and *Whole Living*, and she's been interviewed by author Rick Hanson for his Foundations of Well-Being online course. Jones founded the TIMBo Collective (formerly called yogaHOPE) in 2006 and developed the TIMBo program for transforming trauma in 2009. Since its launch, her program has been delivered to over four thousand women in the U.S., Haiti, Kenya, and Iran and helped transform client care at organizations in Massachusetts; Washington, DC; and Georgia, serving women overcoming homelessness, addiction, and domestic violence. Jones also writes a blog for the TIMBo Collective and *Elephant Journal*. *There Is Nothing to Fix* is her first book.

Made in the USA
Lexington, KY
21 November 2019